[英汉对照]
探险与传奇经典文学
双语系列丛书

鲁滨逊漂流记
Robinson Crusoe

[英] 丹尼尔·笛福 / 著　　青闰　安月英　宣碧 / 译

东华大学出版社

图书在版编目(CIP)数据

鲁滨逊漂流记/(英)笛福(Defoe, D.)著;青闰,
安月英,宣碧译.—上海:东华大学出版社,2007.9
(探险与传奇经典文学双语系列丛书)
ISBN 978-7-81111-281-8

Ⅰ.鲁… Ⅱ.①笛…②青…③安…④宣…
Ⅲ.①英语—汉语—对照读物②长篇小说—英国—
近代 Ⅳ.H319.4:I

中国版本图书馆 CIP 数据核字(2007)第 138093 号

鲁滨逊漂流记

(英)丹尼尔·笛福 著

青闰 安月英 宣碧 译

东华大学出版社出版

上海市延安西路 1882 号

邮政编码:200051 电话:(021)62193056

电子信箱:dandes. shen@gmail. com

新华书店上海发行所发行 苏州望电印刷有限公司印刷

开本:890×1240 1/32 印张:11.25 字数:390 千字

2007 年 9 月第 1 版 2007 年 9 月第 1 次印刷

印数:0 001—5 000

ISBN 978—7—81111—281—8/H·107

定价:24.00 元

编者的话

"探险与传奇经典文学双语系列丛书"第一辑《金银岛》、《所罗门王的宝藏》、《冠军的童年》、《死亡诗社》和《月亮宝石》推出后，受到了广大读者的一致好评。应读者的强烈要求，我们又适时组译了第二辑，包括《鲁滨逊漂流记》、《80天环游地球》、《时间机器》和《布哈拉沙漠历险记》。

"探险与传奇经典文学双语系列丛书"顾名思义是在我们营造的探险与传奇的文学氛围中领略大师经典，让你晓畅自如地穿行在英语世界的广阔天地中，采撷芬芳，咀嚼英华，潜移默化，分享知识带给你的快慰和力量。

在选材上，我们披沙拣金，尽可能多方位、多角度、多层面地体现探险与传奇的风姿与魅力。

在翻译上，我们反复斟酌推敲，力求准确到位，传神达韵，让你体味到汉语言的博大精深和独特韵味。

在设计上，我们追求精美韵致、别出心裁，让你一见倾心、爱不释手、一读难忘。

我们推出的这套"探险与传奇经典文学双语系列丛书"既有惊心动魄、缠绵悱恻的迷人故事，又有地道纯正、原汁原味的英语经典。而且，为了照顾多层次读者的阅读需求和欣赏品味，我们尽可能做到兼收并蓄、雅俗共赏。

我们相信她们一定会让你赏心悦目、流连忘返，增加对英语的浓厚兴趣和深切感悟，使你的英语水平在不知不觉中迅速得以提升，同时也使你的汉语悟性更上一层楼。

　　"探险与传奇经典文学双语系列丛书"在翻译过程中得到了东华大学出版社沈衡先生，以及望岳、常明月、黎明春、丹冰、云中君等同志的悉心指导，在此深表谢忱。

青　闰

2007 年 6 月 18 日

前 言

　　《鲁滨逊漂流记》是"探险与传奇经典文学双语系列丛书"奉上的第六道精美大餐。

　　《鲁滨逊漂流记》英国作家丹尼尔·笛福的代表作，也是英国乃至欧洲文学史上的第一部长篇小说。

　　18世纪初，一个英国水手在航行中和船长发生冲突，被遗弃在海上。他在南太平洋漂流了一段时间后，流落到一座荒岛上，独自生活了四年。1719年，英国作家丹尼尔·笛福根据这个故事创作了长篇小说《鲁滨逊漂流记》，并因此成为英国和欧洲小说之父。

　　这部作品通过作者丰富的想像、曲折的情节、朴实的语言，鲜明地反映了18世纪英国社会的时代特征，真实地描写了离开社会28年之久的人所遭遇的逆境和绝望，还有对信仰的感同身受和对生活无尽的挑战。

　　主人公鲁滨逊·克鲁索从小就渴望冒险，终于有一天离家航海。后来，船在海上失事，他历尽艰险，独自漂泊到了一座荒岛上。在岛上，他想出了很多具有创意的办法，努力活了下来，并救出了被土著人俘虏到岛上的星期五，使他成了忠实的仆人，最后还机智地救出了一位英国帆船的船长，帮助船长平息了船上的叛乱，一起回到了阔别35年的故乡。

　　笛福擅长描写环境，细节逼真，令人信服。他的语言自然，不引经据典；故事都是由主人公自述，使读者感到亲切、通俗易懂，具有强烈的艺术魅力。这正是这部作品历久弥新、雅俗共赏的重要原因。

青 闰

2007年6月18日

Contents 目录

　　主人公鲁滨逊·克鲁索从小就渴望冒险，终于有一天离家航海。后来，船在海上失事，他历尽艰险，独自漂泊到了一座荒岛上。在岛上，他想出了很多具有创意的办法，努力活了下来，并救出了被土著人俘虏到岛上的星期五，使他成了忠实的仆人，最后还机智地救出了一位英国帆船的船长，帮助船长平息了船上的叛乱，一起回到了阔别 35 年的故乡。

　　这部作品通过作者丰富的想像、曲折的情节、朴实的语言，鲜明地反映了 18 世纪英国社会的时代特征，真实地描写了离开社会 28 年之久的人所遭遇的逆境和绝望，还有对信仰的感同身受，以及对生活无尽的挑战。

I

I was born in the year 1632, in the City of York, of a good family. I had two elder brothers, one of which was a lieutenant colonel[1] to an English regiment of foot in Flanders[2], killed at the battle near Dunkirk against the Spaniards. What <u>became</u> of my second brother I never knew any more than father or mother did know what was become of me.

Being the third son of the family, and not bred to any trade, my head began to be filled very early with rambling thoughts.

But being one day at Hull, where I went casually, and without any purpose of making an elopement[3] that time; but I say, being there, and one of my companions being going by sea to London, in his father's ship, and prompting me to go with them, with the common allurement[4] of seafaring[5] men, viz.[6], that it should cost me nothing for my passage.

On the first of September 1651, I went on board a ship bound for London. The ship was no sooner gotten out of the Humber but the wind began to blow hard; and as I had never been at sea before, I was sick and terrified. I began now seriously to reflect upon what I had done.

---

[1] lieutenant colonel　*n.* 陆军中校
[2] Flanders 佛兰德斯(包括现比利时东佛兰德省和西佛兰德省及法国北部部分地区)
[3] elopement　*n.* 潜逃，私奔
[4] allurement　*n.* 诱惑物，魅力
[5] seafaring　*adj.* 航海事业的，水手工作的
[6] viz.　<拉> 即，就是(读做 namely)

1

1632 年，我出生在约克城的一个体面家庭。我有两个哥哥：其中一个是驻佛兰德斯的英国步兵团的一名中校，在敦克尔克附近与西班牙人作战时阵亡；第二个的下落，我至今一无所知，就像父母亲对我后来的下落一无所知那样。

因为我在家里排行老三，而且学无所长，所以从小我的脑海里就充满了浪迹天涯的念头。

有一天，我偶然来到了赫尔城，当时还没有离家出走的念头；而我到了那里，我的一个伙伴正要乘他父亲的船去伦敦，并用引诱水手的普通方式怂恿我跟他们一起去，也就是说，不收我任何船钱。

1651 年 9 月 1 日，我登上了开往伦敦的一艘轮船。那艘轮船一出亨伯河，风就开始猛刮起来。我以前从未出过海，所以恶心欲吐、胆战心惊。这时，我开始认真反思自己的所作所为。

All this while the storm increased, and the sea went very high. I expected every wave would have swallowed us up, and that every time the ship fell down, as I thought, in the trough[1] or hollow of the sea, we should never rise more; and in this agony of mind, I made many vows[2] and resolutions[3], that if it would please god here to spare my life this one voyage, if ever I got once my foot upon dry land again, I would go directly home to my father, and never set it into a ship again while I lived.

These wise and sober[4] thoughts continued all the while the storm continued, and indeed some time after; but the next day the wind was abated[5] and the sea calmer, and I began to be a little inured[6] to it. However, I was very grave for all that day, being also a little seasick still; but towards night the weather cleared up, the wind was quite over, and a charming fine evening followed; the sun went down perfectly clear and rose so the next morning; and having little or no wind and a smooth sea, the sun shining upon it, the sight was, as I thought, the most delightful that ever I saw.

I had slept well in the night, and was now no more seasick, but very cheerful, looking with wonder upon the sea that was so rough and terrible the day before, and could be so calm and so pleasant in so little time after.

The sixth day of our being at sea we came into Yarmouth Roads; the wind having been contrary and the weather calm, we had made but little way since the storm. Here we were obliged to come to an anchor, and here we lay, the wind continuing contrary, viz., at southwest, for seven or eight days, during which time a great many ships from Newcastle came into the same Roads, as the common harbour where the ships might wait for a wind for the river.

---

[1] trough   *n.*   槽，水槽
[2] vow   *n.*   誓约
[3] resolution   *n.*   坚定，决心
[4] sober   *adj.*   冷静的，清醒的
[5] abate   *vi.*   (数量、程度等)减少，减轻，缓和
[6] inure   *vt.*   使习惯

此时，风暴越刮越猛，海浪滔天，随时会将我们吞没。每次我们的船跌入浪谷，我就想我们再也升不起来了。在这种极端痛苦的心情中，我一次次地发誓，一次次地下决心，说如果上帝在这次航行中饶我一命，如果我再次踏上干燥的陆地，就马上回到父亲身边，这辈子再也不坐船了。

这些明智而清醒的思想，在暴风肆虐、乃至过后的一段时间，一直萦绕在我的脑海里。但到了第二天，风小了，浪也渐渐静了，我开始对海上生活有点儿习惯了。然而，我整天仍然闷闷不乐，因为我还有点儿晕船。傍晚时分，天晴风停，随之而来的是一个美丽迷人的黄昏。当晚的落日和第二天早上的日出都清澈明朗。此时，风平浪静，阳光照在上面，我想，那种美景最让人心旷神怡，我以前从未见过。

那天夜里，我睡得很香，现在不再晕船了，心情非常愉快，我惊奇地望着昨天还是那样汹涌可怕的大海，没过多时却能如此平静宜人。

在海上航行了六天后，我们驶进了雅茅斯锚地。暴风过后，因为逆风、天气平静，所以我们没走多少路，只得在这里下锚停泊。逆风（即西南风）持续刮了七、八天。在此期间，许多艘来自纽卡斯尔的轮船也都驶进了这个锚地，因为这里是海上公用港口，那些轮船都在这里等候进入河口的顺风。

We had not, however, rid here so long, but should have tided it up the river, but that the wind blew too fresh; and after we had lain four or five days, blew very hard. However, the Roads being reckoned as good as a harbour, the anchorage[1] good, and our ground-tackle very strong, our men were unconcerned, and not in the least apprehensive of danger, but spent the time in rest and mirth[2], after the manner of the sea; but the eighth day in the morning, the wind increased, and we had all hands at work to strike our topmasts[3], and make everything snug[4] and close, that the ship might ride as easy as possible. By noon the sea went very high indeed, and our ship rid forecastle[5] in, shipped several seas, and we thought once or twice our anchor had come home; upon which our master ordered out the sheet anchor[6]; so that we rode with two anchors ahead, and the cables veered[7] out to the bitter end.

Such a dismal sight I never saw: the sea went mountains high, and broke upon us every three or four minutes. When I could look about, I could see nothing but distress round us: two ships that rid near us we found had cut their masts by the board, being deep loaden; and our men cried out, that a ship which rid about a mile ahead of us was foundered[8]. Two more ships being driven from their anchors, were run out of the Roads to sea at all adventures, and that was not a mast standing. The light ships fared the best as not so much labouring in the sea; but two or three of them drove and came close by us, running away with only their spritsail[9] out before the wind.

---

[1] anchorage   *n.* 停泊地点，抛锚地点
[2] mirth   *n.*   欢笑，高兴
[3] topmast   *n.* 中桅
[4] snug   *adj.* 建造良好的，紧密牢固的
[5] forecastle   *n.* 前甲板
[6] sheet anchor   *n.* 备用大锚，最后的希望，最后的手段
[7] veer   *vt.* 使转向，放出（锚）
[8] founder   *vt.* 使沉没，使摔倒
[9] spritsail   *n.* 斜杠帆

我们本来不该在此停泊太久，而是应该趁着潮水驶入河口，但风刮得太紧；而停了四、五天后，风势更猛。然而，由于这块锚地一向被认为是一个良港，是理想的停泊地，而且船上的锚索又很结实，因此水手们都满不在乎，一点儿也不担心有什么危险，而是像在海上那样休息作乐。到第八天早晨，风势增大。于是，我们都一起动手拉下中椼，并把船上的一切东西都捆牢扎紧，以便船尽可能轻松航进。到了中午，大浪滔天，我们的船头钻进了水里，好几次都灌进了海水。有一两次，我们以为船锚已经脱离；因此，船长下令放下备用大锚。这样，我们在船头下了两个锚，而且锚索放到了头。

这种凄惨景象，我以前从未见过：海浪像山一样高，每隔三、四分钟就扑向我们。我环顾四周，只见我们周围危机四伏。我们发现，停泊在我们附近的两艘船因吃水深，已经砍掉了下风板边的那些椼杆。随后，我们船上的人大声呼喊。原来停在我们前面大约一海里远的一艘船已经沉没。还有两艘船被吹得脱了锚，冲出锚地，不顾一切地驶向大海，船上一根椼杆也没有了。那些轻型船境况最好，在海上不那么吃力，但也有两三艘只挂着斜桁帆，被风刮得从我们近旁飞驰而过，向大海漂去。

Towards evening the mate and boatswain[1] begged the master of our ship to let them cut away the foremast, which he was very unwilling to. But the boatswain protesting to him that if he did not the ship would founder, he consented; and when they had cut away the foremast, the mainmast stood so loose, and shook the ship so much, they were obliged to cut her away also, and make a clear deck.

We had a good ship, but she was deep loaden, and wallowed[2] in the sea, that the seamen every now and then cried out, she would founder.

In the middle of the night, and under all the rest of our distresses, one of the men that had been down on purpose to see cried out we had sprung a leak; another said there was four-foot water in the hold. Then all hands were called to the pump.

We worked on pumping, but the water increasing in the hold, it was apparent that the ship would founder, and though the storm began to abate a little, yet as it was not possible she could swim till we might run into a port, so the master fired guns for help; and a light ship who had rid it out just ahead of us ventured a boat out to help us. So, partly rowing and partly driving, our boat went away to the norward[3] sloping wards the shore almost as far as Winterton Ness.

We were not much more than a quarter of an hour out of our ship but we saw her sink, and then I understood for the first time what was meant by a ship foundering in the sea.

While we were in this condition, the men yet labouring the oar to bring the boat near the shore, we could see, when, our boat mounting the waves, we were able to see the shore, a great many people running along the shore to assist us when we should come near, but we made but slow way towards the shore, nor were we able to reach the shore, till being past the lighthouse at Winterton, the shore falls off to the westward towards Cromer, and so the land broke off a little the violence of the wind. Here we got in, and, though not without much difficulty, got all safe on shore.

---

[1] boatswain   *n.* 水手长
[2] wallow   *vi.* 打滚，<喻>颠簸
[3] norward   *n.* 北方，北部

到了傍晚，大副和水手长请求我们的船长砍掉前桅，船长不愿答应。但水手长向他抗议说，他不答应，船就会沉没，船长只好答应了。而当船上砍掉前桅时，主桅随风摇晃，船也晃得越发厉害。他们只得把主桅也砍掉，只剩下一个空荡荡的甲板。

尽管我们的船非常坚固，但因载货重、吃水深，并在海里打晃，水手们不时地大声喊叫，船要沉没了。

到了半夜，更是雪上加霜，其中一个下去到船舱底查看的人跑上来大声喊道：漏水了；另一个水手跑上来说，底舱里的水有四英尺深了。于是，全船的人都被叫去抽水。

尽管我们不断抽水，但底舱里进水越来越多。显然，我们的船将会沉没。这时，尽管暴风开始减小，但我们不可能让船驶进港口了。于是，船长鸣枪求救。有一艘刚刚漂过我们前面的轻型船冒险放下一只小艇来救我们。于是，我们一边划着小艇，一边随浪逐流，歪歪斜斜地向北方的岸边漂去，差不多漂到了温特顿海角。

离开大船不到一刻钟，我们就看到它沉下去了。这时，我才第一次明白大海沉船是怎么回事。

尽管我们处在这种境地，但水手们还是奋力向岸边划动小艇。当小艇被冲上浪峰时，我们能看到海岸，只见岸上有好多人跑来跑去，想等小艇靠岸时援救我们。但小艇前进速度很慢，而且怎么也靠不了岸，最后一直划过了温特顿灯塔。海岸由此向西偏离，朝克罗默伸去。这样，陆地挡住了一点风势。我们在这里靠岸，尽管非常吃力，但大家都安全上了岸。

II

Had I now had the sense to have gone back to Hull, and have gone home, I would have been happy; and though I had several times loud calls from my reason and my more composed judgment to go home, yet I had no power to do it.

And I went on board a vessel bound to the coast of Africa; or, as our sailors vulgarly[1] call it, a voyage to Guinea.

This was the only voyage which I may say was successful in all my adventures, and which I owe to the integrity[2] and honesty of my friend the captain, under whom I got a competent knowledge of the mathematics and the rules of navigation, learned how to keep an account of the ship's course, take an observation. In a word, this voyage made me both a sailor and a merchant; for I brought home five pounds nine ounces of gold dust for my adventure, which yielded me in London at my return, almost 300 pounds, and this filled me with those aspiring thoughts which have since so completed my ruin.

Yet even in this voyage I had my misfortunes too; particularly, that I was continually sick, being thrown into a violent calenture by the excessive heat of the climate; our principal trading being upon the coast, from the latitude of 15 degrees north even to the line it self.

I was now set up for a Guinea trader; and my friend, to my great misfortune, dying soon after his arrival, I resolved to go the same voyage again, and I embarked in the same vessel with one who was his mate in the former voyage, and had now got the command of the ship.

---

[1] vulgarly *adv.* 通俗地，普通地，庸俗地
[2] integrity *n.* 正直，诚实

2

如果我当时理智地返回赫尔，并回到家里，我一定会非常幸福。尽管我的理性和比较冷静的头脑曾向我大声喊过好几次，要我回家，但我却没有力量这样做。

于是，我踏上了一艘驶往非洲海岸的船；就像我们的水手们通常所称的那样，到几内亚去走一趟。

可以说，这是我所有历险中唯一成功的一次航行。我把这归功于那位船长朋友的正直诚实。在他的指导下，我掌握了一些数学知识和航海规则，学会了如何记录轮船航程、如何测天。总之，这次航行使我既成了水手又成了商人，因为这次航行我带回了 5 磅 9 盎司金粉。回到伦敦后，我换回了差不多 300 英镑。这更使我雄心勃勃，也因此断送了我的一生。

不过，这次航行我也有倒霉事儿；尤其是我们做生意主要在从北纬15 度到赤道的岸边，气候异常炎热，所以我得了一种严重的热病，总是不断生病。

我现在自命为几内亚商人。非常倒霉的是，那位朋友抵港后不久就去世了。我决定再到几内亚去一趟，就踏上了同一艘船。这时，船上原来的大副做了船长。

This was the unhappiest voyage that ever man made; for though I did not carry quite 100 pounds of my new gained wealth, so that I had 200 left, and which I lodged[1] with my friend's widow, yet I fell into terrible misfortunes in this voyage.

Our ship making her course towards the Canary Islands, or rather between those islands and the African shore, was surprised in the grey of the morning, by a Turkish Rover of Sallee, who gave chase to us with all the sail she could make. We crowded also as much canvas as our masts carry, to have got clear; but finding the pirate[2] gained upon us, and would certainly come up with us in a few hours, we prepared to fight; our ship having 12 guns, and the rogue[3] 18. About three in the afternoon he came up with us, and bringing to, by mistake, just athwart[4] our quarter, instead of athwart our stern, as he intended, we brought 8 of our guns to bear on that side, and poured in a broadside upon him, which made him sheer off[5] again, after returning our fire, and pouring in also his small shot from near 200 men which he had on board. However, we had not a man touched, all our men keeping close. He prepared to attack us again, and we to defend ourselves; but laying us on board the next time upon our other quarter, he entered 60 men upon our decks, who immediately fell to cutting and hacking the decks and rigging. We plied them and cleared our deck of them twice. However, our ship being disabled, and three of our men killed, and eight wounded, we were obliged to yield, and were carried all prisoners into Sallee, a port belonging to the Moors[6].

The usage I had there was not so dreadful as at first I apprehended[7], nor was I carried up the country to the emperor's court, as the rest of our men were, but was kept by the captain of the rover, as his proper prize, and made his slave, being young and nimble[8], and fit for his business.

---

[1] lodge   *vt.* 容纳，寄存
[2] pirate   *n.* 海盗，盗版者
[3] rogue   *n.*   流氓，无赖
[4] athwart   *prep.* 横过，逆
[5] sheer off   避开，转向
[6] Moor   摩尔人（非洲西北部伊斯兰教民族）
[7] apprehend   *vt.* 理解；害怕，忧虑
[8] nimble   *adj.*   敏捷的

这是有史以来最不幸的一次航行，因为尽管我只带了刚赚的其中100英镑，余下的200英镑寄存在了朋友遗孀那里，但在这次航行中，我却屡遭可怕的不幸。

我们的船向加那利群岛驶去，或者更确切地说，正航行在那些群岛和非洲海岸之间。一天拂晓时分，突然有一艘来自萨利的土耳其海盗船张满帆，向我们追来。我们的船也张满帆，试图逃跑。但我们发现海盗船渐渐逼近我们，再过几小时它肯定会追上我们。我们做好了战斗准备。我们船上有12门炮，海盗船上则有18门。大约到了下午3点，他们的船追上了我们。它本想横冲我们的船尾，却误冲到了我们的后舷上。我们把其中八门炮瞄准了那边，一齐向它开火。海盗船一边后退，一边还击，同时船上将近200人也一齐用枪向我们射击。然而，因为我们的人隐蔽得好，所以没有一个人受伤。海盗船准备向我们再次发动攻击，我们也准备自卫。这次，他们从后舷的另一侧靠上我们的船，60人跳上了我们的甲板。他们一上船，就马上对我们的舱面和索具一阵乱劈乱砍。我们不断向他们发动进攻，并把他们从我们的甲板上击退了两次。然而，我们的船最后失去了战斗力，而且死了三个，伤了八个，我们被迫投降，全被俘虏到了摩尔人的一个港口——萨利。

我在那里受到的待遇并没有像我当初担心的那样可怕，也没有像其他人那样被押到皇宫，而是被海盗船长作为特有的战利品留下，成了他的奴隶，因为我年轻伶俐，正合他意。

As my master had taken me home to his house, so I was in hopes that he would take me with him when he went to sea again, believing that it would some time or other be his fate to be taken by a Spanish or Portugal man-of-war; and that then I should be set at liberty. But this hope of mine was soon taken away; for when he went to sea, he left me on shore to look after his little garden, and do the common drudgery[1] of slaves about his house; and when he came home again from his cruise, he ordered me to lie in the cabin to look after the ship.

Here I meditated nothing but my escape and what method I might take to effect it, but found no way that had the least probability in it.

---

[1] drudgery   *n.* 苦差事，苦工

主人把我带回他的家里，我一直希望他再次出海时会带上我，我相信总有一天他会被西班牙或葡萄牙的战舰俘获，那时我就可以自由了。但我这个希望很快就破灭了，因为每次出海，他总把我留在岸上照看他的小花园，并在家里做一些奴隶的苦活儿；而他巡航回来时，又吩咐我躺到船舱里看船。

　　我在这里只想着逃跑和采取什么办法能实现这个愿望，但根本找不到任何可能的办法。

III

After about two years my master used constantly, once or twice a week, sometimes oftener, if the weather was fair, to take the ship's pinnace[1], and go out into the road a-fishing; and as he always took me and a young Moor with him to row the boat, we made him very merry, and I proved very dexterous[2] in catching fish; insomuch, that sometimes he would send me with a Moor, one of his kinsmen[3], and the youth, the Maresco, as they called him, to catch a dish of fish for him.

It happened one time, that going a-fishing in a stark[4] calm morning, a fog rose so thick, that though we were not half a league[5] from the shore we lost sight of it; and rowing we knew not whither or which way, we laboured all day and all the next night, and when the morning came we found we had pulled off to sea instead of pulling in for the shore; and that we were at least two leagues from the shore. However, we got well in again with a great deal of labour, and some danger.

But our patron, warned by this disaster, resolved to take more care of himself for the future; and having lying by him the longboat of our English ship we had taken, he resolved he would not go a-fishing any more without a compass and some provision; so he ordered the carpenter of his ship, who also was an English slave, to build a little stateroom or cabin in the middle of the longboat, with a place to stand behind it to steer and hale[6] home the mainsheet; and room before for a hand or two to stand and work the sails.

---

[1] pinnace   _n._ 装载于舰上的中型艇
[2] dexterous   _adj._ 灵巧的，惯用右手的
[3] kinsman   _n._   亲戚
[4] stark   _adv._ 完全地
[5] league   _n._ 里格(长度单位=3 哩)
[6] hale   _vt._   <古>强拉，硬拖

3

大约两年后，主人经常坐舢舨去外面的锚地捕鱼；每星期至少一两次，天气晴朗的话，去的更勤。他总是让我和一个摩尔族男孩替他划船。我们让他非常开心，而我也确实是一个捕鱼能手。因此，有时他就让我和他的一个摩尔族亲戚以及那个名叫莫里斯科的摩尔族男孩一起去为他打点儿鱼吃。

一天早晨，风平浪静，我们又出海打鱼。突然，大雾弥漫。我们才划了半里格，就看不见海岸了。当时，我们分不清东南西北，只顾划船。我们这样划了一天一夜，到第二天早晨才发现，我们不仅没有划近海岸，反而划向外海去了，离岸至少有两里格。不过，我们费了很大劲儿，冒了一些险，才又平安返航。

这次不幸给我们主人敲了个警钟，他决定以后更加小心，不带指南针和一些食物绝不出海捕鱼。正好在他俘获的我们那艘英国船上有一只大艇。他吩咐船上的木匠——也是他的一个英国奴隶——在大艇中间做一个小客舱，舱后留了一些空间，可让一个人站在那里掌舵和拉主帆；舱前也有一些空档，可让一两个人站在那里升降帆。

We went frequently out with this boat a-fishing, and as I was most dextrous to catch fish for him, he never went without me. It happened that he had appointed to go out in this boat, either for pleasure or for fish, with two or three Moors of some distinction in that place, and for whom he had provided extraordinarily; and had therefore sent on board the boat over night, a larger store of provisions than ordinary; and had ordered me to get ready three fuzees[1] with powder and shot, which were on board his ship; for that they designed some sport of fowling[2] as well as fishing.

I got all things ready as he had directed. The next morning my patron came on board alone, and told me his guests had put off going, upon some business that fell out, and ordered me with the man and boy, as usual, to go out with the boat and catch them some fish, for that his friends were to sup[3] at his house; and commanded that as soon as I had got some fish I should bring it home to his house.

This moment my former notions of deliverance[4] darted into my thoughts, for now I found I was like to have a little ship at my command; and my master being gone, I prepared to furnish myself, not for a fishing business but for a voyage.

My first contrivance[5] was to make a pretence[6] to speak to this Moor, to get something for our substance on board; for I told him we must not presume to eat of our patron's bread, he said that was true; so he brought a large basket of rusk[7], and three jars with fresh water into the boat; I knew where my patron's case of bottles stood; and I conveyed them into the boat while the Moor was on shore. I conveyed also a great lump of beeswax[8] into the boat, which weighed above half a hundredweight, with a parcel of twine, a hatchet[9], a saw and a hammer, all which were of great use to us afterwards; especially the wax to make candles.

---

1 fuzee   *n.* 短枪
2 fowling   *n.*   捕鸟，打鸟
3 sup   *vi.* 吃晚饭，啜饮
4 deliverance   *n.*   释放；判决
5 contrivance   *n.* 发明，想出的办法
6 pretence   *n.* 伪装
7 rusk   *n.* 甜面包干，一片甜面包干
8 beeswax   *n.* 蜂蜡
9 hatchet   *n.* 短柄斧

我们从此就经常坐这只大艇出海捕鱼。因为我捕鱼手艺很高，所以他没有一次不带着我去。有一次，他约定要和当地两三位有声望的摩尔人坐我们的大艇出海解闷或捕鱼。为了款待客人，他为他们特地准备了比平常多的食品，并在前一天晚上就送上了船。他还吩咐我把他的大船上的三支短枪备好弹药。看来，他们不仅想捕鱼，还想打鸟儿玩。

我按照他的指示，把一切都准备停当。第二天早晨，主人独自走上船来，对我说，因为客人们临时有事，行程延期，然后又吩咐我、那个摩尔人和男孩像往常一样出去打一些鱼，因为他的朋友们要在他的家里吃晚饭，他命令，我一打到鱼，就马上送到家里。

这时，我先前想逃跑的念头又突然冒了出来，因为我现在发现自己可以支配一条小船了。主人一走，我就着手准备起来，不是准备去捕鱼，而是准备去航行。

我想出的第一个办法就是假装对这个摩尔人说，我们要自己动手准备船上吃的东西，因为我们不应该擅自吃主人的面包。他说我说的不错，就向船里提来了一大篮甜饼干，以及三罐子淡水。我知道主人装酒的箱子放在什么地方，便趁那个摩尔人上岸时把那箱酒搬到了船上。我又把半英担多蜂蜡搬到船上，还拿了一小包麻绳、一把短柄斧、一条锯子和一把锤子；这些东西后来对我们都大有用处，尤其是可用来做蜡烛的蜂蜡。

Another trick I tried upon him, which he innocently came into also; his name was Ismael, who they call Moely, so I called to him, "Moely, our patron's guns are on board the boat; can you not get a little powder and shot? It may be we may kill some curlews[1] for ourselves, for I know he keeps the gunner's stores in the ship." "Yes," said he, "I'll bring some," and accordingly he brought a great leather pouch[2] which held about a pound and half of powder; and another with shot, that had five or six pound, with some bullets. At the same time I had found some powder of my master's in the great cabin, with which I filled one of the large bottles in the case, which was almost empty; pouring what was in it into another; and thus furnished with everything needful, we sailed out of the port to fish. The castle, which is at the entrance of the port, knew who we were, and took no notice of us; and we were not above a mile out of the port before we haled in our sail, and set us down to fish: The wind blew from the north-northeast, which was contrary to my desire; for had it blown southerly I had been sure to have made the coast of Spain, and at least reached to the bay of Cadiz; but my resolutions were, blow which way it would, I would be gone from that horrid place where I was, and leave the rest to fate.

After we had fished some time and caught nothing, for when I had fish on my hook, I would not pull them up; I said to the Moor, "This will not do, our master will not be thus served, we must stand farther off." He, thinking no harm, agreed, and being in the head of the boat, set the sails; and as I had the helm[3], I ran the boat out near a league farther and then brought her to stop as if I would fish; when giving the boy the helm, I stepped forward to where the Moor was, and making as if I stooped for something behind him, I took him by surprise with my arm under his twist, and tossed him clear overboard into the sea; he rose immediately, for he swam like a cork[4], and called to me, begged to be taken in, told me he would go all over the world with me.

---

[1] curlew *n.* 一种鸟
[2] pouch *n.* 小袋，烟草袋
[3] helm *n.* 舵
[4] cork *n.* 软木塞，软木

20

随后，我又想出了一个窍门，他也信以为真。他的名字叫伊斯梅尔，大家都叫他穆利，所以我向他喊道："穆利，我们主人的枪都在小船上，你不能去搞点儿弹药来吗？也许我们还能给自己打几只鸟儿呢，因为我知道他把弹药放在大船上。""好，"他说，"我去弄些来。"于是，他就去弄来了一大皮袋火药，大约有一磅半重。他还拎来了一大皮袋鸟枪子弹和其他子弹，足有五、六磅重。同时，我又在大舱里找到了主人的一些火药，从箱子里找出一只几乎喝完的大酒瓶，把剩下的酒倒进另一只瓶子，将空瓶装满火药。于是，准备好一切所需的东西后，我们就出港捕鱼。港口城堡里的人都知道我们是谁，所以就没有理会我们。我们出港不到一英里，就落下帆，开始捕鱼。这时，风向东北偏北，正好和我的愿望相反，因为如果刮南风，我就有把握将船开到西班牙海岸，至少可以开到加的斯海湾，但我决心已定，无论什么风向，只要离开我呆的这个可怕地方，剩下的就听天由命吧。

　　我们捕了一阵鱼，什么也没有捕到，因为有鱼上钩时，我总不把它们钓上来。我对那个摩尔人说："这不行，我们拿什么招待自己的主人呀，我们必须走远点儿。"他认为这样做无妨，就表示同意。因为他在船头，所以就张起了帆；我在船尾掌舵，把船驶出了将近一里格，然后把船停下，仿佛我要捕鱼。我把舵递给那个男孩，向摩尔人站的地方走去。我弯下腰，装作像在他身后寻找什么东西的样子，出其不意拦腰抱住他，把他一下抛进了海里。因为他水性好，所以马上就凫出了海面，向我喊叫，求我拉他上船，说他愿意跟我走遍世界。

He swam so strong after the boat that he would have reached me very quickly; upon which I stepped into the cabin and fetching one of the fowling-pieces, I presented it at him, and told him I had done him no hurt and, if he would be quiet I would do him none.

I said, "You swim well enough to reach to the shore, and the sea is calm, make the best of your way to shore and I will do you no harm, but if you come near the boat I'll shoot you through the head." So he turned himself about and swam for the shore.

I could have been content to have taken this Moor with me, and have drowned the boy, but there was no venturing[1] to trust him. When he was gone I turned to the boy, who they called Xury, and said to him, "Xury, if you will be faithful to me I'll make you a great man, but if you will not be true to me, I must throw you into the sea too." The boy smiled in my face and swore to be faithful to me and go all over the world with me.

While I was in view of the Moor that was swimming, I stood out directly to sea with the boat, rather stretching to windward, that they might think me gone towards the Straits' mouth, for who would have supposed we were sailed on to the southward to the truly barbarian coast, where whole nations of Negroes were sure to surround us with their canoes, and destroy us; where we could ne'er once go on shore but we should be devoured by savage beasts, or more merciless savages of human kind.

But as soon as it grew dusk[2] in the evening, I changed my course, and steered directly south and by east, bending my course a little toward the east, that I might keep in with the shore; and having a fair fresh gale of wind, and a smooth quiet sea, I made such sail that I believe by the next day at three o'clock in the afternoon, when I first made the land, I could not be less than 150 miles south of Sallee; quite beyond the emperor of Morocco's dominions[3], or indeed of any other king thereabouts, for we saw no people.

Yet such was the fright I had taken at the Moors, and the dreadful apprehensions I had of falling into their hands, that I would not stop, or go on shore, or come to an anchor; the wind continuing fair, till I had sailed in that manner five days.

---

[1] venture   *v.* 冒险，冒昧
[2] dusk   *adj.* 幽暗的，微黑的
[3] dominion   *n.* 主权，领土

他跟在船后面游得很猛，很快就会追上我。我走进船舱，拿出一支鸟枪，举枪瞄准了他，然后对他说，我没想伤害他，如果他不惹事生非，我绝不会伤害他。

我说："你水性够好的，能游到岸边。再说，海上风平浪静，你尽力游回岸边，我绝不会伤害你，但如果你靠近船，我就射穿你的脑袋。"于是，他回转身，向海岸方向游去。

我本可以带上这个摩尔人、淹死那个男孩，但我不敢冒昧信任他。他走后，我转向那个男孩（人们都叫他苏利）对他说："苏利，如果你对我忠诚，我会让你成为一个了不起的人。但如果你不对我忠心耿耿，我也把你扔进海里。"那个男孩向我露出了微笑，并发誓对我忠诚，跟我走遍世界。

在那个凫水的摩尔人看见我的同时，我直接让小船逆风向大海驶去。这样，他们就可能会以为我是驶向直布罗陀海峡口，谁会想到我们会继续朝南驶向真正野人出没的海岸。到了那里，所有的黑人部族就会用独木舟把我们团团包围，并消灭我们；到了那里，我们根本上不了岸，就会被野兽们或更残忍的野人吞吃掉。

但傍晚天一黑，我就改变航向，直接朝南偏东方向驶去，同时又拐了点弯向东驶去，这样我就可以沿着海岸航行了。这时，一路顺风，海面平滑如镜，我张起帆，相信第二天下午三点到达陆地时，我肯定会在萨利以南 150 英里，完全超过了摩洛哥皇帝的领土或任何国王的地界，因为我们根本看不到人。

然而，我心惊胆战，害怕摩尔人，恐怕再落入他们的手里，一路上不敢停留，不敢上岸，也不敢抛锚，一路顺风，就这样航行了五天。

And then the wind shifting to the southward, I concluded also that if any of their vessels were in chase of me, they also would now give over; so I ventured to make to the coast, and came to an anchor in the mouth of a little river. I knew not where; I neither saw or desired to see any people; the principal thing I wanted was fresh water. We came into this creek in the evening, resolving to swim on shore as soon as it was dark; but as soon as it was quite dark, we heard such dreadful noises of the barking, roaring, and howling of wild creatures that the poor boy was ready to die with fear, and begged of me not to go on shore till day.

I took his advice. We dropped our little anchor and lay still all night; I say still, for we slept none! For in two or three hours we saw vast great creatures of many sorts, come down to the seashore and run into the water, wallowing and washing themselves; and they made such hideous[1] howlings and yellings, that I never indeed heard the like.

Xury was dreadfully frightened, and indeed so was I too; but we were both more frightened when we heard one of these mighty creatures come swimming towards our boat; we could not see him, but we might hear him by his blowing to be a monstrous, huge and furious beast; Xury said it was a lion and cried to me to weigh the anchor and row away.

"No," said I, "Xury, we can slip our cable with the buoy[2] to it and go off to sea; they cannot follow us far."

I had no sooner said so but I perceived the creature within two oars' length; I immediately stepped to the cabin door, and taking up my gun, fired at him, upon which he immediately turned about and swam towards the shore again.

Be that as it would, we were obliged to go on shore somewhere or other for water, for we had not a pint[3] left in the boat; when or where to get to it was the point. Xury said if I would let him go on shore with one of the jars, he would find if there was any water and bring some to me. I asked him why he would go and why I should not go and he stay in the boat. The boy answered with so much affection that made me love him ever after.

---

[1] hideous *adj.* 骇人听闻的，可怕的
[2] buoy *n.* (湖、河等中的)浮标，浮筒，救生圈
[3] pint *n.* 品脱（英＝0.568 升，美＝0.473 升）

这时，风向转成了南风。我断定，就是他们有船追我，现在也肯定会偃旗息鼓。于是，我斗胆驶向海岸，在一个小河口抛锚。我不知道是在什么地方，看不到一个人，也不想看到任何人；我现在想要的主要东西是淡水。我们傍晚驶进了这条小河，决定天一黑就游上岸。但天一黑，我们就听到了各种野兽狂吠、咆哮和嚎叫，那个可怜的男孩吓得要死，哀求我等天亮后再上岸。

我接受了他的建议。我们抛下小锚，静静地躺了一夜。我之所以说"静静地"，是因为我们都没有合眼！因为两三个小时后，我们看到好多种巨兽来到海边，跳进水里，又是打滚，又是洗澡；它们发出骇人听闻的嚎叫和吼声，我确实从未听过这种声音。

苏利吓得心惊肉跳，我也吓得要死。但更让我们心惊胆战的是，我们听到有一头巨兽向我们船边游来；尽管我们看不见它，但从它的喘息声，我们听出它可能是一头凶暴狂怒的巨兽。苏利说是一头狮子，向我哭叫，要我起锚把船划走。

"不，"我说，"苏利，我们可以悄悄把锚索和浮筒一起放出来，把船向海里移动，它们跟不了我们多远。"

我话音刚落，就察觉到巨兽离船不到两桨远了。我马上走到舱门口，拿起枪，对它开了一枪。它立即转过身，又向岸边游去。

无论如何，我们必须得上岸到什么地方弄点儿淡水，因为船上剩下的水不到一品脱了。问题是什么时候、到什么地方去弄。苏利说，如果我让他拿个罐子上岸，他会去找找看有没有水，有的话就给我带回来。我问他，为什么他要自己去，为什么不让我去，让他留在船上。这个男孩回答得情深意长，这使我从此爱上了他。

He said, "If wild men come, they can eat me; you can go away."

"Well, Xury," said I, "we will both go, and if the wild men come, we will kill them; they shall eat neither of us."

So we waded on shore, carrying nothing but our arms and two jars for water.

I did not care to go out of sight of the boat, fearing the coming of canoes with savages down the river; but the boy seeing a low place about a mile up the country rambled[1] to it; and by and by I saw him come running towards me. I thought he was pursued by some savage, or frightened with some wild beast, and I run forward towards him to help him, but when I came nearer to him, I saw something hanging over his shoulders which was a creature that he had shot, like a hare, but different in colour, and longer legs, however, we were very glad of it, and it was very good meat; but the great joy that Xury came with was that he had found good water and seen no wild men.

But we found afterwards that we need not take such pains for water, for a little higher up the creek where we were, we found the water fresh when the tide was out; so we filled our jars and feasted on the hare we had killed, and prepared to go on our way.

As I had been one voyage to this coast before, I knew very well that the islands of the Canaries and the Cape Verde Islands also lay not far off from the coast. But as I had no instruments to take an observation to know what latitude[2] we were in, and did not exactly know or at least remember what latitude they were in, I knew not where to look for them or when to stand off to sea towards them; otherwise I might now easily have found some of these islands. But my hope was, that if I stood along this coast till I came to that part where the English traded, I should find some of their vessels upon their usual design of trade, that would relieve and take us in.

By the best of my calculation, that place where I now was must be that country, which lying between the Emperor of Morocco's dominions and the Negroes', lies waste and uninhabited, except by wild beasts.

---

[1] ramble *v.* 漫游
[2] latitude *n.* 纬度，范围

他说："如果野人来了，他们吃掉我，你可以逃走。"

"好吧，苏利，"我说，"我们一块去。野人来了，我们就打死他们，我们俩谁也不会让他们吃掉。"

于是，我们就只带了武器和两只水罐，一起涉水上岸。

我不敢走得离船太远，害怕野人的独木舟从河上游顺流而下，但那男孩看到一英里外的地带有一块凹地，就漫步走去。不一会儿，我就见他朝我跑来。我以为是有野人追他，或是受了什么野兽的惊吓，就赶忙跑上前去救他，但我跑近时，才看到他肩上背着一个什么东西，原来是他打到的一只像野兔一样的动物，但颜色和野兔的不一样，腿也比较长。我们为此非常高兴，而且这东西的肉很好吃。但苏利带来的更大喜讯是，他已经找到了淡水，也没见到有野人。

但后来我们发现，我们不必费那么大劲儿去取水，因为沿着我们所在的小河往上走一点儿，潮水一退，便可找到淡水。于是，我们把所有的罐子都灌满了水，又饱餐了一顿我们打来的野兔，准备继续赶路。

我以前曾到这个海岸航行过一次，很清楚加那利群岛和佛得角群岛离海岸不远。但因为我没有任何仪器测天，来了解我们所在的是什么纬度，或者至少不记得这些群岛所在的纬度，所以不知道到哪里寻找这些群岛，也不知道什么时候该离开海岸，向这些群岛驶去，否则我现在可能会轻而易举找到其中一些海岛。不过，我希望，如果沿着这个海岸航行，一直走到英国人做生意的那个地方，我会在那里找到经常来往的一些商船，他们一定会解救并收留我们。

按我最好的估计，我眼下所在的地方很可能是在摩洛哥王国和黑人部落之间的那个地带，除了野兽，这里荒无人烟。

The Negroes having abandoned it and gone farther south for fear of the Moors; and the Moors not thinking it worth inhabiting, by reason of its barrenness[1]; and indeed both forsaking[2] it because of the prodigious[3] numbers of tigers, lions, leopards and other furious creatures which harbour there; so that the Moors use it for their hunting only, where they go like an army, two or three thousand men at a time; and indeed for near a hundred miles together upon this coast, we saw nothing but a waste uninhabited country by day and heard nothing but howlings and roaring of wild beasts by night.

Once or twice in the daytime, I thought I saw the high top of the Mountain Teneriffe in the Canaries; and had a great mind to venture out, in hopes of reaching thither[4]; but having tried twice, I was forced in again by contrary winds, the sea also going too high for my little vessel, so I resolved to pursue my first design and keep along the shore.

Several times I was obliged to land for fresh water, after we had left this place; and once in particular, being early in the morning, we came to an anchor under a little point of land; Xury called softly to me, and told me that we had best go farther off the shore.

He said, "Look, yonder[5] lies a dreadful monster on the side of that hillock[6] fast asleep."

I looked where he pointed, and saw a dreadful monster indeed, for it was a terrible great lion that lay on the side of the shore.

"Xury," said I, "you shall go on shore and kill him."

Xury looked frightened, and said, "I kill him? He'll eat me at one mouthful."

So I took our biggest gun and loaded it with a good charge of powder, and with two slugs; then I loaded another gun with two bullets, and the third, I loaded with five smaller bullets.

---

[1] barrenness   *n.*   荒凉，荒芜
[2] forsake   *vt.* 放弃，抛弃
[3] prodigious   *adj.* 巨大的
[4] thither   *adv.* 到那边，向那方
[5] yonder   *adv.* 在那边
[6] hillock   *n.* 小丘

黑人因害怕摩尔人而放弃此地迁往了南方；摩尔人认为这里土地贫瘠，不值得居住。其实，摩尔人和黑人都放弃这块地方，是因为这里野兽众多，是老虎、狮子、豹子和其他猛兽的栖息地。因此，摩尔人只是把它作为狩猎场。他们每次来时有两三千人，浩浩荡荡像军队似的。事实上，我们沿海岸走了将近100英里，白天只看到一片荒芜，杳无人迹，夜里只听到野兽的嚎叫和咆哮。

　　白天有一两次，我想自己看到了加那利群岛上泰尼利夫山高高的山顶，便很想冒险把船开过去，希望到达那里。但我试了两次，都被逆风推了回来。同时，对我们的小船来说海浪太高，所以我决定按照原先的计划，继续沿海岸行驶。

　　我们离开这个地方后，也有好几次不得不上岸取淡水。特别是有一天大清早，我们来到一个小尖岬地抛了锚。苏利向我轻声叫喊，我们最好离岸远点儿。

　　他说：“看，那里的小山坡上有一个可怕的怪物正在熟睡。”

　　我朝他手指的方向望去，果然看到一个可怕的怪物，原来是一头可怕的巨狮躺在岸边。

　　“苏利，”我说。“你上岸去把它打死。”

　　苏利露出惊恐的神情，说：“我把它打死？它会一口吃了我。”

　　于是，我拿起最大的一支枪，装了大量火药，又装了两颗大子弹，然后给另一支枪装了两颗子弹，给第三支枪装了五颗小子弹。

I took the best aim I could with the first piece to have shot him into the head, but he lay so with his leg raised a little above his nose, that the slugs[1] hit his leg about the knee, and broke the bone. He started up growling at first, but finding his leg broke fell down again, and then got up upon three legs and gave the most hideous roar that ever I heard; I was a little surprised that I had not hit him on the head. I took up the second piece immediately and though he began to move off fired again, and shot him into the head, and had the pleasure to see him drop, and make but little noise, but lay struggling for life.

Then Xury took heart, and would have me let him go on shore.

"Well, go," said I.

So the boy jumped into the water, and taking a little gun in one hand swam to shore with the other hand, and coming close to the creature, put the muzzle[2] of the piece to his ear, and shot him into the head again, which dispatched him quite.

After this stop we made on to the southward continually for ten or twelve days, living very sparing on our provisions, which began to abate very much, and going no oftener into the shore than we were obliged to for fresh water; my design in this was to make the River Gambia or Senegal, that is to say, anywhere about the Cape Verde, where I was in hopes to meet with some European ship, and if I did not, I knew not what course I had to take, but to seek out for the islands, or perish there among the Negroes.

I knew that all the ships from Europe, which sailed either to the coast of Guinea, or to Brazil, or to the East Indies, made this cape or those islands; and in a word, I put the whole of fortune upon this single point, either that I must meet with some ship, or must perish.

When I had pursued this resolution about ten days longer, I began to see that the land was inhabited, and in two or three places as we sailed by, we saw people stand upon the shore to look at us; we could also perceive they were quite black and stark-naked. I was once inclined to have gone on shore to them; but Xury said to me, "Don't go. Don't go."

---

[1] slug   *n.*   （形状不规则的）子弹，弹丸
[2] muzzle   *n.* 动物之鼻口；枪口，喷嘴

我拿起第一支大枪，尽力瞄准那狮子的脑袋开了一枪。但那狮子躺着时，一条腿微微抬到了鼻子上方，子弹打在了它的膝盖上，打断了腿骨。狮子先是吼叫着惊跳起来，但发现那条腿断了，便又跌倒在地，然后用三条腿站起来，发出了我有生以来听到过的最可怕的咆哮。我见自己没有打中狮子的头部，微微吃了一惊。这时，尽管狮子开始走开，但我还是马上拿起第二支枪，又开了一枪，打中了它的头部。我开心地看到它倒下，只轻轻地吼了一声，便躺在那里拼命挣扎起来。

这时，苏利来了精神，要求我让他上岸。

"好，去吧！"我说。

于是，那男孩跳进水里，一只手举着短枪，另一只手划着水，游近那头狮子，把枪口放在它的耳边，向它的头部又开了一枪，彻底结果了它的性命。

这次停船后，我们向南连续航行了十一二天，我们的粮食开始大大减少，吃得非常节省，而且要不是必须取淡水上岸，我们通常不靠岸。我这样做的计划是要把船开到冈比亚河或塞内加尔河，也就是说，佛得海角附近的任何地方，我希望在那里遇上欧洲的某个商船。如果遇不到，我就不知道该走哪条航线了，只好去寻找那些群岛，或者死在黑人那里了。

我知道，所有从欧洲开往几内亚海岸、巴西或东印度群岛的商船都要经过这个海角或那些群岛。总之，我把整个命运都押在了这一点上，要么很可能遇上某个商船，要么很可能死路一条。

我抱着这个决心又向前航行了大约 10 天，这时开始看到了陆地上有人居住。我们开船经过时，看到有两三个地方的人们站在岸上望着我们，同时还可以看到，他们浑身黝黑、一丝不挂。有一次，我很想上岸到他们身边去，但苏利对我说："别去。别去。"

However, I haled in nearer the shore that I might talk to them, and I found they ran along the shore by me a good way. I observed they had no weapons in their hands, except one who had a slender stick, which Xury said was a lance[1], and that they could throw them a great way with good aim; so I kept at a distance, but talked with them by signs as well as I could, and particularly made signs for something to eat. They beckoned[2] me to stop my boat, and that they would fetch me some meat; upon this I lowered the top of my sail, and two of them ran up into the country, and in less than half an hour came back and brought with them two pieces of dry flesh and some corn. We were willing to accept it, but how to come at it was our next dispute, for I was not for venturing on shore to them, and they were as much afraid of us; but they took a safe way for us all, for they brought it to the shore and laid it down, and went and stood a great way off till we fetched it on board and then they came close to us again.

We made signs of thanks to them, for we had nothing to make them amends; but an opportunity offered that very instant to oblige them wonderfully, for while we were lying by the shore, came two mighty creatures, one pursuing the other (as we took it) with great fury from the mountains towards the sea. I had loaded my gun with all possible expedition, and bade[3] Xury load both the other; as soon as he came fairly within my reach, I fired, and shot him directly into the head; immediately he sunk down into the water, but rose instantly and plunged up and down as if he was struggling for life; he immediately made to the shore, but because of his mortal hurt and the strangling[4] of the water, he died just before he reached the shore.

It is impossible to express the astonishment of these poor creatures at the noise and the fire of my gun. But when they saw the creature dead and sunk in the water, and that I made signs to them to come to the shore; they took heart and came to the shore and began to search for the creature. I found him by his blood staining the water, and by the help of a rope which I flung round him and gave the Negroes to haul; they dragged him on shore, and found that it was a most curious leopard, spotted and fine to an admirable degree, and the Negroes held up their hands with admiration to think what it was I had killed him with.

---

[1] lance   *n.* 标枪，长矛

[2] beckon   *v.* 招手，召唤

[3] bid   *vt.* 投标；命令，吩咐

[4] strangling   *n.* 勒死；窒息

然而，我还是驶近海岸，想跟他们说话。我发现他们沿着海岸跟着我的船跑了好长一段路。我观察到，他们手里都没有武器，只有一个人拿了一根细长棍子。苏利说，那是一种长矛，他们能投得又远又准。所以，我保持了一段距离，尽量用手势和他们交谈，特别作出了要吃东西的手势。他们招手让我把船停下，答应给我去取一些肉。于是，我落下顶帆，停住船。随后，便有两个人朝村里跑去，不到半小时就带回来了两块干肉和一些谷物。尽管我们很想要，但接下来我们怎么去拿却是一个问题，因为我不敢上岸接近他们，他们也同样很怕我们。最后，他们想出了一个两全其美的办法。他们把东西带在岸边放下来，然后远远地走开，站在那里，直到我们把那东西拿上船，他们才又走近我们。

　　我们打手势向他们表示感谢，因为我们拿不出什么东西来报答他们。但正在这时，出现了一个良机，让我们好好感谢了他们一番，因为我们正停在岸边时，只见两头巨兽从山上向海岸边气势汹汹地冲过来。我尽可能快地把枪装上弹药，并吩咐苏利把另两支枪也装好弹药。巨兽一进入射程，我就立即开火，一枪正打中了它的头部。它即刻沉进了水里，但又立刻浮起来，在水里上下扑腾，像是在拼命挣扎。随后，它马上向岸边游去，但由于受了致命伤，加上呛水，它还没游到岸边就死了。

　　这些可怜的黑人听到枪声、看到枪里发出的火光后的惊讶之情真是难以言表。但当他们看到那怪兽死去并沉到了水里，又见我向他们招手叫他们到岸边来，他们才壮起胆来到岸边，开始寻找那只巨兽。我根据水里冒出的血迹找到了它，又用绳子套住它，然后递过绳子让那些黑人去拖。他们把它拖到岸上，发现那是一只非常奇特的花斑豹，漂亮极了。黑人们钦佩地举起双手，想着我是用什么东西打死豹子的。

The other creature, frightened with the flash of fire and the noise of the gun, swam on shore, and ran up directly to the mountains from whence they came.

I found quickly the Negroes were eating the flesh of this creature, so I was willing to have them take it as a favour from me, for which they were very thankful. They gave me the skin and brought me a great deal more of their provision; then I made signs to them for some water. Soon there came two women and brought a great vessel; this they set down for me as before, and I sent Xury on shore with my jars, and filled them all three. The women were as stark naked as the men.

Leaving my friendly Negroes, I made forward for about eleven days more without offering to go near the shore, till I saw the land run out a great length into the sea, at about the distance of four or five leagues before me, and the sea being very calm, I kept a large offing to make this point; at length, doubling the point at about two leagues from the land, I saw plainly land on the other side, to seaward; then I concluded that this was the Cape Verde and those islands, called from thence Cape Verde Islands. However, they were at a great distance, and I could not well tell what I had best to do, for if I should be taken with a fresh of wind, I might neither reach one or other.

In this dilemma, as I was very pensive[1], I stepped into the cabin and sat me down, Xury having the helm; when on a sudden the boy cried out, "Master, master, a ship with a sail!" and the foolish boy was frightened out of his wits, thinking it must be some of his master's ships sent to pursue us, when I knew we were gotten far enough out of their reach. I jumped out of the cabin, and immediately saw not only the ship, but what she was, viz., that it was a Portuguese ship, and, as I thought was bound to the coast of Guinea for Negroes. But when I observed the course she steered, I was soon convinced they were bound some other way, and did not design to come any nearer to the shore; upon which I stretched out to sea as much as I could, resolving to speak with them, if possible.

---

[1] pensive   *adj.* 沉思的

另一头巨兽因受到火光和枪声的惊吓，游到了岸上，立即朝它们来的山里跑去。

我马上发现那些黑人吃起了豹肉，于是就心甘情愿作为个人情送给了他们。他们为此非常感激。他们把豹皮送给了我，又给我送了好多粮食。随后，我打手势向他们要水。不久便有两个女人抬来一只大桶。她们像先前那样把桶放下。随后，我派苏利带了三只水罐上岸取水，并把它们全部灌满。那些女人跟那些男人一样一丝不挂。

离别了那些慷慨相助的黑人，我又向前航行了大约 11 天，没有主动靠过一次岸。后来，我看到有一片陆地长长地伸进海里，距离我前面大约有四、五里格。这时，风平浪静，我开过一大片海面，想抵达这个尖岬；最后，在离陆地大约两里格处绕过这个小尖岬时，我清晰地看到了海岬另一边的陆地。这时，我推断，这就是佛得角和以佛得角得名的那些群岛。然而，它们距离很远，我不知道该怎么办才好，因为如果刮起一阵强风，我可能连一个地方也到不了。

在这进退两难之际，我愁眉不展，走进船舱，坐了下来，让苏利去掌舵。突然，那男孩子大声喊道："主人，主人，有一艘大帆船！"这个傻小子吓昏了头，以为一定是他原来的主人派船追上了我们。这时，我明白，我们走得已经够远了，他们追不到这里。我跳出船舱，不仅马上看到了大船，而且看出那是一艘什么船，也就是说，那是一艘葡萄牙船；我想那是开往几内亚海岸贩卖黑人的船。但当我观察它行驶的航向时，我马上确信，他们走的是另一个方向，并不打算靠近海岸。因此，我拼命张帆向海里航行，并决心尽可能跟他们搭上话。

After I had crowded to the utmost, and began to despair, they, it seemed, saw me by the help of their perspective-glasses, so they shortened sail to let me come up. In about three hours' time I came up with them.

They asked me what I was, in Portuguese, and in Spanish, and in French, but I understood none of them; but at last a Scots sailor who was on board, called to me, and I told him I was an Englishman, that I had made my escape out of slavery from the Moors at Sallee; then they bade me come on board, and very kindly took me in.

I immediately offered all I had to the captain of the ship, as a return for my deliverance; but he generously told me, he would take nothing from me.

He said, "I have saved your life on no other terms than I would be glad to be saved myself and it may one time or other be my lot to be taken up in the same condition; besides, when I carry you to Brazil, so great a way from your own country, if I should take from you what you have, you will be starved there, and then I only take away that life I have given. No, no, Mr. Englishman, I will carry you thither in charity, and those things will help you to buy your substance there and your passage home again."

We had a very good voyage to Brazil, and arrived in All-Saints Bay in about twenty-two days after.

The generous treatment the captain gave me, I can never enough remember; he took nothing of me for my passage, gave me twenty ducats[1] for the leopard's skin, and forty for the lion's skin, and what I was willing to sell he bought. In a word, I made about 220 pieces of eight of all my cargo, and with this stock I went on shore in Brazil.

---

[1] ducat   *n.* 达克特（旧时在欧洲各国通用的金币或银币名）

4

　　我扬帆全速前进追了一阵，正要开始绝望时，他们好像凭借望远镜看到了我，所以他们就缩帆，让我赶上来。大约三小时后，我才赶上他们。

　　他们先后用葡萄牙语、西班牙语和法语问我是什么人，但他们的话我一句都听不懂。最后，船上一个苏格兰水手向我喊话，我告诉他说我是英国人，是从萨利的摩尔人手里逃出来的。于是，他们便吩咐我上船，非常和善地收留了我。

　　我马上把自己所有的东西都送给了船长，以报答他的救命之恩。但他慷慨大方地告诉我说，他不要我任何东西。

　　他说："我救你的命没有任何其他条件，我也乐意将来别人救我的命，说不定哪一天我也会遇到同样的命运。再说，我把你带到巴西，远离自己的故土，假如我要你的东西，你就会在那里饿死，那我仅仅送你一命，又夺你一命。不，不，英人先生，我是出于恻隐之心把你带到那里。你那些东西会帮你在那里买一些物品，并作为你回家的路费。"

　　我们去巴西的航程一帆风顺，大约22天后到达了万圣湾。

　　船长对我慷慨相待，我永远都记不够。他不收我一分钱船费，并送给我20枚达克特金币买下那张豹皮，40枚达克特金币买下狮子皮。我愿出卖的东西，他都一一买下。总之，我变卖所有的船货，得了大约220枚八里亚尔金币；我带着这笔钱在巴西上了岸。

I had not been long here, but being recommended to the house of a good honest man like himself, who had a plantation and a sugarhouse. I lived with him some time, and acquainted myself by that means with the manner of their planting and making of sugar; and seeing how well the planters lived, and how they grew rich suddenly, I resolved, if I could get licence to settle there, I would turn planter among them, resolving in the meantime to find out some way to get my money which I had left in London remitted to me. To this purpose, getting a kind of a letter of naturalization, I purchased as much land that was uncured as my money would reach, and formed a plan for my plantation and settlement, and such a one as might be suitable to the stock which I proposed to myself to receive from England.

I had a neighbour, a Portuguese of Lisbon, but born of English parents, whose name was Wells, and in much such circumstances as I was. I call him my neighbour, because his plantation lay next to mine, and we went on very sociably together. My stock was but low as well as his; and we rather planted for food than anything else for about two years. However, we began to increase, and our land began to come into order; so that the third year we planted some tobacco, and made each of us a large piece of ground ready for planting canes in the year to come; but we both wanted help, and now I found, more than before, I had done wrong in parting with Xury.

I went on the next year with great success in my plantation. I raised fifty great rolls of tobacco on my own ground; and these fifty rolls being each of above a hundredweight[1], were well cured and laid by against the return of the fleet from Lisbon. And now increasing in business and in wealth, my head began to be full of projects and undertakings beyond my reach.

Having now lived almost four years in Brazil, I had not only learned the language, but had contracted[2] acquaintance and friendship among my fellow-planters, as well as among the merchants at St. Salvadore, which was our port. I had frequently given them an account of my two voyages to the coast of Guinea and the manner of trading with the Negroes there.

---

[1] hundredweight   *n.*   （重量单位）英担，半公担（英＝50.802 公斤，美＝45.359 公斤）

[2] contract   *vt.*   缔结；结交（朋友等）

我到这里不久，船长把我介绍到了和他一样正直的一个好人的家里。那人开有一个甘蔗种植园和一家制糖作坊。我跟他住了一段时间，熟悉了他们种甘蔗和制糖的方法。我看到，这些种植园主生活条件优越，发家致富很快，所以便打定主意，如果我能获得在此定居的居留证，我也要成为种植园主，同时还决定设法让人把我留在伦敦的那笔钱汇给我。为了达到这个目的，我搞到了一张入籍证，倾囊买下了一些没有开垦过的土地，然后根据我将从伦敦收到的汇款，制订了一个种植和定居的计划。

　　我有一个邻居，是葡萄牙人，生于里斯本，但他的父母是英国人。他名叫威尔斯。当时他的情况和我很相似。我之所以称他为邻居，是因为他和我的种植园相邻，而且我们经常来往。我的本钱和他的一样少。开始的大约两年，我们种的东西只够吃。然而，我们渐渐开始有了收益，我们的土地也开始走上正轨。因此，我们第三年种了一些烟草，又各自买了一大块土地，准备来年种甘蔗。但我们都缺帮手。现在，我比以前更加强烈地发现自己和苏利分手是一个错误。

　　第二年，我的种植园大获成功。我从自己的地里收了50大捆烟叶。这50捆烟叶，每捆都有一英担重；我都把它们晒好存放起来，等着船队从里斯本回来。此时，事业兴旺，财源滚滚，我的头脑里又开始充满了各种力所不及的计划和企图。

　　此时，我已经在巴西生活了差不多四年，我不仅学会了当地的语言，而且已经在种植园主和我们的港口圣萨尔瓦多的商人中有了熟人和朋友。我经常向他们谈起我去几内亚海岸的两次航行，以及跟那里的黑人交易的方式。

They listened always very attentively to my discourses[1] on these heads, but especially to that part which related to the buying Negroes, which was a trade at that time engrossed[2] in the public, so that few Negroes were brought, and those excessive dear.

It happened, being in company with some merchants and planters of my acquaintance, and talking of those things very earnestly, three of them came to me the next morning and told me they had been musing[3] very much upon what I had discoursed with them of, the last night, and they came to make a secret proposal to me; and after enjoining[4] me secrecy, they told me, that they had a mind to fit out a ship to go to Guinea, that they had all plantations as well as I, and were straitened[5] for nothing so much as servants; that as it was a trade that could not be carried on, because they could not publicly sell the Negroes when they came home, so they desired to make but one voyage, to bring the Negroes on shore privately, and divide them among their own plantations; and in a word, the question was whether I would go their supercargo[6] in the ship to manage the trading part upon the coast of Guinea; and they offered me that I should have my equal share of the Negroes without providing any part of the stock.

This was a fair proposal it must be confessed, had it been made to one that had not had a settlement and plantation of his own to look after. However, for me to think of such a voyage was the most preposterous[7] thing.

---

1 discourse   n. 演讲，论述，谈话
2 engross   vt. 吸引，占用，使全神贯注
3 muse   vi. 沉思，冥想
4 enjoin   vt. 吩咐，命令，嘱咐
5 straiten   vt. 使穷困，使为难；使缺乏
6 supercargo   n. (商船上的)押运员，货物管理员
7 preposterous   adj. 荒谬的

每当我谈起这些话题时，他们总是侧耳倾听，尤其是和购买黑人有关的那部分。贩运黑人当时是一种垄断贸易，所以在巴西购买的黑人寥寥无几，而且价格昂贵。

有一次，我跟一些熟悉的商人和种植园主又非常认真地谈起了这些事。第二天上午，就有三个人来找我。他们对我说，他们一直在非常慎重地考虑我昨晚和他们的谈话，他们来是向我悄悄提出一个建议。他们嘱咐我保密后，告诉我说，他们想装备一条船去几内亚。他们说，他们都像我一样有种植园，但最缺乏的是雇工。他们不可能专门购买黑人，因为他们回来后不可能公开出售黑人，所以他们打算只去几内亚一次，把黑人秘密带上岸，然后平分到各自的种植园里去。总之，问题是我是不是愿意管理他们船上的货物，并负责处理几内亚海岸的交易。他们主动提出，我不拿任何本钱，但可以一起平分带回的黑人。

必须承认，如果是向一个没有在此定居、也没有自己的种植园需要照管的人提出来，这个建议大有希望。而让我再去想这次航行却是再荒唐不过的事儿。

But I could no more resist the offer. I told them I would go with all my heart, if they would undertake to look after my plantation in my absence, and would dispose of it to such as I should direct if I miscarried. This they all engaged to do, and entered into writings or covenants[1] to do so; and I made a formal will, disposing of my plantation and effects, in case of my death, making the captain of the ship that had saved my life as before, my universal heir, but obliging him to dispose of my effects as I had directed in my will, one half of the produce being to himself and the other to be shipped to England.

In short, I took all possible caution to preserve my effects, and keep up my plantation; had I used half as much prudence to have looked into my own interest, and have made a judgment of what I ought to have done, and not to have done, I had certainly never gone away from so prosperous an undertaking, leaving all the probable views of a thriving circumstance, and gone upon a voyage to sea.

I went on board in an evil hour, the first of September, 1659, being the same day eight year that I went from my father and mother at Hull.

Our ship was about 120 ton burden, carried 6 guns, and 14 men, besides the master, his boy, and myself; we had on board no large cargo of goods, except of such toys and odd trifles[2] as were fit for our trade with the Negroes.

The same day I went on board we set sail, standing away to the northward upon our own coast, with design to stretch over for the African coast, when they came about 10 or 12 degrees of northern latitude.

---

[1] covenant *n.* 契约，盟约
[2] trifle *n.* 琐碎的东西；无价值的事物

5

可是，我无法拒绝这个提议。我告诉他们说，如果他们保证我不在时照料我的种植园，如果我万一出事，能按我的吩咐处理种植园，那我非常愿意前往。他们都一一答应，并立了字据或契约。而且我还立了一份正式遗嘱来处置我的种植园和财产，万一我死去，先前曾救过我一命的船长将作为我的全权继承人，但责成他要按我在遗嘱中的指示处置我的财产：一半归他自己，一半运到英国。

简而言之，我尽可能小心翼翼来保护自己的财产，并维持种植园的经营。但如果我能用一半心思来关注自己的利益，判断一下自己该做什么、不该做什么，我就绝不会远离自己日益兴旺的事业，把一切致富的希望前景抛到脑后，踏上这次航程。

1659 年 9 月 1 日，我上了船。这是一个不幸的日子。八年前，我离开父母亲，从赫尔城上船离家，也是 9 月 1 日。

我们的船载重大约 120 吨，装有六门炮，除了船长、男仆和我自己，另外还有 14 人。船上没有什么大件货物，只是一些适合与黑人交易的玩具和新奇的小玩意儿。

我上船当天，我们就扬帆起航了。我们沿着海岸向北，计划航行到北纬 10 至 12 度左右，横渡大洋，驶向非洲海岸。

We had very good weather, only excessive hot, all the way upon our own coast, till we came the height of Cape St. Augustino, from whence keeping farther off at sea we steered for the Isle Fernand de Horonha holding our course N.E. by N.; in this course we passed the line in about 12 days' time, and were by our last observation in 7 degrees 22 minutes northern latitude, when a violent tornado[1] took us quite out of our knowledge; it began from the southeast, came about to the northwest, and then settled into the northeast, from whence it blew in such a terrible manner, that for twelve days together we could do nothing but drive, and scudding[2] away before it, let it carry us whither[3] ever fate and the fury of the winds directed.

In this distress, we had besides the terror of the storm, one of our men died of the calenture[4], and one man and the boy washed over board; about the 12th day the weather abating a little, the master made an observation as well as he could, and found that he was in about 11 degrees north latitude, but that he was 22 degrees of longitude difference west from Cape St. Augustino; so that he found he was gotten upon the coast of Guinea, or the north part of Brazil, beyond the river Amazon, toward that of the river Oronoque, commonly called the Great River, and began to consult with me what course he should take, for the ship was leaky and very much disabled, and he was going directly back to the coast of Brazil.

I was positively against that, and looking over the charts of the seacoast of America with him, we concluded there was no inhabited country for us to had recourse[5] to till we came within the circle of the Caribbee Islands, and therefore resolved to stand away for Barbadoes, which by keeping off at sea, to avoid the indraft[6] of the Bay of Mexico, we might easily perform, as we hoped, in about fifteen days' sail.

---

[1] tornado   *n.* 旋风，龙卷风
[2] scud   *vi.* （云朵）疾行，疾飞;（船只）疾驰
[3] whither   *adv.* 到哪里，什么目的
[4] calenture   *n.* 热带地方的热病，中暑
[5] recourse   *n.* 求援，求助
[6] indraft   *n.* 吸入

我们沿着海岸一直开到了圣奥古斯丁角。一路上天气很好，就是热得不行。过了圣奥古斯丁角，我们航向东北偏北，驶向费尔南德霍伦哈小岛。我们沿着这条航线航行，大约 12 天后穿过了赤道。根据最后一次测天，我们已经到了北纬 7 度 22 分。这时，我们突然遭到了一股强烈飓风的袭击。这股飓风开始从东南方刮来，接着转向西北方，最后转成了东北风。狂风这样可怕地刮了 12 天，我们无可奈何，只得随波逐流，任凭命运和狂风的摆布。

　　在这危难之际，除了恐怖的风暴，船上一个人患热病死去，还有一个人和那个男仆被大浪卷走。大约到第 12 天，风浪减小了点儿；船长尽其所能地进行测天，随后发现我们的船处在北纬 11 度左右，但在圣奥古斯丁角以西 22 经度。船长发现，我们的船被刮到了圭亚那海岸或巴西北部，驶过了亚马逊河，向那条通称为"大河"的俄利诺科河驶去。于是，船长和我协商该走哪条航线，因为船渗漏，而且严重受损，他要直接开回巴西海岸。

　　我断然反对那样做。我和他一起查看了美洲沿岸的航海图，最后得出结论，我们要开到加勒比群岛，才能找到有人烟的地方求援。因此，我们决定离岸，驶向巴尔巴多群岛。据我们估计，只要能避开墨西哥湾的逆流，在大海里航行大约 15 天后，便可到达。

With this design we changed our course and steered away N.W. by W. in order to reach some of our English islands, where I hoped for relief; but our voyage was otherwise determined, for being in the latitude of 12 degrees 18 minutes a second storm came upon us, which carried us away with the same impetuosity[1] westward.

One of our men early in the morning cried out, "Land!" and we had no sooner run out of the cabin to look out in hopes of seeing whereabouts in the world we were; but the ship struck upon a sand, and in a moment her motion being so stopped, the sea broke over her in such a manner, that we expected we should all have perished immediately, and we were immediately driven into our close quarters to shelter us the very foam[2] and spray of the sea.

We sat looking upon one another, and expecting death every moment, for there was little or nothing more for us to do in this; and all the comfort we had, was, that contrary to our expectation, the ship did not break yet, and that the master said the wind began to abate.

Now though we thought that the wind did a little abate, yet the ship having thus struck upon the sand, and sticking too fast for us to expect her getting off, we were in a dreadful condition indeed, and had nothing to do but to think of saving our lives as well as we could; we had a boat at our stern just before the storm, but she was first staved[3] by dashing against the ship's rudder, and in the next place she broke away, and either sunk or was driven off to sea, so there was no hope from her; we had another boat on board, but how to get her off into the sea was a doubtful thing; however, there was no room to debate, for we fancied the ship would break in pieces every minute, and some told us she was actually broken already.

In this distress the mate of our vessel laid hold of the boat, and with the help of the rest of the men, they got her flung over the ship's side and, getting all into her, let go and committed ourselves being eleven in number, to God's mercy and the wild sea; for though the storm was abated considerably, yet the sea went dreadful high upon the shore.

---

[1] impetuosity   *n.* 激烈; 冲动
[2] foam   *n.* 泡沫, 水沫
[3] stave   *vt.* 击穿, 弄破

我们根据这个计划，改变航向，向西北偏西方向驶去，以便到达某个英属海岛，我希望在那里获救。但航行方向我们决定不了，因为在北纬 12 度 18 分第二次暴风又向我们袭来，风势与前一次那样猛烈，把我们卷向西方。

　　一天早上，船上有个人突然大喊一声："陆地！"我们刚想跑出舱外，想看看我们究竟到了什么地方，船却撞在了一片沙滩上，马上停了下来。巨浪就这样撞击着船，我们料想肯定都马上要死定了。我们立即退进封闭舱里，躲避浪花飞沫的冲击。

　　我们坐在那里，面面相觑，时刻都在等待着死亡，因为我们在这个世界上已经无能为力。这时，让我们唯一安慰的是，船并没有像我们预料的那样破碎，而且船长说风开始减弱。

　　尽管现在风势确实减小了点儿，但船搁浅在沙里，而且搁浅得非常牢固，别指望让它脱离沙地，因此我们的确处在非常可怕的境地。我们只能尽力想法挽救自己的生命。风暴到来前，船尾曾有一只小艇。但小艇先是被刮到大船的舵上撞了个窟窿，后又挣断，不知是沉了，还是漂向了大海，所以小艇是没有什么指望了。船上还有一只小艇，但如何把它放到海里却是一个问题。然而，没有时间讨论了，因为我们认为大船每时每刻都会粉身碎骨。有些人告诉我们说，大船实际上已经破了。

　　在这危难之际，大副抓住那只小艇，在其他人的帮助下，把小艇抛到了大船边。随后，我们 11 个人都上了小艇，解开小艇，听凭上帝和狂涛巨浪的摆布，因为尽管风势大大减弱，但大海仍然惊涛拍岸。

And now our case was very dismal indeed; for we all saw plainly that the sea went so high that the boat could not live and that we should be inevitably drowned. As to making sail, we had none; nor, if we had, could we have done anything with it; so we worked at the oar towards the land, though with heavy hearts, like men going to execution; for we all knew that when the boat came nearer the shore, she would be dashed in a thousand pieces by the breach[1] of the sea. However, we committed our souls to God in the most earnest manner, and the wind driving us towards the shore, we hastened our destruction with our own hands, pulling as well as we could towards land.

What the shore was, whether rock or sand, whether steep or shoal, we knew not; the only hope that could rationally give us the least shadow of expectation, was, if we might happen into some bay, or the mouth of some river, where by great chance we might have run our boat in, or got under the lee[2] of the land, and perhaps made smooth water. But there was nothing of this appeared; but as we made nearer and nearer the shore, the land looked more frightful than the sea.

After we had rowed, or rather driven, about a league and half, a raging wave, mountain-like, came rolling astern[3] of us, and plainly bade us expect the coup de grace. It took us with such a fury that it overset the boat at once; and it gave us not time hardly to say, "O God!" for we were all swallowed up in a moment.

Nothing can describe the confusion of thought which I felt when I sunk into the water; for though I swam very well, yet I could not deliver myself from the waves so as to draw breath, till that wave having driven me a vast way on towards the shore, and having spent itself, went back, and left me upon the land almost dry, but half-dead with the water I took in. I had so much presence of mind as well as breath left, that seeing myself nearer the main land than I expected, I got upon my feet, and endeavoured to make on towards the land as fast as I could, before another wave should return, and take me up again.

---

[1] breach   n. 缺口，裂口；【航】波浪的碎溅

[2] lee   *n.* 庇荫，保护

[3] astern   *adv.* 在船尾，向船尾

我们当时的处境确实非常可怕，因为我们都清楚，巨浪滔天，小艇不可能生存，我们不可避免地都要被淹死。我们没有帆，即使有，也派不上用场，所以我们用力划桨向岸边靠去，尽管我们心情沉重，就像要走上刑场的犯人一样，因为我们知道小艇一靠近海岸，就会被海浪撞得千疮百孔。然而，我们只能听天由命，顺着风势拼命向岸边划，加速自己的毁灭。

　　海岸是什么情形，是石岸还是沙岸，是陡岸还是浅滩，我们不得而知。所能给我们的唯一的一线合理希望就是，如果我们有可能碰巧进入某个海湾或河口，极其偶然地把小艇划进去，或者划到背风面，也许能找到平静的水面。但我们什么也没有遇上；我们越靠近海岸，陆地比大海越可怕。

　　我们划了，或者更准确地说，被风刮了大约一里格半。突然，一个巨浪排山倒海从我们后面滚滚而来，显然要给我们的小艇致命一击。它立马将我们的小艇掀了个底朝天；我们来不及说"噢，上帝啊！"因为我们马上就被吞没了。

　　我沉入水里时，思想混乱，无法言表，因为尽管我水性很好，但我无法从巨浪中凫上来喘口气。最后，海浪把我冲了好长一段冲上了岸，等浪势使尽退回去时，把我留在了半干的岸上，但我已被海水灌得半死。我当时头脑清醒，还剩有一口气，看到大陆比自己预料的要近，就爬起来，趁第二个浪头还没打来再把我卷入大海，尽可能快地向陆上奔去。

But I soon found it was impossible to avoid it; for I saw the sea come after me as high as a great hill, and as furious as an enemy which I had no means or strength to contend with; my business was to hold my breath, and raise myself upon the water, if I could; and so by swimming to preserve my breathing, and pilot myself towards the shore, if possible; my greatest concern now being that the sea, as it would carry me a great way towards the shore when it came on, might not carry me back again with it when it gave back towards the sea.

The wave that came upon me again buried me at once 20 or 30 feet deep in its own body; and I could feel myself carried with a mighty force and swiftness towards the shore; but I held my breath, and assisted myself to swim still forward with all my might. I was ready to burst with holding my breath, when, as I felt myself rising up, so to my immediate relief, I found my head and hands shoot out above the surface of the water. I was covered again with water, but not so long but I held it out; and finding the water had spent itself and began to return, I struck forward against the return of the waves, and felt ground again with my feet. I stood still a few moments to recover breath, and till the water went from me, and then took to my heels, and run with what strength I had farther towards the shore. But neither would this deliver me from the fury of the sea, which came pouring in after me again, and twice more I was lifted up by the waves, and carried forwards as before, shore being very flat.

The last time of these two had well near been fatal to me; for the sea, having hurried me along as before, dashed me against a piece of a rock, and that with such force as it left me senseless; for the blow, taking my side and breast, beat the breath as it were quite out of my body; and had it returned again immediately, I must have been strangled in the water; but I recovered a little before the return of the waves, and seeing I should be covered again with the water, I resolved to hold fast by a piece of the rock, and so to hold my breath, if possible, till the wave went back; now as the waves were not so high as at first, being near land, I held my hold till the wave abated, and then fetched another run, which brought me so near the shore that the next wave, though it went over me, yet did not so swallow me up as to carry me away, and the next run I took, I got to the mainland, where I clambered[1] up the clifts of the shore, and sat me down upon the grass, free from danger.

---

[1] clamber *vi.* 爬上，攀登

但我很快发现这不可能回避了，因为我看到高山似的海浪向我扑来，就像一个气势汹汹的敌人，我根本无法也无力与其抗争。我现在要做的是，屏住呼吸，浮出水面，设法向岸边游去。我现在最关心的是，海浪来时把我冲上岸，回去时别把我再卷回大海。

　　巨浪再次扑来，立刻把我埋入水中二三十英尺深处。我感到自己被海浪迅速有力地推向岸边，便屏住呼吸，拼命向岸上游去。我屏息屏得快要爆炸时，感到自己浮出了水面，便马上松了口气，头和两只手蹿出了水面。紧接着，我又被埋入水中，但这次时间没有那么长，我总算挺住了。我发现海浪力量耗尽开始回落时，拼命逆水向前挣扎，脚终于又触到了滩地。我静静地站了一会儿，喘了口气。海水一退去，我就拔脚拼命向岸上奔去。但我还是无法逃脱再次从背后冲涌而来的狂涛，一连两次又像以前那样被卷起来，推向平坦的海岸。

　　这两次大浪冲击，最后一次差点儿要了我的命，因为海浪像先前那样把我急速向前推时，让我撞到了一块岩石上，冲力非常大，使我马上失去了知觉，因为这一撞正好撞在我的侧胸部，把我憋住的一口气给撞了出来。如果现在马上再来一个浪头，我一定会憋死在水里。但在第二个浪头打来之前，我恢复了一点儿知觉，看到自己还会海水吞没，就决定紧紧抱住一块岩石，尽可能屏住呼吸，一直等到浪头退去。因为现在接近陆地，所以浪头不像开始那样高了。我紧紧抱住那块岩石，等浪头一退，便又往前跑一阵子，一直跑到了离海岸很近的地方。所以，后一个浪头赶来时，尽管从我头上盖了过去，但已经无法再那样把我吞没或卷走了。我又继续向前跑，跑到了陆地边，爬上岸边的断崖，然后在草地上坐下来，脱离了危险。

VI

I was now landed, and safe on shore, and began to look up and thank God that my life was saved in a case wherein there was some minutes before scarce any room to hope. I believe it is impossible to express to the life what the ecstasies[1] and transports of the soul are when it is so saved.

I cast my eyes to the stranded[2] vessel, when the breach and froth[3] of the sea being so big, I could hardly see it, it lay so far off, and considered, Lord! How was it possible I could get on shore?

I had nothing about me but a knife, a tobacco-pipe, and a little tobacco in a box; for a while I ran about like a madman; night coming upon me, I began with a heavy heart to consider what would be my lot if there were any ravenous[4] beasts in that country.

All the remedy that offered to my thoughts at that time, was, to get up into a thick bushy tree like a fir[5], but thorny[6], which grew near me, and where I resolved to set all night; I walked about a furlong from the shore, to see if I could find any fresh water to drink, which I did, to my great joy; and having drank and put a little tobacco in my mouth to prevent hunger, I went to the tree, and getting up into it, endeavoured to place myself so as that if I should sleep I might not fall; and having cut me a short stick for my defence, I took up my lodging, and having been excessively fatigued, I fell fast asleep.

---

[1] ecstasy   *n.* 入迷，心醉神迷
[2] strand   *vt.* 搁浅；束手无策
[3] froth   *n.* 泡，泡沫
[4] ravenous   *adj.* 贪婪的，渴望的，狼吞虎咽的
[5] fir   *n.* 冷杉，枞树，杉木
[6] thorny   *adj.* 多刺的；痛苦的

6

　　我现已登陆，安全上岸，抬起头，感谢上帝救了我一命，因为几分钟前，我还几乎没有任何生还的希望。现在我相信，当一个人这样死里逃生时，那种心醉神迷、喜不自胜的心情真是难以言表。

　　我眺望那艘搁浅的大船，这时海浪翻腾，烟波浩淼，船离岸是那样远，我简直无法看清，心里想道：上帝啊！我怎么会有可能上岸呢？

　　我身上只有一把小刀、一只烟斗和一小匣烟叶。我像疯子似的来回跑了一阵。夜幕降临，我开始心思重重地想，如果这个地方有猛兽出没，我的命运将会如何？

　　此时，我能想到的所有办法就是，爬上附近一棵枝叶茂密的粗树，像是枞树，但有刺。我决定上去坐一夜。我从海岸向里走了大约一浪远，想看看是不是能找一些淡水喝，让我大为高兴的是，居然找到了。喝完水，我往嘴里放了一点儿烟叶充饥，然后爬上树，尽力躺稳，以免睡熟后从树上掉下来。我还从树上砍了一根短棍防身，然后就睡下了。由于筋疲力尽，我很快就睡着了。

When I woke it was broad day, the weather clear, and the storm abated, so that the sea did not rage and swell as before. But what surprised me most was that the ship was lifted off in the night from the sand where she lay by the swelling of the tide, and was driven up almost as far as the rock where I had been so bruised by the dashing me against it; this being within about a mile from the shore where I was, and the ship seeming to stand upright still, I wished myself on board, that, at least, I might save some necessary things for my use.

When I came down from my apartment in the tree, I looked about me again, and the first thing I found was the boat, which lay as the wind and the sea had tossed her up upon the land, about two miles on my right hand. I walked as far as I could upon the shore to have got to her, but found a neck or inlet of water between me and the boat, which was about half a mile broad, so I came back for the present, being more intent upon getting at the ship, where I hoped to find something for my present subsistence.

A little afternoon I found the sea very calm, and the tide ebbed[1] so far out that I could come within a quarter of a mile of the ship. So I pulled off my clothes and took the water, but when I came to the ship, my difficulty was still greater to know how to get on board, for she lay aground[2], and high out of the water, there was nothing within my reach to lay hold of; I swam round her twice, and the second time I spied a small piece of a rope, which hang down by the fore-chains so low as that with great difficulty I got hold of it, and got up into the forecastle of the ship; here I found that the ship was bulged[3], and had a great deal of water in her hold, but that she lay so on the side of a bank of hard sand that her stern lay lifted up upon the bank, and her head low almost to the water; by this means all her quarter was free. First I found that all the ship's provisions were dry and untouched by the water, and being very well disposed to eat, I went to the bread-room and filled my pockets with biscuit, and eat it as I went about other things, for I had no time to lose; I also found some rum in the great cabin, of which I took a large dram. Now I wanted nothing but a boat to furnish myself with many things I foresaw would be very necessary to me.

---

[1] ebb   *vi.* 潮退，衰退
[2] aground   *adv.* 搁浅地，地面上
[3] bulge *vi.* 膨胀，鼓起

我醒来时，天已大亮。这时，天气晴朗，风暴减弱，海面上也不像以前那样怒涛滚滚、巨浪翻腾了。但最让我吃惊的是，那艘搁浅的大船夜里被潮水浮出沙滩后，差不多又给冲到了我先前被撞伤的那块岩石附近。现在这船离我所在的岸边大约只有一英里，好像还一动不动地直立在那里。我希望能登上大船，至少可以拿出一些必需品为我所用。

我从树上睡觉的地方下来，又环顾了一下四周，发现的第一件东西就是那只小艇，它被风浪冲到陆地上，躺在那里，离我右首大约两英里。我尽可能走上海岸，向小艇走去，但发现小艇和我之间有一个小水湾，大约有半英里宽。于是，我就暂时返回，因为更迫切的是我要上大船，我希望在上面找到一些现在能用的生活必需品。

午后过了一会儿，我发现海面风平浪静，潮水远去。我游不到四分之一英里便可到达大船。我便脱掉衣服，跳下水，但当我游到船边时，上船困难却仍然较大，因为船已搁浅，而且离水面很高，所以没有任何可以抓的东西。我绕船游了两圈，第二圈发现了一小截绳子。绳子从船头上垂下来，绳头垂得很低。我费了很大劲儿抓住绳子，进了船上的前舱。上去后，我发现船已漏水，舱里进了好多水。因为船搁浅在一片坚硬的沙岸的一侧，船尾上翘靠在岸上，船头低得几乎贴住了水，所以船的后半截没有进水。首先，我发现船上所有的粮食都很干燥，没有浸水。因为我很想吃些东西，所以就走进了面包房，把口袋里都装满了饼干，同时一边吃一边干其他事儿，我必须抓紧时间。我还在大舱里找到了一些朗姆酒，就喝了一杯。我现在只想有一只小船，把我认为将来对我非常必需的许多东西装上去运走。

It was in vain to sit still and wish for what was not to be had; we had several spare yards and two or three large spars[1] of wood and a spare topmast[2] or two in the ship; I resolved to fall to work with these, and I flung as many of them overboard as I could manage for their weight, tying every one with a rope that they might not drive away; when this was done I went down the ship's side, and pulling them to me, I tied four of them fast together at both ends as well as I could, in the form of a raft, and laying two or three short pieces of plank upon them crossways, I found I could walk upon it very well, but that it was not able to bear any great weight, the pieces being too light; so I went to work, and with the carpenter's saw I cut a spare topmast into three lengths, and added them to my raft.

My raft was now strong enough to bear any reasonable weight; my next care was what to load it with, and how to preserve what I laid upon it from the surf of the sea; But I was not long considering this; I first laid all the plank or boards upon it that I could get, and having considered well what I most wanted, I first got three of the seamen's chests, which I had broken open and emptied, and lowered them down upon my raft; the first of these I filled with provision, viz., bread, rice, three Dutch cheeses, five pieces of dried goat's flesh and a little remainder of European corn; as for liquors, I found several cases of bottles belonging to our skipper[3]. While I was doing this, I found the tide began to flow, though very calm, and I had the mortification[4] to see my coat, shirt, and waistcoat which I had left on shore upon the sand, swim away; as for my breeches which were only linen and open-kneed, I swam on board in them and my stockings. This put me upon rummaging[5] for clothes, of which I found enough, but took no more than I wanted for present use, for I had other things which my eye was more upon, as first tools to work with on shore, and it was after long searching that I found out the carpenter's chest; I got it down to my raft.

---

[1] spar   *n.* 杆子，原木料；圆材(船舶的桅杆、帆桁等)
[2] topmast   *n.* 中桅
[3] skipper   *n.* 船长
[4] mortification   *n.* 羞辱，耻辱
[5] rummage   *v.* 到处翻寻，搜出，检查

光坐着去想获得并不存在的东西无济于事。船上有几根备用的帆桁、两三块大木板和一两根备用中桅。我决定由此开始着手行动。凡是能搬动的，我都扔下船。扔之前，我先用绳子——一绑好，以免被海水冲走。之后，我下到船边，将它们拉到身边，把其中四根绑在一起，两头尽可能扎紧，扎成木排的形状，又用两三块短厚木板交叉放在上面，我踩上去走了走，发现还算不错，但因为木头太轻，所以承受不了多大重量。于是，我又动手用木匠的锯子把一根中桅锯成三段，加到了木排上。

我的木排现在做得很牢固，足以承受适度的重量。接着，我就考虑该装载什么东西，以及如何防止我装上去的东西给海浪打湿。我不久就想出了办法。我先把船上所能找到的各种木板都铺在木排上，然后仔细考虑了一下自己最需要的东西。我先找到三只船员箱，将它们打开，倒空里面的东西，再把它们吊到木排上。第一只箱子里我装满了食品，也就是面包、大米、三块荷兰干酪、五块干羊肉，以及一点剩下来的欧洲玉米。至于酒类，我找到了几箱，那都是船长的。我在这样做时，只见潮水开始上涨，尽管风平浪静，但还是把我留在岸上的上衣、衬衫和背心都冲走了。这让我窘迫不已，因为我游泳上船时，只穿了一条开膝亚麻裤和一双长袜。这让我又翻找起了衣服。船里衣服真够多的，但我只挑了几件现在要穿的，因为我的目光注意到了更重要的东西——上岸首先要用的工具。我找了好久，终于找到了那只木工箱。我把箱子放到了木排上。

My next care was for some ammunition[1] and arms; there were two very good fowling-pieces in the great cabin, and two pistols, these I secured first, with some powder-horns, and a small bag of shot, and two old rusty swords; I knew there were three barrels of powder in the ship, but knew not where our gunner had stowed[2] them, but with much search I found them, two of them dry and good, the third had taken water, those two I got to my raft, with the arms, and now I thought myself pretty well freighted, and began to think how I should get to shore with them, having neither sail, oar, or rudder, and the least capful of wind would have overset all my navigation.

I had three encouragements: 1. A smooth calm sea. 2. The tide rising and setting in to the shore. 3. What little wind there was blew me towards the land; and thus, having found two or three broken oars belonging to the boat, and besides the tools which were in the chest, I found two saws, an axe, and a hammer, and with this cargo I put to sea. For a mile or thereabouts, my raft went very well, only that I found it drive a little distant from the place where I had landed before, by which I perceived that there was some indraft[3] of the water, and consequently I hoped to find some creek or river there, which I might make use of as a port to get to land with my cargo.

As I imagined, so it was, there appeared before me a little opening of the land, and I found a strong current of the tide set into it, so I guided my raft as well as I could to keep in the middle of the stream. But here I had like to have suffered a second shipwreck, for knowing nothing of the coast, my raft run aground at one end of it upon a shoal[4], and not being aground at the other end, it wanted but a little that all my cargo had slipped off towards that end that was afloat, and so fallen into the water. I did my utmost by setting my back against the chests, to keep them in their places, but could not thrust off the raft with all my strength, neither durst[5] I stir from the posture I was in, but holding up the chests with all my might, stood in that manner near half an hour, in which time the rising of the water brought me a little more upon a level, and a little after, the water still rising, my raft floated again, and I thrust her off with the oar I had, into the channel, and then driving up higher, I at length found myself in the mouth of a little river, with land on both sides, and a strong current running up, I looked on both sides for a proper place to get to shore.

---

[1] ammunition　*n.* 军火，弹药
[2] stow　*v.* 装载
[3] indraft　*n.* 吸入
[4] shoal　*n.* 浅滩，沙洲
[5] durst　*vbl.* dare 的过去分词

下一步我要关心的是弹药和武器。大舱里原来存放着两支很好的鸟枪和两支手枪，我先把这些东西拿到手，然后又拿了几只装火药的角筒、一小包子弹和两把生锈的旧剑。我知道船上还有三桶火药，但不知道炮手把它们放在什么地方了。我找了好一阵子，终于找到了。其中有两桶仍干燥无损，第三桶已经沾水。我把那两桶干燥的火药连同武器放到了木排上。这时，我认为木排上装的东西够多了，就开始想自己应该如何把它们运上岸，因为既没有帆，又没有桨和舵，只要有点儿风，我的木排就会整个翻倒。

　　当时有三点令我鼓舞：一、海面风平浪静；二、潮水上涨，正流向岸边；三、阵阵微风正把我吹向岸边。于是，我找到了原来小艇上用的两三支断桨；除了工具箱里的那些工具，我还找到了两把锯子、一把斧头和一把锤子。我载着这货物下了海。我的木排顺顺当当走了一英里左右，只是我发现稍微偏离了我先前登陆的那个地方。由此，我察觉到，有一股流向岸边的回流。因此，我希望在此找到一条小溪或小河，可以用来作为港口，卸货上岸。

　　果然如我想像的那样，陆地在我面前出现一个小小的缺口，而且我发现一股强劲的潮水正向里涌。于是，我驾着木排，尽可能向急流的中心漂去。在这里，我差点儿又遭到一次海难。因为我对海岸一无所知，所以木排的一头搁浅在沙滩上，另一头却还漂在水里。我的货物只差一点儿就会滑向漂在水里的一头，最后滑到水里。我竭尽全力用背顶住那些箱子，不让它们下滑，但我用尽全力也无法撑开木排，就这样一动不动拼命顶着那些箱子，站了将近半小时。此时，潮水上涨，木排才稍微平衡了点儿。又过了一会儿，潮水持续上涨，木排又浮了起来。我用桨把木排划向水里，然后又向上划了一阵，终于划进了一条河的入口处。这里两边是岸，一股强劲的潮水不断涌进来。我看了一下小河两岸，想找一个合适地方靠岸。

At length I spied a little cove[1] on the right shore of the creek, to which with great pain and difficulty I guided my raft, and at last got so near, as that, reaching ground with my oar, I could thrust her directly in, but here I had like to have dipped all my cargo in the sea again; for that shore lying pretty steep, there was no place to land, but where one end of my float, if it ran on shore, would lie so high and the other sink lower as before, that it would endanger my cargo again. All that I could do was to wait till the tide was at highest, keeping the raft with my oar like an anchor to hold the side of it fast to the shore, near a flat piece of ground, which I expected the water would flow over; and so it did. As soon as I found water enough, for my raft drew about a foot of water, I thrust her on upon that flat piece of ground, and there fastened or moored her by sticking my two broken oars into the ground; one on one side near one end, and one on the other side near the other end; and thus I lay till the water ebbed away, and left my raft and all my cargo safe on shore.

My next work was to view the country, and seek a proper place for my habitation, and where to stow my goods to secure them from whatever might happen; where I was I yet knew not, whether on the continent or on an island, whether inhabited or not inhabited, whether in danger of wild beasts or not. There was a hill not above a mile from me, which rose up very steep and high, and which seemed to overtop some other hills which lay as in a ridge from it northward; I took out one of the fowling pieces, and one of the pistols, and an horn of powder, and thus armed, I travelled for discovery up to the top of that hill, where, after I had with great labour and difficulty got to the top, I saw that I was in an island environed every way with the sea, no land to be seen, except some rocks which lay a great way off, and two small islands less than this, which lay about three leagues to the west.

I found also that the island I was in was barren and uninhabited, yet I saw abundance of fowls; at my coming back, I shot at a great bird which I saw sitting upon a tree on the side of a great wood; I had no sooner fired but from all the parts of the wood there arose an innumerable number of fowls of many sorts. As for the creature I killed, I took it to be a kind of a hawk, its colour and beak resembling it, but had no talons[2], its flesh was carrion[3], and fit for nothing.

---

[1] cove   *n.* 山凹，小湾

[2] talon   *n.* 爪，魔爪

[3] carrion   *adj.* 腐肉的，腐肉的，令人作呕的

我终于在小河右岸发现一个小湾，费了九牛二虎之力才把木排转到那个方向，最后靠近了水湾。我用桨抵住河底，把直接木排撑了进去。但在这里，我差点儿又把货物全都倒在水里，因为这一带河岸很陡，没有可以登岸的地方，但如果木排一头高高地搁浅在岸上，另一头像先前那样下沉，我的货物又会有滑向水里的危险。我所能做的就是用桨作锚，把木排一边固定在一片靠近河岸的浅滩上，等待潮水涨高，漫过浅滩。后来，潮水果然漫过了浅滩。我一发现潮水涨得够高，就把木排划过去，因为木排吃水大约有一英尺。到了那里，我用两支断桨插入浅滩，在木排前后两端各插一支，把木排固定好或停好，等潮水退去，便可以把木排和所有货物安全地留在岸上了。

　　我接下来的工作就是察看周围地形，找一个合适地方安置我的住处和货物，以防发生意外。我还不知道自己身在何处，是在陆地还是在小岛上，是在有人烟的地方还是在没人烟的地方，会不会有野兽袭击的危险。离我不到一英里的地方有一座小山，又高又陡，比北面其他的小山都高，看上去那是一道山脊。我拿出一支鸟枪、一支手枪和一角筒火药，向那座山的山顶走去。我历尽艰辛和努力爬上山顶后，看到自己置身在一个四面环海的海岛，看不到一片陆地，只见很远处有几块岩石，西边有两个比该岛还小的小岛，大约在三里格开外。

　　我还发现，我所在的这个岛一片贫瘠、荒无人烟，却看到好多飞禽。回来路上，我朝一只落在一片大树林旁的一棵树上的大鸟开了一枪。枪声一响，整个森林里飞出无数各种各样的飞鸟。至于我打死的那只鸟，我认为是一种隼，毛色和嘴很像，但没有利爪，它的肉令人作呕，根本不能吃。

I came back to my raft, and fell to work to bring my cargo on shore, which took me up the rest of that day, and what to do with myself at night I knew not, nor indeed where to rest; for I was afraid to lie down on the ground, not knowing but some wild beast might devour me, though, as I afterwards found, there was really no need for those fears.

However, as well as I could, I barricaded myself round with the chests and boards that I had brought on shore, and made a kind of a hut for that night's lodging; as for food, I yet saw not which way to supply myself, except that I had seen two or three creatures like hares run out of the wood where I shot the fowl.

I now began to consider that I might yet get a great many things out of the ship, which would be useful to me, and particularly some of the rigging, and sails, and such other things as might come to land, and I resolved to make another voyage on board the vessel, if possible; and as I knew that the first storm that blew must necessarily break her all in pieces, I resolved to set all other things apart, till I got everything out of the ship that I could get; then I called a council whether I should take back the raft, but this appeared impracticable; so I resolved to go as before, when the tide was down, and I did so, only that I stripped before I went from my hut, having nothing on but a chequered shirt, and a pair of linen drawers, and a pair of pumps on my feet.

I got on board the ship as before, prepared a second raft and brought away several things very useful to me; as first, in the carpenter's stores I found two or three bags full of nails and spikes, a great screw jack, a dozen or two of hatchets, and above all, that most useful thing called a grindstone[1]; all these I secured together, with several things belonging to the gunner, particularly two or three iron crows, and two barrels of musket bullets, seven muskets, and another fowling piece, with some small quantity of powder more; a large bag full of small shot, and a great roll of sheet lead. But this last was so heavy I could not hoist it up to get it over the ship's side.

Besides these things, I took all the men's clothes that I could find, and a spare foretopsail, a hammock[2], and some bedding; and with this I loaded my second raft, and brought them all safe on shore.

---

[1] grindstone   *n.*   旋转磨石
[2] hammock   *n.*   吊床

我回到木排边，动手把货物搬上岸。那天剩下的时间，我都用来搬货物了。我不知道夜里怎么办，其实也不知道在什么地方休息，因为我不敢躺在地上，不知道可能会被什么野兽吃掉。后来，我才发现，那些担心其实没有必要。

　　然而，我还是尽我所能把搬到岸上的那些箱子和木板，挡在自己四周，搭成了一种棚屋，作为夜宿的地方。至于吃的，我还搞不清楚从何处为自己提供。我只看见从我打鸟的地方跑出来两三只野兔似的动物。

　　这时，我开始考虑，我还可能从船上搞到许多有用的东西，尤其是一些索具、帆和其他一些可以搬上岸来的东西。我决定，如有可能，就再上一次船。我知道，要再刮一次风暴，船肯定会粉身碎骨，所以我决定把其他所有的事儿都放在一边，先把船上能搬下来的一切东西都搬下来。随后，我就琢磨自己是不是把木排再划回去，但似乎行不通。所以，我决定像上次那样，等潮水一退，就游过去。而且我这样做了。只是在走出小屋前，我先脱掉衣服，只穿着一件方格衬衫、一条亚麻衬裤和一双浅口无带皮鞋。

　　我像先前那样爬上船，又做了一个木排，载走了好几件有用的东西。像第一次那样，我在木匠舱房里找到了两三袋长短钉子、一只大螺旋千斤顶、一两打短柄斧，首先最有用的是一个磨刀砂轮。我把所有这些东西和炮手的几样东西安放在一起，尤其是两三只起货铁钩、两桶步枪子弹、七支步枪，还有一支鸟枪和一小堆火药、一大袋小子弹，以及一大卷铅皮。但这铅皮太重，我无法把它从船上吊到木排上。

　　除了这些东西，我还拿了所能找到的所有男人的衣服，以及一个备用前桅中桅帆、一张吊床和一些被褥。我把这东西装上第二只木排，并将它们都平安地运到岸上。

Having got my second cargo on shore, though I was fain[1] to open the barrels of powder, and bring them by parcels, for they were too heavy, being large casks[2], I went to work to make me a little tent with the sail and some poles which I cut for that purpose, and into this tent I brought everything that I knew would spoil, either with rain or sun, and I piled all the empty chests and casks up in a circle round the tent, to fortify it from any sudden attempt, either from man or beast.

When I had done this I blocked up the door of the tent with some boards within, and an empty chest set up on end without, and spreading one of the beds upon the ground, laying my two pistols just at my head, and my gun at length by me, I went to bed for the first time, and slept very quietly all night.

I had the biggest magazine[3] of all kinds now that ever were laid up, I believe, for one man, but I was not satisfied still; for while the ship sat upright in that posture, I thought I ought to get everything out of her that I could; so every day at low water I went on board, and brought away something or other.

But that which comforted me more still was that at last of all, after I had made five or six such voyages as these, and thought I had nothing more to expect from the ship that was worth my meddling with, I found a great hogshead[4] of bread and three large runlets[5] of rum, and a box of sugar, and a barrel of fine flour.

The next day I made another voyage; and I got two cables and a hawser[6] on shore, with all the ironwork I could get; and having cut down the spritsail yard, the mizzen[7] yard and everything I could to make a large raft.

---

[1] fain   *adj.* 乐意的，愿意的，勉强的
[2] cask   *n.* 桶，木桶
[3] magazine   *n.* 杂志；军火库，弹药库
[4] hogshead   *n.* 大桶
[5] runlet   *n.* 桶，小河
[6] hawser   *n.* 大缆，曳船索，系船索
[7] mizzen   *n.* 后桅

第二批货物上岸后，尽管我很想打开两桶火药，分成小包带着，因为两大桶的火药太重，但我还要用船上的帆和特意砍的一些木杆做一顶小帐篷，把经不起雨淋日晒的东西搬进去，又把那些空箱和空桶围在帐篷四周，以防人或野兽的突然袭击。

　　帐篷搭好后，我用几块木板在里面顶住帐篷门，在门外竖起一只空箱，然后在地上铺了一张床，在头边放了两支手枪，在身边横放了一支长枪，第一次上床睡觉。我整夜都睡得很安静。

　　我相信，我现在拥有的是一个人所能储备的种类齐全的最大弹药库，但我仍不满足，因为我想趁那只船还在那里竖着时，应该尽可能把所有的东西都拿出来，所以我每天趁退潮时上船，每次都拿走一些东西。

　　但更让我安慰的是，我这样跑了五、六个来回后，认为船上没有什么值得我去拿的东西时，我居然发现了一大桶面包、三大桶朗姆酒、一箱食糖和一桶优质面粉。

　　第二天，我又到船上去了一次。我把两根锚索和一根锚链以及其他我能搬动的铁器都搬到了岸上，然后又把前帆桁、后帆桁和所有能扎成一个大木排的东西都砍了下来。

But my good luck began now to leave me; for this raft was so unwieldy and so overloaden that after I was entered the little cove, where I had landed the rest of my goods, not being able to guide it handily, it overset, and threw me and all my cargo into the water; as for myself it was no great harm, for I was near the shore; but as to my cargo, it was great part of it lost, especially the iron, which I expected would have been of great use to me. However, when the tide was out, I got most of the pieces of cable ashore, and some of the iron. After this I went every day on board, and brought away what I could get.

I had been now thirteen days on shore, and had been eleven times on board the ship; in which time I had brought away all that one pair of hands could well be supposed capable to bring. But preparing the 12th time to go on board, I found the wind begin to rise; however, at low water I went on board, and discovered a locker with drawers in it, in one of which I found two or three razors, and one pair of large scissors, with some ten or a dozen of good knives and forks; in another I found about thirty-six pounds value in money.

Wrapping all this in a piece of canvas, I began to think of making another raft, but while I was preparing this, I found the sky overcast[1], and in a quarter of an hour it blew a fresh gale from the shore; it presently occurred to me that it was in vain to pretend to make a raft with the wind off shore, and that it was my business to be gone before the tide of flood began, otherwise I might not be able to reach the shore at all.

Accordingly I let myself down into the water, and swam across the channel, which lay between the ship and the sands, and even that with difficulty enough, partly with the weight of the things I had about me, and partly the roughness of the water, for the wind rose very hastily, and before it was quite high water, it blew a storm.

But I was gotten home to my little tent, where I lay with all my wealth about me very secure. It blew very hard all that night, and in the morning, when I looked out, no more ship was to be seen.

---

[1] overcast   *adj.* 阴天的，阴暗的

但现在好运开始离我而去，因为这个木排太笨重，而且超载太多，所以木排驶进卸货的小湾后，无法得心应手地操纵它，结果木排一翻，将我和所有货物都掉进了水里。我自己没有受多大伤，因为我离岸很近，但我的货物却大部分都掉了，尤其是那些铁器，我本指望会对我大有用处。然而，退潮后，我还是把大部分锚索和一些铁器从水里捞上了岸。之后，我每天上一次船，把能搬动的东西都搬走。

　　我现已上岸 13 天了，到船上去了 11 次。在这段时间里，我已经把双手能拿得动的东西都搬了下来。我正准备第 12 次上船时，发现风开始刮了起来。不过，我还是在退潮时又上了船，发现了一个带抽屉的存物柜。我在其中一个抽屉里找出了两三把剃刀、一把大剪刀、十几把上好的刀叉，在另一个抽屉里还发现了大约价值 36 英镑的钱币。

　　我一边用一块帆布包所有东西，一边开始想再做一只木排。但我正准备做时，发现天空阴云密布，不到一刻钟就从岸上刮来一股强风。我马上想到，风从岸上刮来，再做木排徒劳无益，我要在涨潮之前赶快离开，否则就根本无法回到岸上去了。

　　于是，我跳下水，游过船和沙滩之间的狭长水湾。这次真够吃力的，一部分是因为身上带的东西太重，一部分是因为水势汹涌，因为风起得很急，还没等潮水完全涨起来，就已经刮起了风暴。

　　不过，我还是回到了自己的小帐篷。我躺下来，四周都是自己的财产，心里感到安稳。整个晚上，风都刮得很猛。第二天早晨，我向外望去，发现那只船已经不见了踪影。

VII

I soon found the place I was in was not for my settlement, because it was upon a low moorish[1] ground near the sea, and I believed would not be wholesome[2], and because there was no fresh water near it, I resolved to find a more healthy and more convenient spot.

I found a little plain on the side of a rising hill, whose front towards this little plain was steep as a house-side so that nothing could come down upon me from the top; on the side of this rock there was a hollow place.

On the flat of the green, just before this hollow place, I resolved to pitch my tent. This plain was not above an hundred yards broad, and about twice as long, and lay like a green before my door, and at the end of it descended irregularly every way down into the low-grounds by the seaside. It was on the N.N.W. side of the hill, so that I was almost sheltered from the heat every day.

Before I set up my tent, I drew a half circle before the hollow place. In this half circle I pitched two rows of strong stakes, driving them into the ground till they stood very firm like piles, the biggest end being out of the ground about five feet and a half, and sharpened on the top. The two rows did not stand above six inches from one another.

Then I took the pieces of cable which I had cut in the ship, and I laid them in rows one upon another, within the circle, between these two rows of stakes, up to the top, placing other stakes in the inside, leaning against them, about two foot and a half high, and this fence was so strong, that neither man or beast could get into it or over it.

---

[1] moorish   *adj.* 沼地的；荒野的
[2] wholesome   *adj.* 有益于健康的

7

　　我很快发现自己所在的地方不宜居住，一是因为离海太近，地势低湿，我相信也不会卫生；二是因为附近没有淡水，所以我决定找一个更卫生、更方便的地点。

　　我在一个隆起的小山坡上找到了一小片平原。面向小平原小山正面像山墙一样陡，所以什么东西都无法从山顶来袭击我。这块山岩边上有一块凹地。

　　我决定就在这凹地前面的一片平坦的草地上搭个帐篷。这块平原不足 100 码宽，长大约是宽的两倍，就像门前的草坪一样。平原尽头，地势参差不齐渐渐降低，一路通到了海边低地。这里正处在小山西北偏北处，所以小山每天几乎都可以把太阳遮住。

　　搭帐篷前，我先在凹地前划了个半圆形。在这个半圆形中，我插了两排结实的树桩，并将木桩打入地里，插在地里像木桩一样结实，大头朝下，露出地面大约 5 英尺半，顶上削得尖尖的。两排木桩相距不超过 6 英寸。

　　随后，我用从船上砍下来的那些锚索，沿着半圆形一层一层堆放在这两排木桩之间，一直堆到顶上，再用一些大约两英尺半高的木桩插进圈内撑住锚索。这个栅栏非常牢固，无论是人还是野兽都无法冲进来，也无法越过去。

The entrance into this place I made to be not by a door, but by a short ladder to go over the top, which ladder, when I was in, I lifted over after me, and so I slept secure in the night.

Into this fence, with infinite labour, I carried all my riches, all my provisions, ammunition and stores, and I made me a large tent, which, to preserve me from the rains, I made double, viz., one smaller tent within, and one larger tent above it, and covered the uppermost with a large tarpaulin[1].

And now I lay no more for a while in the bed which I had brought on shore, but in a hammock.

Into this tent I brought all my provisions, and everything that would spoil by the wet, and having thus enclosed all my goods, I made up the entrance, which till now I had left open, and so passed and re-passed by a short ladder.

When I had done this, I began to work my way into the rock, and bringing all the earth and stones that I dug down out through my tent, I laid them up within my fence in the nature of a terrace about a foot and a half; and thus I made me a cave just behind my tent.

It cost me much labour, and many days, before all these things were brought to perfection. At the same time it happened after I had laid my scheme for the setting up my tent and making the cave, that a storm of rain falling from a thick dark cloud, a sudden flash of lightning happened, and after that a great clap of thunder; I was not so much surprised with the lightning as I was with a thought which darted into my mind as swift as the lightning it self: O my powder! My very heart sunk within me when I thought that at one blast all my powder might be destroyed, on which, not my defence only, but the providing me food, as I thought, entirely depended; I was nothing near so anxious about my own danger, though had the powder took fire, I had never known who had hurt me.

So after the storm was over, I laid aside all my works, applied myself to make bags and boxes to separate the powder, and keep it a little and a little in a parcel, in hope that whatever might come, it might not all take fire at once, and to keep it so apart that it should not be possible to make one part fire another; I finished this work in about a fortnight[2].

---

[1] tarpaulin *n.* 防水油布
[2] fortnight *n.* 两星期

我搭的这个地方的入口不是一扇门，而是由一个短梯从栅栏顶上翻进来，进到里面后再收起梯子。这样，我夜里就可以放心睡觉了。

　　我又千辛万苦把所有财产、所有粮食、弹药和储备都搬进了栅栏，然后给自己搭了一个大帐篷用来遮雨。我把帐篷做成双层的，也就是说，里面一个小的，上面再盖一个大的，大的上面又罩了一大块油布。

　　现在我不再睡在搬上岸的那张床上，而是睡在一张吊床上。

　　我把所有粮食和所有会受潮损坏的东西都搬进了这个帐篷。我把所有东西都搬进来后，便将栅栏的出入口堵起来，由一个短梯进出。

　　这个做完后，我开始在岩壁上挖洞，把挖出来的土石方通过帐篷运到外面，在栅栏内堆成一个大约一英尺半高的土台。这样，我就在帐篷后面挖了一个洞穴。

　　所有这些工作费了我好多力气和时间才圆满完成。在我计划搭帐篷、挖岩洞的同时，突然乌云密布，暴雨倾盆，电光突闪，随后霹雳炸响。让我大为吃惊的不是闪电，而是像闪电一样快地飞进我的脑海里的一个念头：噢，我的火药！一想到一个霹雳就可能会把我所有的火药都炸毁，我的心就一沉，因为我不仅全靠它自卫，而且全靠它来猎食糊口。我几乎没有想到自己的危险，尽管火药一旦爆炸，我都不知道是谁害了自己。

　　于是，暴风雨过后，我把所有工作都放在一边，集中精力做一些袋子和盒子，把火药分成许多小包，希望万一发生什么情况，不致全部马上起火。我把火药分开放，以免一包着火引燃另一包。我用了大约两个星期才完成这项工作。

And I think my powder, which in all was about 240 pounds' weight was divided in not less than a hundred parcels; as to the barrel that had been wet, I did not apprehend any danger from that, so I placed it in my new cave, which I called my kitchen, and the rest I hid up and down in holes among the rocks, so that no wet might come to it, marking very carefully where I laid it.

In the interval of time while this was doing, I went out once at least every day with my gun. The first time I went out I presently discovered that there were goats in the island; but they were so shy, so subtle, and so swift of foot that it was the most difficult thing in the world to come at them. But I was not discouraged at this, not doubting but I might now and then shoot one, as it soon happened, for after I had found their haunts, I laid wait in this manner for them: I observed if they saw me in the valleys, though they were upon the rocks, they would run away as in a terrible fright; but if they were feeding in the valleys, and I was upon the rocks, they took no notice of me; so I always climbed the rocks first to get above them, and then had frequently a fair mark.

After I had been there about ten or twelve days, it came into my thoughts, that I should lose my reckoning of time for want of books and pen and ink, and should even forget the Sabbath days from the working days; but to prevent this I cut it with my knife upon a large post in capital letters, "I came on shore here on the 30th of September 1659", and making it into a great cross I set it up on the shore where I first landed. Upon the sides of this square post I cut every day a notch[1] with my knife, and every seventh notch was as long again as the rest, and every first day of the month as long again as that long one, and thus I kept my calendar.

Also I found three very good Bibles, some Portuguese books, among which two or three popish prayer books, and several other books. And we had in the ship a dog and two cats; I carried both the cats with me, and as for the dog, he jumped out of the ship of himself and swam on shore to me the day after I went on shore with my first cargo, and was a trusty servant to me many years. Later I found pen, ink and paper, and I husbanded[2] them to the utmost.

---

[1] notch   *n.* 槽口，凹口，刻痕
[2] husband   *vt.* 节用

我想所有火药大概 240 磅重，我把它们分成 100 多包。至于那桶受潮的火药，我倒不担心有什么危险，所以我把它放在新挖的洞穴里，将这洞穴称为我的厨房，其余的火药我都藏在岩石缝里，以免最后受潮，并在我藏的地方小心翼翼地标上记号。

　　在进行这项工作的这段时间，我至少每天带枪出去一次。第一次外出，我便很快发现岛上有山羊，但它们都很胆小、狡猾，而且跑得飞快，要想袭击它们是再难不过的事儿。但我并不气馁，我相信迟早会打到一只，这件事不久便应验了，因为我发现了山羊经常出没的地方，就对它们采用了打埋伏的方法。我注意到，如果它们看到我在山谷里，哪怕它们是在山岩上，也会惊慌失措地逃跑；但如果它们在山谷里吃草，我站在山岩上，它们就注意不到我。于是，我总是先爬上那些岩石，埋伏在它们上方，常常打得很准。

　　上岛大约十一二天后，我突然想到，我没有书，没有笔墨，一定会忘记计算日期，甚至会忘记安息日和工作日。但为了防止发生这种情况，我用刀子以大写字母在一根大柱子上刻下了："1659 年 9 月 30 日我在此上岸"，并把柱子做成一个大十字架，竖在我第一次上岸的地方。我在这方柱的四边每天用刀刻一个凹痕，每七天刻一个长一倍的凹痕，每个月刻一个再长一倍的凹痕。这样，我就有了自己的日历。

　　同时，我又找到了三本漂亮的《圣经》、几本葡萄牙文的书籍，其中有两三本天主教祈祷书和几本别的书。船上还有一条狗和两只猫。我随身带着那两只猫；至于那条狗，我第一次上船搬东西时，它就跟我游上了岸，它后来做了我多年的忠实仆人。后来，我还找到了纸和笔墨，而且用得极其节省。

This want of tools made every work I did go on heavily, and it was near a whole year before I had entirely finished my little pale or surrounded habitation.

Having now brought my mind a little to relish[1] my condition, and given over looking out to sea to see if I could spy a ship, I began to apply myself to accommodate my way of living, and to make things as easy to me as I could.

I have already described my habitation, which was a tent under the side of a rock, surrounded with a strong pale[2] of posts and cables, but I might now rather call it a wall, for I raised a kind of wall up against it of turfs[3], about two feet thick on the outside, and after some time, I think it was a year and half, I raised rafters[4] from it leaning to the rock, and thatched[5] or covered it with bows of trees and such things as I could get to keep out the rain, which I found at some times of the year very violent.

I have already observed how I brought all my goods into this pale, and into the cave which I had made behind me. But I must observe too, that at first this was a confused heap of goods, so they took up all my place and I had no room to turn myself; so I set myself to enlarge my cave and works farther into the earth, for it was a loose sandy rock. When I found I was pretty safe as to beasts of prey, I worked sideways to the right hand into the rock, and then turning to the right again, worked quite out and made me a door to come out on the outside of my pale.

This gave me not only egress[6] and regress[7], as it were a back way to my tent and to my storehouse, but gave me room to stow my goods.

And now I began to apply myself to make such necessary things I most wanted. I made me a table and a chair in the first place, and this I did out of the short pieces of boards that I brought on my raft from the ship.

---

[1] relish *vt.* 喜欢，爱好
[2] pale *n.* 栅栏，界线，(围篱用的)尖板条
[3] turf *n.* 草根土，草皮
[4] rafter *n.* 椽，筏夫
[5] thatch *vt.* 用茅草覆盖屋顶
[6] egress *n.* 出口，外出
[7] regress *n.* 退回，回归

由于缺乏工具，一切工作进行得都非常吃力。我花了差不多整整一年时间才把小木栅或围墙全部垒好。

我现在对自己的处境稍微有了兴趣，不再望着海面，看能不能看到一艘船了。我开始集中精力考虑自己的生活方式，并尽可能让自己过得舒适。

我已经描述过自己的住所，那是一个搭在一块山岩下的帐篷，四周用木桩和锚索做成坚固的栅栏围起来，但我现在可以把它叫做围墙了，因为我在栅栏外面用草皮垒成了一道大约两英尺厚的墙，而且过了一段时间，我想是一年半后，在围墙和岩壁之间搭了一些屋椽，上面盖了一些树枝或能找到的遮盖物用来挡雨，因为我发现一年中总有某段时期大雨倾盆。

我已经说过我把所有东西都搬进了这个围墙，搬进了我在帐篷后面挖的洞穴。现在我必须再说一下，那些东西起初都杂乱无章地堆在那里，所以它们占满了住所，连我转身的空间都没有。于是，我开始扩大洞穴，并向里深挖，因为这是一种疏松的沙石。当我发现自己非常安全，足以抵挡猛兽袭击时，便向岩壁右边挖去，然后又转向右面，挖穿岩壁，做成了一个门，通到围墙外面。

这不仅给我提供出入口，成了我的帐篷和储藏室的后门，而且给我提供了更多空间放置东西。

现在，我开始集中精力做自己最必需的东西。我先给自己做了一张桌子和一把椅子，这是用我从船上运回来的几块短木板做成的。

And I made large shelves of the breadth of a foot and half one over another, all along one side of my cave, to lay all my tools, nails, and ironwork, and in a word, to separate everything at large in their places, that I might come easily at them; I knocked pieces into the wall of the rock to hang my guns and all things that would hang up.

And now it was when I began to keep a journal of every day's employment. I shall here give you the copy, though in it will be told all these particulars[1] over again.

---

[1] particular *n.* 细节，详情

我还沿洞穴一侧搭了几层一英尺半宽的大木架，把所有工具、钉子和铁制品一层一层放好，总之把所有东西都分类放在上面，以便随时取用。我又在岩壁上钉了许多钉子，用来挂枪和所有可以挂起来的东西。

　　我就是这个时候开始写起了日记，把每天的工作都记下来。我要把它抄给你们，尽管日记里要把所有细节都要重述一遍。

VIII

September 30, 1659. I, being shipwrecked, during a dreadful storm, in the offing, came on shore on this dismal unfortunate island, which I called "the Island of Despair," all the rest of the ship's company being drowned, and myself almost dead.

All the rest of that day I spent in afflicting myself at the dismal circumstances I was brought to. I had neither food, house, clothes, weapon, or place to fly to, and in despair of any relief, saw nothing but death before me, either that I should be devoured by wild beasts, murdered by savages, or starved to death for want of food. At the approach of night, I slept in a tree for fear of wild creatures, but slept soundly though it rained all night.

October 1. In the morning I saw to my great surprise the ship had floated with the high tide, and was driven on shore again much nearer the island, which as it was some comfort on one hand, for seeing her sit upright, and not broken to pieces, I hoped, if the wind abated, I might get on board, and get some food and necessaries out of her for my relief; so on the other hand, it renewed my grief at the loss of my comrades, who I imagined if we had all stayed on board might have saved the ship, or at least that they would not have been all drowned as they were; and that had the men been saved, we might perhaps have built us a boat out of the ruins of the ship, to have carried us to some other part of the world. I spent great part of this day in perplexing myself on these things; but at length seeing the ship almost dry, I went upon the sand as near as I could, and then swam on board; this day also it continued raining, though with no wind at all.

From the 1st of October to the 24th. All these days entirely spent in many several voyages to get all I could out of the ship, which I brought on shore, every tide of flood, upon rafts. Much rain also in these days, though with some intervals of fair weather. But, it seems, this was the rainy season.

8

1659 年 9 月 30 日。在一场可怕的风暴中，由于近海船只遇难，我登上了这个不幸的荒岛，我把它称为"绝望岛"。同船的其他人都被淹死了，我自己也差点儿送命。

那天剩下的时间，我都为自己被带到这个凄凉的境地而痛苦。我既没有食物、房屋、衣服、武器，也没有地方可逃，没有获救的希望，只有死路一条，不是被野兽吞吃、被野人残杀，就是因缺少食物而饿死。夜幕降临，因为害怕野兽，我睡在一棵树上。尽管整整下了一夜雨，但我睡得很香。

10 月 1 日。早晨，让我大为吃惊的是，我看到那只船已经随着涨潮浮起，又被冲到了离岸近得多的地方。这件事虽然一方面给了我一些安慰，因为我看到船仍然挺立在那里，没有被海浪打成碎片，我希望，如果风势减弱，我可以登上船去弄一些食物和必需品来救急，另一方面又唤起了我对失去同伴的痛苦。我想，如果我们当时都留在船上，也许会保住船，或者至少他们不会都被淹死，如果那些人得救，我们也许可以用大船的残骸为自己造一只小船，把我们载到世界上的其他地方去。这一天的大部分时间，我都为这些事困扰。但当看到船里几乎没有进水时，我便尽可能走到离船最近的沙滩，然后凫水上了船。这一天，雨继续下个不停，但连一点儿风都没有。

10 月 1 日到 24 日。这几天，我都一直来回上船，把我能搬动的东西都搬了下来，趁每次涨潮时用木排把它们运上岸。这几天，雨水还是很多，尽管有时天也放晴，但好像现在正是雨季。

October 20. I overset[1] my raft, and all the goods I had got upon it, but being in shoal water, and the things being chiefly heavy, I recovered many of them when the tide was out.

October 25. It rained all night and all day, with some gusts of wind, during which time the ship broke in pieces, the wind blowing a little harder than before, and was no more to be seen, except the wreck of her, and that only at low water. I spent this day in covering and securing the goods which I had saved, that the rain might not spoil them.

October 26. I walked about the shore almost all day to find out a place to fix my habitation, greatly concerned to secure myself from an attack in the night, either from wild beasts or men. Towards night I fixed upon a proper place under a rock, and marked out a semicircle for my encampment, which I resolved to strengthen with a work, wall, or fortification[2] made of double piles, lined within with cables, and without with turf.

From the 26th to the 30th I worked very hard in carrying all my goods to my new habitation, though some part of the time it rained exceeding hard.

The 31st in the morning I went out into the island with my gun to see for some food, and discover the country, when I killed a she-goat, and her kid followed me home, which I afterwards killed also, because it would not feed.

November 1. I set up my tent under a rock, and lay there for the first night, making it as large as I could with stakes driven in to swing my hammock upon.

November 2. I set up all my chests and boards, and the pieces of timber which made my rafts, and with them formed a fence round me.

November 3. I went out with my gun and killed two fowls like ducks, which were very good food. In the afternoon went to work to make me a table.

November 4. This morning I began to order my times of work, of going out with my gun, time of sleep, and time of diversion, viz., every morning I walked out with my gun for two or three hours if it did not rain, then employed myself to work till about eleven o'clock, then eat what I had to live on, and from twelve to two I lay down to sleep, the weather being excessive hot, and then in the evening to work again. The working part of this day and of the next were wholly employed in making my table.

---

[1] overset   *vt.* 打翻，颠覆
[2] fortification   *n.* 防御工事，要塞

10 月 20 日。我把木排和上面的货物都翻到了水里，但因为是在浅水区，而那些东西又都很重，所以潮水一退，我又捞回了许多东西。

10 月 25 日。雨整整下了一天一夜，天还刮着一阵阵大风。此时，风刮得比先前更猛了点儿，船撞成了碎片，再也见不到它的踪影，只是低潮时看到了船的残骸。我花了一天功夫把从船上抢救出来的东西遮盖起来，妥善保管，这样雨水就淋不坏它们了。

10 月 26 日。我在岸上走了差不多一天，想寻找一个地方作为自己的住所。我极为关心的是不让野兽或野人夜间袭击我。傍晚，我在一块岩石下找到了一个合适的地方，然后划了一个半圆形作为自己的宿营地。我决定沿着那个半圆形筑一道坚固的工事、围墙或堡垒，插上两层木桩，中间盘上锚索，外面再堆上草皮。

26 日到 30 日，我非常努力，把所有货物都搬到了新住地，尽管有一段时间雨下得特别大。

31 日早上，我带着枪向岛内走去，一来是为了找点吃的，二来是为了察看小岛地形。我打死了一只母山羊，它的一只小羊跟着我回了家，后来我把它也杀了，因为它不愿吃食。

11 月 1 日。我在一块岩石下搭起了一个帐篷，尽可能把帐篷搭大一些，同时插上几根木桩挂吊床，这是我第一次在帐篷里过夜。

11 月 2 日。我堆起所有的箱子、木板和做木排用的船骨，然后沿着半圆形在我四周堆成了一道围墙。

11 月 3 日。我带枪出去，打死了两只野鸭似的飞鸟，这种鸟的肉很好吃。下午开始着手做一张桌子。

11 月 4 日。今天早上，我开始规定工作的时间、带枪外出的时间、睡觉的时间和解闷的时间，也就是说，每天早晨，如果不下雨，我就带枪出去两三小时，回来后再工作到大约 11 点，然后吃点儿东西聊以为生，12 点到两点我躺下睡觉，因为天气特别热，傍晚再接着干。今天和明天的工作时间，我全都用来做桌子。

November 5. This day went abroad with my gun and my dog, and killed a wild cat, her skin pretty soft, but her flesh good for nothing. Every creature I killed I took off the skins and preserved them. Coming back by the seashore, I saw many sorts of sea fowls which I did not understand, but was surprised and almost frightened with two or three seals, which, while I was gazing at, not well knowing what they were, got into the sea and escaped me.

November 6. After my morning walk I went to work with my table again, and finished it, though not to my liking; nor was it long before I learned to mend it.

November 7. Now it began to be settled fair weather. The 7th, 8th, 9th, 10th, and part of the 12th. (for the 11th was Sunday) I took wholly up to make me a chair, and with much ado brought it to a tolerable shape, but never to please me, and even in the making I pulled it in pieces several times.

I soon neglected my keeping Sundays, for omitting my mark for them on my post, I forgot which was which.

November 13. This day it rained, which refreshed me exceedingly, and cooled the earth, but it was accompanied with terrible thunder and lightning, which frightened me dreadfully for fear of my powder; as soon as it was over, I resolved to separate my stock of powder into as many little parcels as possible, that it might not be in danger.

November 14, 15, 16. These three days I spent in making little square boxes, which might hold about one or two pounds, at most, of powder, and so putting the powder in, I stowed it in places as secure and remote from one another as possible. On one of these three days I killed a large bird that was good to eat, but I know not what to call it.

November 17. This day I began to dig behind my tent into the rock to make room for my farther conveniency.

Three things I wanted exceedingly for this work, viz., a pickaxe[1], a shovel and a wheelbarrow[2] or basket, so I desisted[3] from my work, and began to consider how to make me some tools; as for a pickaxe, I made use of the iron crows; but the next thing was a shovel. I knew not what kind of one to make.

---

[1] pickaxe *n.* 镐

[2] wheelbarrow *n.* 独轮手推车，手推车

[3] desist *vi.* 终止

11月5日。今天带枪和狗外出。打死了一只野猫，它的毛皮非常柔软，但肉却不能吃。我每打死一只动物，就剥下毛皮保存起来。从海岸边回来时，我看到许多种叫不上名字的水鸟。但让我吃惊、几乎吓了一跳的是两三只海豹。我盯着它们，还不熟悉是什么动物，它们就跳进了海里，从我眼皮底下逃走了。

11月6日。早晨外出回来后，我又继续做桌子，最后终于做成了，但我不大喜欢。没过多久，我又想法修补了一下。

11月7日。现在天气开始晴好。7日、8日、9日、10日和12日的一部分时间（因为11日是礼拜天），我都用来做一把椅子，费尽周折才凑合做成了椅子的样子，但我一点儿都不满意。甚至在做的过程中，我就把它拆了好几次。

我不久便不再注意记礼拜天了，因为没有在木桩上标记，所以我忘记哪天是礼拜天了。

11月13日。今天下雨，这让我特别爽快，地上也凉快了，但这场雨伴随着电闪雷鸣，让我胆战心惊，因为我担心火药。雨一停，我就决定把库存的火药分成许许多多小包，以免发生危险。

11月14日、15日、16日。我用这三天做了许多小方盒，每个盒子至多大约可以装一两磅火药。我把火药装进盒里，尽可能远地妥善分开储藏。其中有一天，我打到了一只大鸟，肉很好吃，但我不知道叫什么鸟。

11月17日。今天我开始在帐篷后面的岩壁上挖洞，扩大空间，使自己行动更方便些。

这工作我最缺三样工具，也就是一把镐、一把铁铲、一辆手推车或一只箩筐。于是，我停下手头的工作，开始考虑如何制作一些工具。至于镐，我用起货钩代替，此外还需要一把铁铲。我不知道如何去做这种铁铲。

November 18. The next day in searching the woods I found a tree of that wood, or like it, which, in Brazil they call the iron tree, for its exceeding hardness; of this, with great labour and almost spoiling my axe, I cut a piece, and brought it home too with difficulty enough, for it was exceedingly heavy.

The excessive hardness of the wood, and having no other way, made me a long while upon this machine, for I worked it effectually by little and little into the form of a shovel, the handle exactly shaped like ours in England, only that the broad part having no iron shod upon it at bottom, it would not last me so long; however, it served well enough for the uses which I had occasion to put it to; but never was a shovel, I believe, made after that fashion, or so long a-making.

I was still deficient, for I wanted a basket or a wheelbarrow, a basket I could not make by any means, having no such things as twigs that would bend to make wicker ware, at least none yet found out; and as to a wheelbarrow, I fancied I could make all but the wheel, but that I had no notion of, neither did I know how to go about it; besides I had no possible way to make the iron gudgeons for the spindle or axis of the wheel to run in, so I gave it over; and so for carrying away the earth which I dug out of the cave, I made me a thing like a hod[1] which the labourers carry mortar[2] in when they serve the bricklayers[3].

This was not so difficult to me as the making the shovel; and yet this, and the shovel, and the attempt which I made in vain to make a wheelbarrow took me up no less than four days, I mean except my morning walk with my gun.

November 23. My other work having now stood still, because of my making these tools; when they were finished, I went on, and working every day, as my strength and time allowed, I spent eighteen days entirely in widening and deepening my cave, that it might hold my goods commodiously[4].

---

[1] hod   *n.* 灰浆桶
[2] mortar   *n.* 灰泥
[3] bricklayer   *n.* 砖匠
[4] commodiously   *adv.* 宽阔地，方便地

11月18日。第二天，我去树林里搜寻时，发现一种在巴西见过的树，或者类似的树，因为特别坚硬，人们称为铁树。我费了好大劲儿才砍下了一块，差点儿把斧头砍坏，又费了不少劲儿才把木块带回住所，因为这种木料特别重。

这种木料特别坚硬，又没有别的办法，我花了好一阵子才做成一把铁铲。我一点一点行之有效地把木块削成了铁铲的形状，铲柄完全像我们英国的铁铲，只是宽的部分没有包铁，所以我用不了那么久。然而，必要时用一下也还可以对付。但我相信，从来没有一把铁铲做成那个样子，也绝不会花那么长时间才做成。

我还缺少工具，因为我缺少一只箩筐或一辆手推车。箩筐我没办法做，因为我没有编柳条编织品那样的细软枝条，至少还没找到。至于手推车，我想，除了轮子，其他都能做。但我对做轮子一窍不通，也不知道该如何着手。此外，我也无法为轮轴做一个铁轴心，让轮子转动。所以，我放弃了这个想法。这样，为了把洞里挖出来的土运走，我做了一个小工们替泥瓦匠运泥灰用的灰斗那样的东西。

这对我来说不像做铁铲那么难，但制作这个东西和铁铲，以及试图做手推车而又半途而废，花了我多达四天的时间，我是说除了每天早晨带枪外出的时间。

11月23日。因为做这些工具，所以其他工作都停了下来。这些工具制成后，我又继续干了起来，只要力气和时间许可，我每天都工作，花了整整18天加宽加深了洞穴。这样，存放东西就更宽敞方便了。

During all this time, I worked to make this room or cave spacious enough to accommodate me as a warehouse or magazine, a kitchen, a dining-room, and a cellar; as for my lodging, I kept to the tent, except that some times in the wet season of the year, it rained so hard that I could not keep myself dry, which caused me afterwards to cover all my place within my pale with long poles in the form of rafters leaning against the rock, and load them with flags and large leaves of trees like a thatch.

December 10th. I began now to think my cave finished, when on a sudden a great quantity of earth fell down from the top and one side, so much that it frightened me, and not without reason too; for if I had been under it I had never wanted a gravedigger[1]. Upon this disaster I had a great deal of work to do over again; for I had the loose earth to carry out and the ceiling to prop up, so that I might be sure no more would come down.

December 11. This day I went to work with it accordingly and got two posts pitched upright to the top, with two pieces of boards across over each post. This I finished the next day; and setting more posts up with boards, in about a week more I had the roof secured; and the posts standing in rows, served me for partitions to part of my house.

December 17. From this day to the twentieth I placed shelves and knocked up nails on the posts to hang everything up that could be hung up, and now I began to be in some order within doors.

December 20. Now I carried everything into the cave, began to furnish my house, and set up some pieces of boards, like a dresser, to order my victuals[2] upon, but boards began to be very scarce with me; also I made me another table.

December 24. Much rain all night and all day, no stirring out.

December 25. Rain all day.

December 26. No rain, and the earth much cooler than before, and pleasanter.

---

[1] gravedigger   *n.*   挖墓者
[2] victual   *n.*   食物

这几天时间，我做的工作就是扩大这个房间或洞穴，使它足以成为我的储藏室或军火库，也成为我的厨房、餐室和地窖。我仍住在帐篷里，除了雨季的某些时候，因为雨下得很大，我无法使自己保持干燥，所以我后来把围墙里的所有地方都用长木杆搭成屋椽的样子靠在岩石上，再在上面铺一些菖蒲草和大树叶，搭成像茅屋那样。

12月10日。我开始以为洞穴已经大功告成，这时突然大量的泥土从洞顶上和一侧的岩壁上塌下来，落下来的泥土很多，把我给吓坏了。我这样惊恐也不是没有理由，因为如果塌方时我正在下面，我就再也不要挖墓人了。发生了这场灾祸后，我又有许多工作要做了，因为我要把落下来的松土运出去，把天花板撑起来，确保泥土不再掉下来。

12月11日。今天我按计划着手工作，用两根柱子撑住洞顶，每根柱子上交叉搭上两块木板。这我第二天就完成了，接着又撑起了更多的柱子、搭起了更多的木板，大约一星期后终于把洞顶加固。柱子一排排竖立在那里，把我的房间隔成了好几个小间。

12月17日。从今天到20日，我在洞里装了几个木架，又在柱子上钉了钉子，把所有能挂起来的东西都挂起来。现在，我的房里开始有些条理了。

12月20日。现在我把所有的东西都搬进洞里，开始布置自己的房子，像碗柜似的架起了一些木板，好把我吃的东西摆上去，但木板越来越不够用了。另外，我又做了一张桌子。

12月24日。大雨整整下了一天一夜。没有出去。

12月25日。雨下了一天。

12月26日。无雨，地上比先前凉爽多了，也更舒适了。

December 27. Killed a young goat, and lamed[1] another so as that I caught it, and led it home in a string; when I had it home, I bound and splintered up its leg which was broken. I took such care of it, that it lived, and the leg grew well, and as strong as ever; but by my nursing it so long it grew tame, and fed upon the little green at my door, and would not go away. This was the first time that I entertained[2] a thought of breeding up some tame creatures, that I might have food when my powder and shot was all spent.

December 28, 29, 30. Great heats and no breeze; so that there was no stirring abroad, except in the evening for food; this time I spent in putting all my things in order within doors.

January 1. Very hot still, but I went abroad early and late with my gun, and lay still in the middle of the day; this evening going farther into the valleys which lay towards the center of the island, I found there were plenty of goats, though exceeding shy and hard to come at; however, I resolved to try if I could not bring my dog to hunt them down.

January 2. I went out with my dog and set him upon the goats; but I was mistaken, for they all faced about upon the dog, and he knew his danger too well, for he would not come near them.

January 3. I began my fence; which, being still jealous of my being attacked by somebody, I resolved to make very thick and strong.

From the 3rd of January to the 14th of April I was working, finishing and perfecting this wall, though it was no more than about 24 yards in length, being a half circle from one place in the rock to another place about eight yards from it, the door of the cave being in the center behind it.

All this time I worked very hard, the rains hindering me many days; but I thought I should never be perfectly secure till this wall was finished. When this wall was finished, and the outside double-fenced with a turf-wall raised up close to it, I persuaded myself that if any people were to come on shore there, they would not perceive anything like a habitation; and it was very well I did so, as may be observed hereafter upon a very remarkable occasion.

---

[1] lame *vt.* 使成残废
[2] entertain *vt.* 娱乐，招待；怀有

12 月 27 日。打死了一只小山羊，又打瘸了另一只小山羊，于是捉住了它，并用绳子绑住牵回了家。到家后，我绑起了山羊的那条断腿，还上了夹板。在我这样照料下，受伤的小山羊活了下来，那条腿也长好了，而且像以前那样结实。由于我饲养了那么长时间，小山羊渐渐驯服，吃着我门前的小草，不愿离开。这是我第一次想到我可以饲养一些驯服的动物，在弹药都用完时可以有东西吃。

12 月 28 日、29 日、30 日。酷热无风，没有出去，只是傍晚才外出猎食。我这几天都在家里整理所有的东西。

1 月 1 日。仍然很热，但我早晚带枪各出去一次，中午睡觉。傍晚，我走进伸向岛中心的山谷，发现有许多山羊，但非常容易受惊，难以捉到。不过，我决定带狗试一下，看是不是能追捕到它们。

1 月 2 日。我带狗出去，让它去追捕那些山羊，但我想错了，因为那些山羊大胆面向我的狗。狗深知其中的危险，不敢接近他们。

1 月 3 日。我开始修筑栅栏，因为我仍然戒备着，怕受到某个人的袭击。我决定修得又厚又牢。

从 1 月 3 日到 4 月 14 日，我一直都在垒墙、修整、完善。围墙呈半圆形，从岩壁的一边围向另一边大约 8 码，围墙全长不过 24 码，洞门处于围墙中央后部。

这段时间，我拼命工作，尽管雨水耽搁了我许多天。但我认为，围墙不垒好，我就绝不会平安无事。墙垒好后，我又在墙外堆了一层和墙差不多一样高的草皮。我相信，如果有人到岛上来，他们不会察觉到会有这样的一个住所。我这样做很好，因为后来的事实非常鲜明地说明了这一点。

During this time, I made my rounds in the woods for game every day when the rain admitted me, and made frequent discoveries in these walks of something or other to my advantage; particularly I found a kind of wild pigeons, who built not as wood pigeons in a tree, but rather as house pigeons, in the holes of the rocks; and taking some young ones, I endeavoured to bread them up tame, and did so; but when they grew older they flew all away, which perhaps was at first for want of feeding them, for I had nothing to give them; however, I frequently found their nests, and got their young ones, which were very good meat.

In the managing my household affairs, I found myself wanting in many things, which I thought it was impossible for me to make; for instance, I could never make a cask to be hoped.

In the next place, I was at a great loss for candle, so that as soon as ever it was dark, which was generally by seven o'clock, I was obliged to go to bed. I remembered the lump of beeswax with which I made candles in my African adventure, but I had none of that now; the only remedy had was, that when I had killed a goat, saved the tallow[1], and with a little dish made of clay, which I baked in the sun, to which I added a wick of some oakum[2], I made me a lamp; and this gave me light, though not a clear steady light like a candle; in the middle of all my labours it happened, that rummaging my things, I found a little bag, which had been filled with corn when the ship came from Lisbon; what little remainder of corn had been in the bag was all devoured with the rats, and I saw nothing in the bag but husks and dust; and being willing to have the bag for some other use, I think it was to put powder in, when I divided it for fear of the lightning, I shook the husks of corn out of it on one side of my fortification under the rock.

About a month after, I saw some few stalks of something green, shooting out of the ground, which I fancied might be some plant I had not seen, but I was surprised and perfectly astonished, when, after a little longer time, I saw about ten or twelve ears come out, which were perfect green barley of the same kind as our English barley; and more strange to me, I saw near it still all along by the side of the rock, some other straggling stalks, which proved to be stalks of rice, and which I knew, because I had seen it grow in Africa when I was ashore there.

---

[1] tallow   *n.* 牛脂，动物脂
[2] oakum   *n.* 麻絮，填絮

在此期间，不下雨时，我每天就到树林里去打猎，常常发现对自己有用的各种东西，尤其是我发现了一种野鸽，它们不是像斑尾林鸽那样在树上筑巢，而是像家鸽一样在石洞里垒窝。我逮了几只小鸽子，想把它们驯养大。但养大时，它们都飞走了。也许是我起初没有经常喂它们，因为我没有什么东西喂它们。然而，我经常找到它们的窝，逮一些小鸽子，它们的肉很好吃。

在处理家务时，我发现自己还缺少许多东西，我认为有些东西我不可能做出来。比如，我根本不会做带箍的木桶。

其次，我很缺蜡烛。所以，天一黑，我就得上床睡觉。这里一般7点天就黑了。我想起了自己从萨利的海盗船长手里逃到非洲沿岸的航程中做蜡烛用的那一小块蜂蜡，但现在已经没有了。我唯一的补救办法就是，我每杀死一只山羊，就把羊油留下来。我用粘土做成一个小碟子，在太阳下晒干，然后放上一些麻絮做灯芯，做成了一盏灯，虽然光线没有蜡烛那样明亮稳定，但给我带来了光明。在做这些事时，我翻找东西，偶尔翻到了一个小袋子。船从里斯本出发时袋子里曾装满了谷类。袋子里剩下的一点谷类已被老鼠吃光了，我看到只剩下了外壳和尘土。因为我很想把这个袋子用到别处，我想是用来装火药，当时我害怕闪电，就把火药分开装，顺手将袋子里的外壳抖落在岩石下的围墙边。

大约一个月后，我看到地上长出了一些绿色茎干。我以为那可能是自己以前没有注意到的某种植物，但不久以后，我看到长出了十一二个穗子，这和我们英国的大麦苗完全一样，让我大为惊讶。更让我吃惊的是，我看到在大麦茎干旁边沿着岩壁零零星星长出了几枝其他的茎干，原来是稻茎；我知道那是稻子，因为我在非洲上岸时曾见过。

I not only thought these the pure productions of Providence for my support, but not doubting but that there was more in the place, I went all over that part of the island where I had been before, peering in every corner, and under every rock, to see for more of it, but I could not find any; at last it occurred to my thoughts that I had shaken a bag of chickens' meal out in that place.

I carefully saved the ears of this corn in their season, which was about the end of June; laying up every corn, resolved to sow them all again, hoping in time to have some quantity sufficient to supply me with bread; but it was not till the 4th year that I could allow myself the least grain of this corn to eat. I lost all that I sowed the first season, by not observing the proper time; for I sowed it just before the dry season.

Besides this barley, there was 20 or 30 stalks of rice, which I preserved with the same care. But to return to my journal.

我当时不仅认为这些谷类纯粹是上帝为了让我活命送给我的，而且相信岛上其他地方还有。于是，我走遍了岛上自己以前曾到过的那个地方，把每个角落、每块岩石下面都查看了一遍，想找到更多的麦穗和稻茎，但我再也没找到。最后，我突然想起自己曾把一袋鸡食抖落到了那个地方。

　　大约 6 月底，到了大麦成熟的季节，我小心翼翼地收起麦穗，每一颗麦粒都储存好，决定再次播种，希望将来再收获一些足以供我做面包。但直到第四年，我才允许自己吃到一点儿种的粮食。第一次播种没有看好时节，我把全部种子都损失了，因为我正好在旱季来临前播种。

　　除了这大麦，还有二三十根稻茎，我同样小心翼翼地存了起来。还是回到我的日记上来吧。

IX

I worked excessive hard these three or four months to get my wall done; and the 14th of April I closed it up, contriving to go into it, not by a door, but over the wall by a ladder, that there might be no sign in the outside of my habitation.

April 16. I finished the ladder, so I went up with the ladder to the top, and then pulled it up after me, and let it down in the inside. This was a complete enclosure[1] to men for within I had room enough, and nothing could come at me from without, unless it could first mount my wall.

The very next day after this wall was finished, I had almost had all my labour overthrown at once, and myself killed; the case was thus, as I was busy in the inside of it, behind my tent, just in the entrance into my cave, all on a sudden I found the earth come crumbling down from the roof of my cave, and from the edge of the hill over my head, and two of the posts I had set up in the cave cracked in a frightful manner; I was heartily scared, but thought nothing of what was really the cause, only thinking that the top of my cave was falling in, as some of it had done before; and for fear I should be buried in it, I ran forward to my ladder, and not thinking myself safe there either, I got over my wall for fear of the pieces of the hill which I expected might roll down upon me. I was no sooner stepped down upon the firm ground but I plainly saw it was a terrible earthquake, for the ground I stood on shook three times at about eight minutes' distance, with three such shocks, as would have overturned the strongest building that could be supposed to have stood on the earth, and a great piece of the top of a rock, which stood about half a mile from me next the sea, fell down with such a terrible noise, as I never heard in all my life. I perceived also, the very sea was put into violent motion by it; and I believe the shocks were stronger under the water than on the island.

---

[1] enclosure *n.* 围住，围栏，围墙

9

　　这三、四个月，我要把围墙垒好，工作非常辛苦，4 月 14 日终于合拢，因为我设计的就是不从门进，而是由梯子翻墙而过。这样，外面就看不出我住所的任何迹象了。

　　4 月 16 日。我做好了梯子，于是就用梯子爬上墙头，然后再收起来，放到围墙内。围墙完全封闭，墙内我有足够的空间，任何东西都无法从墙外袭击我，除非先爬上墙头。

　　垒好围墙后的第二天，我差点儿前功尽弃，而且差点儿送命。事情是这样的：我正在帐篷后面的洞穴口忙活，发现泥土从洞顶上和头顶岩壁上泥土塌了下来，把我竖在洞里的两根柱子都压断了，发出了可怕的断裂声。我胆战心惊，不知道究竟发生了什么事，以为只不过像上次那样发生了部分塌方，我怕自己被土石埋在里面，就跑向梯子，后来认为在那里也不安全，怕山上滚下来的石块滚落在我身上，就爬过了围墙。我一下到坚实的地上，才明白那是一场可怕的地震，因为我所站的地方在大约八分钟内震动了三次。这三次震动可以震倒地球上最坚固的建筑。离我大约半英里靠近海边的一个巨大岩顶都因可怕的震动而滚落下来，这声音我一辈子都没听到过。我还察觉到，大海因震动而汹涌澎湃，我相信水下比岛上震动得更强烈。

I was so amazed with the thing it self, having never felt the like, or discoursed with anyone that had, that I was like one dead or stupefied; and the motion of the earth made my stomach sick like one that was tossed at sea; but the noise of the falling of the rock awoke me as it were, and rousing me from the stupefied condition I was in, filled me with horror, and I thought of nothing then but the hill falling upon my tent and all my household goods, and burying all at once; and this sunk my very soul within me a second time.

After the third shock was over, and I felt no more for some time, I began to take courage, and yet I had not heart enough to go over my wall again, for fear of being buried alive, but sat still upon the ground, greatly cast down and disconsolate[1], not knowing what to do.

While I sat thus, I found the air overcast, and grow cloudy, as if it would rain; soon after that the wind rose by little and little, so that, in less than half an hour, it blew a most dreadful hurricane. The sea was all on a sudden covered over with foam and froth, the shore was covered with the breach of the water, the trees were torn up by the roots, and a terrible storm it was; and this held about three hours, and then began to abate, and in two hours more it was stark calm, and began to rain very hard.

All this while I sat upon the ground very much terrified and dejected, when on a sudden it came into my thoughts, that these winds and rain being the consequences of the earthquake, the earthquake itself was spent and over, and I might venture into my cave again. With this thought my spirits began to revive, and I went in and sat down in my tent, but the rain was so violent that my tent was ready to be beaten down with it, and I was forced to go into my cave, though very much afraid and uneasy for fear it should fall on my head.

This violent rain forced me to a new work, viz., to cut a hole through my new fortification like a sink to let the water go out, which would else have drowned my cave. After I had been in my cave some time, and found still no more shocks of the earthquake follow, I began to be more composed; and now to support my spirits, which indeed wanted it very much, I went to my little store and took a small sup of rum, which, however, I did then and always very sparingly, knowing I could have no more when that was gone.

---

[1] disconsolate   *adj.* 孤独的，郁郁不乐的

我从来没经历过地震，也从来没听到经历过地震的人谈起过，所以目瞪口呆、魂不附体。此时，地动山摇，使我像晕船一样恶心欲吐，但岩石滚落的声音把我从原来目瞪口呆的状态中惊醒过来，我感到万分恐惧。我这时只想着小山会倒下来压在帐篷上和所有的家用品上，马上会把所有东西都埋起来。这使我的心一下子又沉了下去。

　　第三次震动过后，我一段时间没再感到震动，才开始有了勇气，但我还是不敢再爬过墙，害怕被活埋。我一动不动地坐在地上，垂头丧气，闷闷不乐，不知道该怎么办。

　　我正这样坐着时，发现阴云密布，好像要下雨。不久之后，风势渐起，不到半小时，就刮起了极其可怕的飓风。海面上突然波涛汹涌，海岸上浪花飞溅，大树连根拔起。真是一场可怕的风暴。风暴持续了大约3小时，然后开始减退；又过了两小时，风平浪静，下起了大雨。

　　此时，我坐在地上，心惊胆战、萎靡不振。后来，我突然想到，这些风雨是地震带来的后果。地震已经过去了，我可以冒险重新回到洞里去了。这样一想，我又精神振作起来，爬进洞里，在帐篷里坐下，但大雨滂沱，都快把帐篷压塌了，我只得躲进洞里，尽管心里惶恐不安，生怕洞顶塌下来。

　　这场暴雨迫使我去做一项新的工作，也就是，在新围墙下挖一个像下水道一样的小洞，把水排出去，否则就会淹没洞穴。我在洞里呆了一段时间，发现没有再发生余震，才开始镇静了些。这时，我感到确实非常需要壮壮胆，就走到小储藏室，倒了一小杯朗姆酒。不过，我喝得一向非常节省，因为我知道喝完就没有了。

It continued raining all that night, and great part of the next day, so that I could not stir abroad, but my mind being more composed, I began to think of what I had best do, concluding that if the island was subject to these earthquakes, there would be no living for me in a cave, but I must consider of building me some little hut in an open place which I might surround with a wall as I had done here, and so make myself secure from wild beasts or men; but concluded, if I stayed where I was, I should certainly, one time or other, be buried alive.

With these thoughts I resolved to remove my tent from the place where it stood, which was just under the hanging precipice[1] of the hill, and which, if it should be shaken again, would certainly fall upon my tent. And I spent the two next days, being the 19th and 20th of April, in contriving[2] where and how to remove my habitation.

The fear of being swallowed up alive made me that I never slept in quiet, and yet the apprehensions of lying broad without any fence was almost equal to it; but still, when I looked about and saw how everything was put in order, how pleasantly concealed I was, and how safe from danger, it made me very loath to remove.

In the meantime it occurred to me that it would require a vast deal of time for me to do this, and that I must be contented to run the venture where I was, till I had formed a camp for myself, and had secured it so as to remove to it. So with this resolution I composed myself for a time, and resolved that I would go to work with all speed to build me a wall with piles and cables in a circle as before, and set my tent up in it when it was finished. This was the 21st.

April 22. The next morning I began to consider of means to put this resolve in execution, but I was at a great loss about my tools; I had three large axes and abundance of hatchets, (for we carried the hatchets for traffic with the Indians), but with much chopping and cutting knotty[3] hard wood, they were all full of notches and dull, and though I had a grindstone, I could not turn it and grind my tools too. At length I contrived a wheel with a string, to turn it with my foot, that I might have both my hands at liberty. My grindstone was very large and heavy. This machine cost me a full week's work to bring it to perfection.

---

[1] precipice   *n.* 悬崖
[2] contrive   *v.* 发明，设计，图谋
[3] knotty   *adj.* （木材等）多结的，多节的

大雨整整下了一夜，第二天又下了大半天，所以我无法出去，但我心里比较镇静，开始想着做什么最好，最后决定，如果岛上容易发生这些地震，我就绝不能住在洞穴里，必须考虑在开阔地上建一间小屋，四面像这里一样围一道墙，以防野兽或野人袭击；如果我呆在原地，迟早肯定会被活埋。

　　想到这些，我决定把帐篷从原来的地方移开，因为帐篷正好搭在小山的悬崖下面。如果再发生地震，悬崖肯定会砸落在帐篷上。于是，我又花了两天时间（即 4 月 19 日和 20 日）来计划将住所移到何处和如何移。

　　我害怕被活埋，所以一直无法安睡，但想到睡在外面，四周没有围墙，心里差不多又同样担忧。而环顾四周，看到一切都井井有条，我住的既隐蔽舒适又没有危险，我又很不愿搬家。

　　同时，我想到，这样做将需要我大量时间，而且我必须安心住在原地，冒点儿险也无妨，要等到我亲自建好一个营地安全可靠后，再搬过去。所以，这样决定后，我就镇静了一段时间，决定尽快用木桩和锚索像以前一样垒一道围墙，建好后再把帐篷搭在里面。这是 4 月 21 日。

　　4 月 22 日。第二天早上，我开始考虑实施搬家的方法，但我很缺工具。我有三把长柄斧和许多短柄斧（我们带了许多小斧，准备和印第安人做交易），但由于经常砍伐多结的硬木，这些工具到处是凹口，都不快了；尽管我有一个旋转磨石，但也无法转动磨轮来磨工具。最后，我想了一个办法，用一根绳子套在一个轮子上，用一只脚转动轮子，这样我就可以腾出两只手来磨工具了。我的磨轮又大又重。我花了整整一个星期才把这个磨刀机器做好。

April 28, 29. These two whole days I took up in grinding my tools, my machine for turning my grindstone performing very well.

April 30. Having perceived my bread had been low a great while, now I took a survey of it, and reduced myself to one biscuit cake a day, which made my heart very heavy.

May 1. In the morning looking towards the seaside, the tide being low, I saw something lie on the shore bigger than ordinary; when I came to it, I found a small barrel, and two or three pieces of the wreck of the ship, which were driven on shore by the late hurricane, and looking towards the wreck itself, I thought it seemed to lie higher out of the water than it used to do; I examined the barrel which was driven on shore, and soon found it was a barrel of gunpowder, but it had taken water, and the powder was caked as hard as a stone; however, I rolled it farther on shore for the present, and went on upon the sands as near as I could to the wreck of the ship to look for more.

When I came down to the ship I found it strangely removed. The forecastle, which lay before buried in sand, was heaved up at least six feet, and the stern which was broken to pieces and parted from the rest by the force of the sea soon after I had left rummaging her, was tossed, as it were, up, and cast on one side, and the sand was thrown so high on that side next her stern that whereas there was a great place of water before, so that I could not come within a quarter of a mile of the wreck without swimming, I could now walk quite up to her when the tide was out; I was surprised with this at first, but soon concluded it must be done by the earthquake, and as by this violence the ship was more broken open than formerly, so many things came daily on shore, which the sea had loosened, and which the winds and water rolled by degrees to the land.

This wholly diverted my thoughts from the design of removing my habitation; and I busied myself mightily that day especially in searching whether I could make any way into the ship, but I found nothing was to be expected of that kind, for that all the inside of the ship was choked up with sand. However, as I had learned not to despair of anything, I resolved to pull everything to pieces that I could of the ship, concluding that everything I could get from her would be of some use or other to me.

4月28日、29日。整整两天，我都忙着磨工具，这个带转动磨轮的机器用起来不错。

4月30日。我好一阵子就察觉到面包不多了，现在查看了一下，把自己的口粮减为每天一块饼干，这使我心情非常沉重。

5月1日。早上向海边望去，潮水已退，我看到一个不同寻常的大东西躺在岸边。我走过去一看，发现是一只小桶，还有两三块破船的残骸，这是被最近的飓风刮到岸上来的。我向那艘破船望去，只见比先前高出了水面。我察看了一下冲上岸边的那只桶，马上发现那是一桶火药，但已经进水，火药像石头一样硬。不过，我还是暂时把它滚到了远处的岸上，然后走上沙滩，尽可能走近那个破船的残骸，想寻找更多的东西。

我走近船边，发现船莫名其妙地移了位。此前埋在沙里的船头现在抬高了至少六英尺。我最后一次上船搜寻东西后不久就被海浪打得粉碎脱离船身的船尾，现在好像被海水冲到了一边。先前那里有一大片水，有四分之一英里，所以我要接近那艘破船，非游泳不可，而现在船尾附近那边沙子堆得很高，所以潮水一退，我就可以直接走到船边。我起初对此感到吃惊，但不久便马上断定，这一定是地震造成的。由于这次地震，船比以前更破了。每天都有许多东西被海浪从船上冲下来，风和水又把这些东西逐步卷到了岸上。

这让我把搬家的计划完全放到了一边。那天，我手忙脚乱，尤其是要想方设法看能不能到船上去，但我发现那没有任何指望，因为船里都堵满了沙子。然而，因为我已经学会了对任何事情都不丧失信心，所以我决定把船上能拆下来的东西都拆下来，同时断定我从船上弄下来的所有东西将来对我都会有用。

May 3. I began with my saw, and cut a piece of a beam through, which I thought held some of the upper part or quarter-deck together, and when I had cut it through, I cleared away the sand as well as I could from the side which lay highest; but the tide coming in, I was obliged to give over for that time.

May 4. I went a-fishing, but caught not one fish that I durst eat of, till I was weary of my sport, when just going to leave off, I caught a young dolphin. I had made me a long line of some rope yarn, but I had no hooks, yet I frequently caught fish enough, as much as I cared to eat; all which I dried in the sun and eat them dry.

May 5. Worked on the wreck, cut another beam asunder[1] and brought three great fir planks off from the decks, which I tied together and made swim on shore when the tide of flood came on.

May 6. Worked on the wreck, got several iron bolts out of her and other pieces of ironwork; worked very hard and came home very much tired and had thoughts of giving it over.

May 7. Went to the wreck again, but with an intent not to work, but found the weight of the wreck had broken itself down, the beams being cut, that several pieces of the ship seemed to lie loose, and the inside of the hold lay so open, that I could see into it, but almost full of water and sand.

May 8. Went to the wreck, and carried an iron crow to wrench up the deck, which lay now quite clear of the water or sand; I wrenched open two planks and brought them on shore also with the tide. I left the iron crow in the wreck for next day.

May 9. Went to the wreck and with the crow made way into the body of the wreck and felt several casks and loosened them with the crow, but could not break them up; I felt also the roll of English lead and could stir it, but it was too heavy to remove.

May 10, 11, 12, 13, 14. Went every day to the wreck, and got a great deal of pieces of timber and plank, and two or three hundredweight of iron.

May 15. I carried two hatchets to try if I could not cut a piece off of the roll of lead, by placing the edge of one hatchet, and driving it with the other; but as it lay about a foot and a half in the water, I could not make any blow to drive the hatchet.

---

[1] asunder   *adv.* 分离，成碎片

5月3日。我开始用锯子锯断了一根横梁。我想这根横梁是支撑上甲板或后甲板的。锯断横梁后，我尽可能清除沙子堆得最高的那边。但此时潮水上涨，我只得放弃。

5月4日。我去钓鱼，但钓到的鱼没有一条我敢吃的。我感到厌倦，正要离开，却钓到了一只小海豚。我用钢索股绳做了一根长长的钓鱼线，但没有鱼钩。不过，我还是常钓到鱼，足够我吃。我把钓到的鱼都在太阳地晒干了再吃。

5月5日。在破船上工作，又锯断了一根横梁。从甲板上取下三大块杉木板，我把板捆在一起，等涨潮时让它们漂到岸上。

5月6日。在破船工作，从船上取下几根铁条和一些铁器。工作很辛苦，回来时筋疲力尽，想放弃这种工作。

5月7日。又到破船上去，但不想工作。只见破船因横梁锯断承受不住自身重量而碎裂，好几块木板散落下来，船舱敞开，一览无余，里面差不多都是水和沙。

5月8日。到破船上去，用一只起货钩撬起甲板，现在甲板上完全没有多少水或沙了。我撬开两块厚木板，又随着涨潮送上岸。我把起货钩留在船上，供明天再用。

5月9日。到破船上去，用起货钩撬入船身，探到了好几只木桶，然后用起货钩撬松这几只桶，却无法把桶打开。我还探到了那卷英国铅皮，并能摇动，但因太重而搬不动。

5月10日、11日、12日、13日、14日。每天都上破船，弄到了很多船骨和厚木板，以及两三英担的铁。

5月15日。我带了两把短柄斧上船，将一把斧刃放在那卷铅皮上，再用另一把去敲，想试试看能不能削掉一块铅，但因为铅皮在水下一英尺半深处，所以我根本无法敲到那把斧。

May 16. It had blown hard in the night, and the wreck appeared more broken by the force of the water; but I stayed so long in the woods to get pigeons for food that the tide prevented me going to the wreck that day.

May 17. I saw some pieces of the wreck blown on shore, at a great distance, near two miles off me, but resolved to see what they were, and found it was a piece of the head, but too heavy for me to bring away.

May 24. Every day to this day I worked on the wreck, and with hard labour I loosened some things so much with the crow, that the first blowing tide several casks floated out, and two of the seamen's chests; but the wind blowing from the shore, nothing came to land that day but pieces of timber and a hogshead which had some Brazil pork in it, but the salt water and the sand had spoiled it.

I continued this work every day to the 15th of June, except the time necessary to get food, which I always appointed, during this part of my employment, to be when the tide was up, that I might be ready when it was ebbed out, and by this time I had gotten timber and plank and ironwork enough to have built a good boat, if I had known how; and also, I got at several times and in several pieces near one hundredweight of the sheet lead.

June 16. Going down to the seaside, I found a large turtle; this was the first I had seen, which it seems was only my misfortune, not any defect of the place, or scarcity; for had I happened to be on the other side of the island, I might have had hundreds of them every day, as I found afterwards.

June 17. I spent in cooking the turtle; I found in her threescore[1] eggs; and her flesh was to me at that time the most savoury[2] and pleasant that ever I tasted in my life, having had no flesh but of goats and fowls since I landed in this horrid place.

---

[1] threescore   *n.* 六十，六十岁
[2] savoury   *adj.* 开胃的，可口的，味香的

5月16日。大风刮了一夜，那条破船因风吹浪打显得更破。我在树林里呆了好长时间想逮鸽子吃，所以那天潮水上涨，使我无法再到船上去了。

5月17日。我看到几块残骸漂到岸上，离我差不多有两英里远，但我决心走过去看个究竟，发现是一块船头木，但太重，我搬不走。

5月24日。至今，我每天都在破船上工作。我费了很大劲儿用起货钩撬松了一些东西。潮水一来，几只木桶和两只水手箱都浮了出来。但因为风是从岸上吹来的，所以那天漂到岸上的东西只有几块船骨和一个装有巴西猪肉的大桶，咸水和沙子早已把肉给损坏了。

我这样每天除了必要的猎食时间就上船继续干这项工作，一直到6月15日。在这段工作时间，我总是规定，涨潮时外出猎食，退潮时上船工作。到这个时候，如果知道怎样造船的话，我弄到的船骨、厚木板和铁器足够造一条不错的小船了。同时，我在不同地方分好几次搞到了将近一英担重的铅皮。

6月16日。我走到海边，发现了一只大海龟。这是我上岛后第一次看见海龟。好像只是我运气不好，并不是这地方缺少海龟。后来我发现，如果我碰巧住在岛的另一边，每天都可以捉到几百只。

6月17日。我花了一些时间煮那只海龟，在它的肚子里发现了60只蛋。对我来说，海龟肉是我有生以来尝到的最鲜美可口的肉，因为自从登上这个可怕的地方以来，我只吃过山羊和飞禽的肉。

IX

June 18. Rained all day, and I stayed within. I thought at this time the rain felt cold, and I was something chilly, which I knew was not usual in that latitude.

June 19. Very ill, and shivering, as if the weather had been cold.

June 20. No rest all night, violent pains in my head, and feverish.

June 21. Very ill, frightened almost to death with the apprehensions[1] of my sad condition, to be sick and no help. Prayed to God for the first time since the storm off of Hull, but scarce knew what I said, or why; my thoughts being all confused.

June 22. A little better, but under dreadful apprehensions of sickness.

June 23. Very bad again, cold and shivering, and then a violent headache.

June 24. Much better.

June 25. An ague[2] very violent; the fit held me seven hours, cold fit and hot, with faint sweats after it.

June 26. Better; and having no victuals to eat, took my gun, but found myself very weak; however, I killed a she-goat, and with much difficulty got it home, and broiled[3] some of it and eat; I would fain have stewed it and made some broth[4], but had no pot.

---

[1] apprehension *n.* 理解，忧惧
[2] ague *n.* 疟疾，冷颤
[3] broil *v.* 烤（肉）
[4] broth *n.* 肉汤

10

6月18日。下了一天雨，我呆在围墙内。我感到这次的雨冷，身上也感到有点儿冷。我知道，在这个纬度上是不常见的。

6月19日。病得很重，浑身发抖，好像天气已经很冷。

6月20日。整夜无法休息，头疼得非常厉害，而且身上发热。

6月21日。病得很重，想到自己生病而无人帮助的惨状，几乎怕得要死。自从离开赫尔城遭遇风暴以来，第一次向上帝祈祷，但我几乎不知道自己说什么、为什么说，因为头脑一片混乱。

6月22日。身子稍好了点儿，但还是非常担心自己的病。

6月23日。病又重了，冷得发抖，接着是头疼得非常厉害。

6月24日。病好多了。

6月25日。疟疾发作。发作一次持续七小时，时冷时热，随后出虚汗。

6月26日。好了点儿。因为没有东西吃，就拿枪出门，但身体十分虚弱。不过，还是打到了一只母山羊，非常吃力地把它弄回了家。烤了些羊肉吃。我很想炖些羊肉，熬些羊肉汤喝，但没有锅。

June 27. The ague was again so violent that I lay abed all day and neither ate or drank. I was ready to perish for thirst, but so weak, I had not strength to stand up or to get myself any water to drink. Prayed to God again, but was lightheaded, and when I was not, I was so ignorant that I knew not what to say; only I lay and cried, "Lord look upon me, Lord pity me, Lord have mercy upon me." I suppose I did nothing else for two or three hours till, the fit wearing off, I fell asleep, and did not wake till far in the night; when I woke, I found myself much refreshed, but weak, and exceeding thirsty. However, as I had no water in my whole habitation, I was forced to lie till morning, and went to sleep again. In this second sleep, I had this terrible dream.

I thought that I was sitting on the ground on the outside of my wall, where I sat when the storm blew after the earthquake, and that I saw a man descend from a great black cloud, in a bright flame of fire, and light upon the ground. He was all over as bright as a flame, so that I could but just bear to look towards him; his countenance[1] was most inexpressibly dreadful; when he stepped upon the ground with his feet, I thought the earth trembled, just as it had done before in the earthquake, and all the air looked, to my apprehension, as if it had been filled with flashes of fire.

He was no sooner landed upon the earth but he moved forward towards me, with a long spear in his hand, to kill me; and when he came to a rising ground, at some distance, he spoke to me, or I heard a voice so terrible that it is impossible to express the terror of it; all that I can say I understood was this, "Seeing all these things have not brought thee to repentance[2], now thou shalt die." At which words, I thought he lifted up the spear that was in his hand, to kill me.

It is impossible to describe the impression that remained upon my mind when I awoke.

---

[1] countenance *n.* 面容，脸色
[2] repentance *n.* 后悔，悔改

6 月 27 日。疟疾再次发作，我在床上整整躺了一天，不吃不喝，渴得要死，但身体非常虚弱，我无力站起来为自己弄点儿水喝。再次向上帝祈祷，但头昏眼花；等头不昏时，我又不知道该说什么，只是躺在床上，喊道："上帝保佑我！上帝可怜我！上帝救救我！"我想我两三个小时什么也没做，等到发作逐渐消失，我才倒头睡去，直到深更半夜才醒。醒来时，我发现身体爽快了许多，但仍然无力，渴得要命。然而，家里连一滴水都没有，我只得躺到第二天早晨。于是，我又睡着了。这二次睡着时，我做了一个可怕的梦。

我想我是坐在围墙外面的地上，就是地震后狂风暴雨时我坐的地方，我看见一个人从一大片乌云中降下来，在一片明亮的火焰中降落到地上。他浑身像火焰一样闪亮，所以我无法正眼看他。他面目狰狞，难以言表。当他两脚踩到地上时，我想大地震动，就像先前曾发生的地震一样。而且让我忧惧的是，空中仿佛充满了闪耀的火光。

他一落到地面，就向我走来，手里拿着一根长矛，要来杀我。他走到不远处的一个高坡上时，对我讲起了话，我听到的声音非常可怕，恐怖得难以形容。他对我说的话，我只听懂了一句："因为所有这一切都无法让你痛改前非，所以现在你必须死。"说完，我想他就举起手中的长矛，要杀我。

我醒来时留在我脑海中的印象真是难以描述。

June 28. Having been somewhat refreshed with the sleep I had had, and the fit being entirely off, I got up; and though the fright and terror of my dream was very great, yet I considered, that the fit of the ague would return again the next day, and now was my time to get something to refresh and support myself when I should be ill; and the first thing I did, I filled a large square case-bottle with water, and set it upon my table, in reach of my bed; and to take off the chill of the water, I put about a quarter of a pint of rum into it; then I got me a piece of the goat's flesh, and broiled it on the coals, but could eat very little; I walked about, but was very weak, and withal[1] very sad and heavy-hearted in the sense of my miserable condition; dreading the return of my distemper[2] the next day; at night I made my supper of three of the turtle's eggs, which I roasted in the ashes; and this was the first bit of meat I had ever asked God's blessing to, even as I could remember, in my whole life.

It occurred to my thought that the Brazilians take no physic but their tobacco for almost all distempers; and I had a piece of a roll of tobacco in one of the chests, which was quite cured, and some also that was green and not quite cured.

I went, directed by Heaven no doubt; for in this chest I found a cure, both for soul and body, I opened the chest, and found the tobacco; and as the few books I had saved lay there too, I took out one of the Bibles and brought it with the tobacco to the table.

What use to make of the tobacco, I knew not, as to my distemper, or whether it was good for it or no; but I tried several experiments with it as if I was resolved it should hit one way or other. I first took a piece of a leaf and chewed it in my mouth, which indeed at first almost stupefied[3] my brain, the tobacco being green and strong, and that I had not been much used to it; then I took some and steeped it an hour or two in some rum, and resolved to take a dose of it when I lay down; and lastly, I burnt some upon a pan of coals, and held my nose close over the smoke of it as long as I could bear.

---

[1] withal   *adv.* 此外，而且
[2] distemper   *n.* 大瘟热，不高兴，病异状
[3] stupefy   *v.* 麻木

6 月 28 日。睡了一觉，精神好了点儿，疟疾也完全退了，我从床上起来。尽管噩梦的恐惧让我心惊肉跳，但我认为，疟疾明天还会再次发作，所以现在正是吃些东西恢复元气维持体力应对即将发病的时机。我做的第一件事就是把一只大方瓶灌满水，放在床边的桌子上。为了减少水的寒气，我又在往瓶里倒了大约四分之一品脱的朗姆酒。随后，我取了一块羊肉，放在煤火上烤，但我吃得很少。我又走动了一下，但非常虚弱。而且一想到自己的悲惨处境，害怕明天再发病，我就愁容满面、心情沉重。夜里，我在火灰里烤了三只海龟蛋。这是我一生中记事以来第一次在吃肉时祈求上帝赐福。

这时，我突然想起，巴西人差不多什么病都不吃药，只嚼烟叶。我的箱子里有一卷烟叶，有些完全烤熟了；也有一些是青烟叶，没有完全烤熟。

毫无疑问，上天在为我指点迷津，因为我在箱子里找到了医治灵魂和肉体的良药。我打开箱子，找到了烟叶。箱子里还有我保存的几本书。我取出一本《圣经》，和烟叶一起放到了桌上。

我不知道怎样服用烟草，也不知道是不是对我的病有疗效，但我还是做了好几种试验，好像我主意已定总会有一种办法能生效似的。我先把一片烟叶放在嘴里嚼，因为烟叶呈青色，劲儿很大，我又不大习惯嚼烟，所以几乎一下就晕头转向了。随后，我又取了些烟叶，放在朗姆酒里泡了一两小时，决定躺下睡觉前服下去。最后，我又拿些烟叶放在炭盆上烧，然后把鼻子凑近烟叶燃起的烟闻，能闻多久就坚持多久。

In the interval of this operation, I took up the Bible and began to read, but my head was too much disturbed with the tobacco to bear reading, at least that time; only having opened the book casually, the first words that occurred to me were these, "Call on Me in the day of trouble, and I will deliver, and thou shalt[1] glorify Me."

Before I lay down, I did what I never had done in all my life, I knelt down and prayed to God to fulfill the promise to me, that if I called upon Him in the day of trouble, He would deliver me; after that, I drunk the rum in which I had steeped the tobacco, which was so strong and rank of the tobacco, that indeed I could scarce get it down; immediately upon this I went to bed; I found presently it flew up in my head violently, but I fell into a sound sleep, and woke no more till by the sun it must necessarily be near three o'clock in the afternoon the next day; nay, to this hour I'm partly of the opinion that I slept all the next day and night, and till almost three that day after; for otherwise I knew not how I should lose a day out of my reckoning in the days of the week, as it appeared some years after I had done; for if I had lost it by crossing and re-crossing the line, I should have lost more than one day. But certainly I lost a day in my account, and never knew which way.

Be that, however, one way or the other, when I awoke I found myself exceedingly refreshed; when I got up, I was stronger than I was the day before, and my stomach better, for I was hungry; and in short, I had no fit the next day, but continued much altered for the better; this was the 29th.

The 30th was my well day, of course, and I went abroad with my gun, but did not care to travel too far. I killed a seafowl or two, something like a brand goose, and brought them home, but was not very forward to eat them; so I ate some more of the turtle's eggs, which were very good. This evening I renewed the medicine which I had supposed did me good the day before, viz., the tobacco steeped[2] in rum, only I did not take so much as before, nor did I chew any of the leaf, or hold my head over the smoke; however, I was not so well the next day, which was the first of July, as I hoped I should have been; for I had a little spice of the cold fit, but it was not much.

---

[1] shalt   *vbl.* shall 的第二人称单数现在式
[2] steep   *v.* 浸，泡，沉浸

在这样治病的空隙，我拿起《圣经》，开始看了起来，但我的头因烟味而昏昏沉沉，至少那段时间看不下去，只是随便翻开了书页，我看到的第一句话就是："患难之时请求我，我将拯救你，你一定会赞美我。"

我躺下睡觉前，做了一件一生从未做过的事儿：我跪下来，向上帝祈祷，求他对我履行诺言，如果我在患难之时请求他，他一定要拯救我。之后，我就喝了浸过烟叶的朗姆酒，酒劲儿很冲，带着刺鼻的烟味，我简直喝不下去。喝过酒后，我立刻上床睡觉。不久，我就感到酒劲儿猛地上了头，倒头酣睡了起来，肯定是到第二天下午将近三点才醒来。不，此时此刻，我还部分认为，我第二天又睡了整整一天一夜，直到第三天下午差不多三点才醒来，因为几年后我不知道自己的日历上这一周怎么漏记了一天，因为如果我来回穿越赤道线失去时间的话，少掉的应该超过一天。我确实漏记了一天，却怎么也不知道是怎么漏记的。

不过，无论怎样，我醒来时发现自己神清气爽。起床后，我也比前一天有劲了，胃口也好了，因为我感到饿了。总之，第二天疟疾没有发作，状况越来越好。这是 29 日。

30 日当然是我的康复日，我又带枪外出，但不敢走得太远。我打死了一两只像黑雁那样的海鸟带回家，却不很想吃它们。所以，我又煮了几只海龟蛋吃，味道很好。晚上，我又喝了点儿浸过烟叶的朗姆酒，因为昨天对我有好处，只是这次我喝得没有先前多，也没有嚼烟叶或烧烟叶熏头。不过，第二天，7 月 1 日，我并没有像希望的那样好，因为我有点儿发冷，但不是太厉害。

July 2. I renewed the medicine all the three ways, and dozed myself with it as at first; and doubled the quantity which I drank.

July 3. I missed the fit[1] for good and all, though I did not recover my full strength for some weeks after; while I was thus gathering strength, my thoughts run exceedingly upon this Scripture, "I will deliver thee." This touched my heart very much, and immediately I knelt down and gave God thanks aloud.

July 4. In the morning I took the Bible, and beginning at the New Testament, I began seriously to read it.

My thoughts being directed by a constant reading the Scripture and praying to God to things of a higher nature, I had a great deal of comfort within.

From the 4th of July to the 24th, I was chiefly employed walking about with my gun in my hand, a little and a little at a time, as a man that was gathering up his strength after a fit of sickness.

I had been now in this unhappy island above 10 months; and I firmly believed that no humane shape had ever set foot upon that place.

It was the 15th of July that I began to take a more particular survey of the island itself. I went up the creek first, where I brought my rafts on shore; I found after I came about two miles up, that the tide did not flow any higher. On the bank of this brook I found many pleasant savannas[2], plain, smooth, and covered with grass; and on the rising parts of them next to the higher grounds, I found a great deal of tobacco, green, and growing to a great and very strong stalk; there were divers other plants which I had no notion of.

I searched for the cassava[3] root, which the Indians in all that climate make their bread of, but I could find none. I saw large plants of aloes[4], but did not then understand them. I saw several sugarcanes[5], but wild, and for want of cultivation, imperfect. I contented myself with these discoveries for this time.

---

[1] fit   *n.* （病痛的）发作，一阵
[2] savanna   *n.* 热带（或亚热带）稀树大草原
[3] cassava   *n.* 木薯
[4] aloe   *n.* 芦荟，芦荟油
[5] sugarcane   *n.* 甘蔗，糖蔗

7月2日。我把三种用药法又都试了一遍，并像第一次那样昏昏欲睡，喝下去的药酒份量增加了一倍。

7月3日。我没有再发作，尽管几星期后我还没有完全恢复体力。在我这样恢复体力时，我念念不忘《圣经》上的这句话："我一定会拯救你。"这大大触动了我的心，我马上跪下来大声感谢上帝。

7月4日。早上，我拿起《圣经》，从《新约》开始。认真读了起来。

由于经常读《圣经》和向上帝祈祷，我的思想转向了更高尚的事情上，内心也有了极大安慰。

从7月4日到14日，我主要忙着手里拿枪四处走动。我像病了一场后恢复体力的人那样，走一阵歇一阵。

我在这个不幸的岛上已经10个多月了。我坚信以前从里没有人到过这个地方。

7月15日，我开始对这个岛进行更详细的勘察。我先走到那条小河边。这条小河是我木排靠岸的地方。我沿河而上走了大约两英里后，发现海潮涨不了再高了。我看到河岸上是一片片宜人的草地，广阔平坦，绿草如茵；在靠近高地的那些地势较高的地方，我发现有许多烟草，绿油油的，茎秆长得高大粗壮。还有我不认识的其他各种各样的植物。

我到处寻找木薯，那是生活在那种气候的印第安人用来做面包的植物，但我什么也没有找到。我看到了大株大株的芦荟，但当时我不了解它们。我还看到好几株甘蔗，却都是野生的，因缺乏人工栽培，显得不太完美。我对自己这次的发现非常满意。

The next day, the 16th, I went up the same way again, and after going something farther than I had gone the day before, I found the brook and the savannas began to cease, and the country became more woody than before; in this part I found different fruits, and particularly I found melons upon the ground in great abundance and grapes upon the trees; the vines had spread indeed over the trees, and the clusters of grapes were just now in their prime[1], very ripe and rich. This was a surprising discovery, and I was exceeding glad of them; but I was warned by my experience to eat sparingly of them. But I found an excellent use for these grapes, and that was to cure them in the sun, and keep them as raisins[2] are kept.

I spent all that evening there, and went not back to my habitation, which was the first night I had lain from home. In the night I took my first contrivance[3] and got up into a tree, where I slept well, and the next morning proceeded upon my discovery, traveling near four miles, as I might judge by the length of the valley, keeping still due north, with a ridge[4] of hills on the south and north side of me.

At the end of this march I came to an opening, where the country seemed to descend to the west, and a little spring of fresh water which issued out of the side of the hill by me, run due east; and the country appeared so fresh, so green, so flourishing.

I descended a little on the side of that delicious vale[5], surveying it, to think that this was all my own, that I was king and lord of all this country indefeasibly[6]. I saw here abundance of cocoa trees, orange and lemon and citron trees; but all wild, and very few bearing any fruit, at least not then. However, the green limes[7] that I gathered were not only pleasant to eat but very wholesome.

I found now I had business enough to gather and carry home to lay up a store, to furnish myself for the wet season, which I knew was approaching.

---

[1] prime *n.* 青春；壮年，全盛期
[2] raisin *n.* 葡萄干
[3] contrivance *n.* 发明，发明物
[4] ridge *n.* 背脊，山脊，屋脊
[5] vale *n.* 谷
[6] indefeasibly *adv.* 难使无效地，不能废弃地
[7] lime *n.* 酸橙；石灰

第二天，16日，我又沿原路上去，比昨天走得更远些后，发现小河和草地到了尽头，而那里的树木比先前更加茂盛。我在这个地方发现了各种水果，尤其发现地上有大量甜瓜，树上有葡萄。事实上，葡萄藤爬满了树枝，一串串葡萄现在长得正盛，圆润透熟。这是一个意外的发现，我对此非常高兴，但经验警告我不能贪吃。不过，我还是想出了一个极好的方法利用这些葡萄，就是把它们放在太阳下晒干，做成葡萄干保存起来。

我在那里过了一夜，没有返回住处。这是我第一次在外面过夜。夜里，我采用老办法，爬上一棵树，在那里睡得很香。第二天早上，我又继续勘察。根据山谷的长度判断，我大约朝正北走了四英里，南面和北面是连绵不断的山岭。

走到尽头时，我来到了一片开阔地，这里地势好似乎向西低下去。一股小小的清泉从我身边的山坡上流下来，朝正东流去。眼前的土地是那样清新，那样翠绿，那样繁茂。

沿着风景秀丽的山谷坡往下走了一小段路，我环顾四周，心里想，这都是我自己的，我是这地方无法废除的君王。我在这里又看到了许多可可树、橘子树、柠檬树和香橼树，但都是野生的，结果子的寥寥无几，至少说当时没有结。然而，我采集的青酸橙不仅好吃，而且非常有益健康。

我现在发现，得采集一些带回家，储藏起来，准备雨季吃，因为我知道雨季即将来临。

Having spent three days in this journey, I came home. But before I got thither, the grapes were spoiled; as to the limes, they were good, but I could bring but a few.

The next day, being the 19th, I went back, having made me two small bags to bring home my harvest. But I was surprised, when coming to my heap of grapes, which were so rich and fine when I gathered them, I found them all spread about, and abundance eaten and devoured. By this I concluded, there were some wild creatures thereabouts, which had done this; but what they were, I knew not.

I found there was no laying them up on heaps, and no carrying them away in a sack, but that one way they would be destroyed, and the other way they would be crushed with their own weight. I took another course; for I gathered a large quantity of the grapes, and hung them up upon the out-branches of the trees, that they might cure and dry in the sun; and as for the limes and lemons, I carried as many back as I could.

When I came home from this journey, I contemplated with great pleasure the fruitfulness of that valley, and the pleasantness of the situation, the security from storms on that side the water and the wood, and concluded that I had pitched upon a place to fix my abode which was by far the worst part of the country. Upon the whole, I began to consider of removing my habitation; and to look out for a place equally safe as where I now was situate, if possible, in that pleasant fruitful part of the island.

This thought ran long in my head, the pleasantness of the place tempting me; but when I came to a nearer view of it, and to consider that I was now by the seaside, where it was at least possible that something might happen to my advantage, and by the same ill fate that brought me hither, might bring some other unhappy wretches to the same place; and though it was scarce probable that any such thing should ever happen, yet to enclose myself among the hills and woods, in the center of the island, was to anticipate my bondage[1]; and therefore I ought not by any means to remove.

---

[1] bondage　*n.* 奴役，束缚

路上花了三天时间，我才回到家。但还没等我到家，葡萄就都烂了。至于酸橙，则完好无损，但我能带的只有寥寥几个。

第二天，也就是19日，我带着两只小袋子回去装我的摘下的果子。但来到葡萄堆前时，发现采集时饱满完好的葡萄现在撒得到处都是，许多都被吃掉了。眼前的情景让我吃了一惊。我由此推断，附近一定有野兽出没，但我不知道它们是什么野兽。

我发现，把葡萄堆成堆不行，用袋子装把它们带走也不行，堆起来会被毁掉，装起来则会因自身的重压而被挤烂。于是，我便又想了一个办法。我采集了大量葡萄，把它们挂在外面的树枝上，这样它们就可以在太阳下晒干。至于柠檬和酸橙，我可以尽可能多地带回去。

这次外出回家后，我想到那个山谷果实累累，地势宜人，靠近河流和树林，不受暴风雨袭击，心里非常高兴，并推断出，我选的是目前岛上最坏的地方安营扎寨。总之，我开始考虑搬家，在岛上那个果实累累、地势宜人的地方寻找一个和我现在所处的位置同样安全的地方。

搬家的念头在我脑海里盘旋了很久，因为那地方可爱宜人诱惑着我，但仔细一想，我现在住在海边，这里至少有可能出现对我有利的事儿，说不定还有一些其他不幸的人被同样的厄运带到这座岛上来。尽管这种事发生的可能性几乎没有，但把自己关在岛中央的山林里，等于把自己禁闭了起来。因此，我绝不应该搬家。

However, I was so enamoured[1] of this place that I spent much of my time there, for the whole remaining part of the month of July; and though upon second thoughts I resolved not to remove, yet I built me a little kind of a bower[2] and surrounded it at a distance with a strong fence, being a double hedge, as high as I could reach, well staked, and filled between with brushwood[3]; and here I lay very secure, sometimes two or three nights together, always going over it with a ladder, as before. This work took me up to the beginning of August.

About the beginning of August, I had finished my bower. The third of August, I found the grapes I had hung up were perfectly dried, and, indeed, were excellent good raisins of the sun; so I began to take them down from the trees, and it was very happy that I did so; for the rains which followed would have spoiled them, and I had lost the best part of my winter food; for I had above two hundred large bunches of them. No sooner had I taken them all down, and carried most of them home to my cave, but it began to rain, and from hence, which was the fourteenth of August, it rained more or less, every day, till the middle of October; and sometimes so violently that I could not stir out of my cave for several days.

From the fourteenth of August to the twenty-sixth, incessant rain, so that I could not stir, and was now very careful not to be much wet. In this confinement I began to be straitened for food, but venturing out twice, I one day killed a goat, and the last day, which was the twenty-sixth, found a very large turtle.

During this confinement in my cover by the rain, I worked daily two or three hours at enlarging my cave, and by degrees worked it on towards one side, till I came to the outside of the hill, and made a door or way out; but I was not perfectly easy at lying so open; for as I had managed myself before, I was in a perfect enclosure, whereas now I lay exposed, and open for anything to come in upon me; and yet I could not perceive that there was any living thing to fear, the biggest creature that I had yet seen upon the island being a goat.

---

[1] enamour   vt. 迷住，使迷恋
[2] bower   n. 凉亭
[3] brushwood   n. 矮灌木丛

然而，我对这个地方是那样恋恋不舍，7 月剩下的时间都是在那里度过的。虽然经过反复考虑不搬家，但我还是在那里建了一间小小的茅屋，并用一道结实的围墙把它从外面围住。围墙是双层树篱，像我那样高，桩子打得很牢，桩子之间塞满了矮灌木丛。我睡在里面非常安全，有时在里面一连睡两三夜，总是像以前那样爬梯子翻墙过去。这项工作我到 8 月初才完工。

　　大约 8 月初，我终于建成了茅屋。8 月 3 日，我发现自己挂在树枝上的那些葡萄都完全晒干了，真正成了上等葡萄干。于是，我开始动手把它们从树上摘下来。我很高兴这样做，因为接踵而至的雨会毁了它们，那样我冬季一大半的食物就没有了。我晒了 200 多大串大串的葡萄。我刚把它们摘下来，并将大部分运到原来的洞穴里，就下起了雨。从那时起，也就是从 8 月 14 日到 10 月中旬，每天或多或少都要下雨；有时下得很猛，一连好几天我都出不了洞口。

　　从 8 月 14 日到 26 日，雨下个不停，所以我无法出门。我现在小心翼翼，不敢过多淋雨了。在这段足不出户的日子里，我的食物开始缺乏起来。不过，我也冒险出去两次，第一次打死了一只山羊，第二次，最后一天，也就是 26 日，找到了一只非常大的海龟。

　　在被雨困在家里这段时间，我每天工作两三个小时扩大洞穴。我把洞渐渐向一边延伸，一直通到山外，作为门或出口。但这样敞开门，我总睡不安稳，因为以前我总是设法把自己围在四面封闭的地方，而现在却敞开门户，什么东西都可以进来袭击我。不过，我还没有发现有什么可怕的生物，我在岛上见到的最大的动物就是山羊。

September the thirtieth, I was now come to the unhappy anniversary of my landing. I cast up the notches on my post, and found I had been on shore three hundred and sixty five days. I kept this day as a solemn fast; and having not tasted the least refreshment for twelve hours, even till the going down of the sun, I then ate a biscuit cake and a bunch of grapes and went to bed.

The rainy season and the dry season began now to appear regular to me, and I learned to divide them so as to provide for them accordingly. Now I thought it a proper time to sow it after the rains, the sun being in its southern position, going from me.

Accordingly I dug up a piece of ground as well as I could with my wooden spade, and dividing it into two parts, I sowed my grain; but as I was sowing, it casually occurred to my thoughts that I would not sow it all at first, because I did not know when was the proper time for it; so I sowed about two thirds of the seed, leaving about a handful of each.

It was a great comfort to me afterwards that I did so, for not one grain of that I sowed this time came to anything; for the dry months following, the earth having had no rain after the seed was sown, it had no moisture[1] to assist its growth, and never came up at all, till the wet season had come again, and then it grew.

I dug up a piece of ground near my new bower, and sowed the rest of my seed in February, a little before the vernal equinox[2]; and this having the rainy months of March and April to water it, sprung up very pleasantly and yielded a very good crop; but having part of the seed left only, and not daring to sow all that I had I had but a small quantity at last, my whole crop not amounting to above half a peck[3] of each kind.

But by this experiment I was made master of my business, and knew exactly when the proper season was to sow; and that I might expect two seed times and two harvests every year.

---

[1] moisture   *n.* 潮湿，湿气

[2] vernal equinox 春分

[3] peck   *n.* 配克（容量单位，等于 2 加仑）

9月30日。今天是登陆这个岛的不幸的纪念日。我加了一下柱子上的凹痕，发现我已上岸365天了。我把这天定为斋戒日。我12小时什么东西都没有吃，直到太阳下山，我才吃了一块饼干和一串葡萄干，上床睡觉。

对我来说，雨季和旱季现在渐渐有规律了，而且我学会了划分这两个季节，以便做好相应的准备。那场雨过后，太阳南移，我认为现在是播种的良机。

于是，我用木铲把一块地挖松，并把地分成两部分播种。但在播种时，我临时想到，起先不能把全部种子播下去，因为我不知道什么时候适合播种，所以我播了大约三分之二的种子，每一样都留了大约一把。

我这样做事后对我是一个极大安慰，我这次播的种子一粒也没有长出来。因为播下种子后，一连几个月不下雨，地面缺雨，没有水份帮助种子生长，所以一直到雨季来临才冒了出来。

二月的春分前几天，我在新茅屋附近挖了一块地，把留下的种子都播了下去。这次有三、四月的雨季浇灌，就非常喜人地冒了出来，而且收成良好。但因为只留了一部分种子，而且不敢全部种下去，所以最后收获量很小，全部产量每一种就半配克多。

但通过这次试验，我成了种田能手，确切知道什么季节适合播种，每年可望播种两次、收获两次。

While this corn was growing, I made a little discovery which was of use to me afterwards. As soon as the rains were over, and the weather began to settle, which was about the month of November, I made a visit up the country to my bower, where though I had not been some months, yet I found all things just as I left them. The double hedge that I had made was not only firm and entire; but the stakes which I had cut out of some trees that grew thereabouts were all shot out and grown with long branches. I was surprised, and yet very well pleased, to see the young trees grow.

This made me resolve to cut some more stakes, and make me a hedge like this in a semicircle round my wall; I mean that of my first dwelling; and placing the trees or stakes in a double row, at about eight yards distance from my first fence, they grew presently, and were at first a fine cover to my habitation, and afterward served for a defence also.

I found now that the seasons of the year might generally be divided, not into summer and winter, as in Europe; but into the rainy seasons and the dry seasons.

I employed myself in planting my second rows of stakes and in this wicker[1] working all the summer, or dry season.

---

[1] wicker   *n.* 柳条

在庄稼生长时，我有了一个小小的发现，后来对我很有用。大约 11 月，雨季一过，天气开始转晴，我去了一趟乡间茅屋。尽管我几个月没去那里了，但发现一切都和我离开时一样。我建的双层围墙不仅牢固完整，而且从附近砍下来的那些树桩都发了芽，长出了长长的枝条。看到这些小树成长，我真是又惊又喜。

这使我决定再砍一些树桩，在我原来的围墙外以半圆形围一圈树篱。我是说在最初的住处外面。我在离栅栏大约 8 码的地方种了两排树或树桩，它们很快就长了起来，起初成了我住处的良好庇护，后来又成了防御工事。

我现在发现，这里的季节通常不像欧洲那样一年分为夏季和冬季，而是分为雨季和旱季。

在整个夏季或旱季，我把时间都花在了栽第二排木桩和编箩筐上。

I mentioned before that I had a great mind to see the whole island and that I had travelled up the brook and so on to where I built my bower and where I had an opening quite to the sea on the other side of the island; I now resolved to travel quite across to the seashore on that side; so taking my gun, a hatchet, and my dog, and a larger quantity of powder and shot than usual, with two biscuit cakes and a great bunch of raisins, I began my journey; when I had passed the vale where my bower stood, I came within view of the sea to the west, and it being a very clear day, I fairly descried land, whether an island or a continent, I could not tell; but it lay very high, extending from the west, to the west-southwest at a very great distance; by my guess it could not be less than fifteen or twenty leagues off.

I concluded by all my observations that it must be near the Spanish dominions and perhaps was all inhabited by savages, where if I should have landed, I had been in a worse condition than I was now.

Besides, I considered that if this land was the Spanish coast, I should certainly, one time or other, see some vessel pass or re-pass one way or other; but if not, then it was the savage coast between the Spanish country and Brazil, which are indeed the worst of savages; for they are cannibals[1].

With these considerations I walked very leisurely forward. I found that side of the island where I now was, much pleasanter than mine, the open or savanna fields sweet, adorned with flowers and grass, and full of very fine woods. I saw abundance of parrots, and fain I would have caught one, if possible to have kept it to be tame, and taught it to speak to me. I did, after some painstaking, catch a young parrot, and brought it home; but it was some years before I could make him speak.

---

[1] cannibal　*n.* 食人者

11

我以前提到过，一心想去看一下全岛。我顺着小河向上走，然后继续向前，走到了我建乡间茅屋的地方，那里有一片开阔地，完全面向小岛另一边的大海。我现在决定穿过小岛，走到另一边的海岸。于是，我带上枪、短柄斧、狗，以及比平常多的火药子弹，另外还带了两块饼干和一大包葡萄干，开始了旅程。我穿过茅屋所在的山谷，向西眺望，可以看到大海。这一天，天气格外晴朗，我可以远远地看清对面的地面，是海岛还是大陆，我说不清楚；只见地势很高，从西向西南偏西延伸了很长一段距离，我估计可能不少于15或20里格。

根据我的种种观察，这一定靠近西班牙领土，也许全都住着野人。如果当时我在那里上岸，情况肯定比现在更糟。

另外，我又想，如果这片陆地是西班牙海岸，我迟早肯定会看到有船只来往；但如果没有的话，那就是位于西班牙领土和巴西之间的蛮荒海岸，那里确实有最坏的野人，因为他们都吃人肉。

我一边这样想，一边慢慢悠悠地向前走。我发现现在所在的小岛这边比我原来住的那边舒适得多。这里草原开阔，花草遍地，林木郁郁葱葱，散发出阵阵芳香。我看到有许多鹦鹉，很想逮一只驯养起来，教它和我说话。经过了一番努力，我真的逮住了一只小鹦鹉，并把它带回了家。但过了好几年，我才教会它说话。

I was exceedingly diverted with this journey. I found in the low grounds hares and foxes, but they differed greatly from all the other kinds I had met with; nor could I satisfy myself to eat them, though I killed several. I had no need to be venturous; for I had no want of food.

I never travelled in this journey above two miles outright in a day; but I took so many turns and returns, to see what discoveries I could make, that I came weary enough to the place where I resolved to sit down for all night; and then I either reposed myself in a tree, or surrounded myself with a row of stakes set upright in the ground, either from one tree to another, or so as no wild creature could come at me without waking me.

As soon as I came to the seashore, I was surprised to see that I had taken up my lot on the worst side of the island; for here indeed the shore was covered with innumerable turtles, whereas on the other side I had found but three in a year and half. Here was also an infinite number of fowls of many kinds, some which I had seen, and some which I had not seen of before, and many of them very good meat.

I confess this side of the country was much pleasanter than mine, but yet I had not the least inclination to remove; for as I was fixed in my habitation, it became natural to me, and I seemed all the while I was here to be, as it were, upon a journey, and from home.

I travelled along the shore of the sea towards the east, I suppose about twelve miles; and then setting up a great pole upon the shore for a mark, I concluded I would go home again; and that the next journey I took should be on the other side of the island, east from my dwelling, and so round till I came to my post again.

I took another way to come back than that I went, thinking I could easily keep all the island so much in my view that I could not miss finding my first dwelling by viewing the country; but I found myself mistaken; for being come about two or three miles, I found myself descended into a very large valley; but so surrounded with hills, and those hills covered with wood, that I could not see which was my way by any direction but that of the sun, nor even then, unless I knew very well the position of the sun at that time of the day.

我对这次旅行非常高兴，还在地势低的地方发现了野兔和狐狸，但它们和我以前碰到过的都完全不一样。尽管我打死了几只，但并不想吃它们。我没必要冒险，因为我不缺食物。

　　在这次旅行中，我一天走的路从来没有超过两英里。我总是绕来绕去，看看能不能有新的发现。因此，当我走到决定停下来过夜的地方时，已经够累了。有时我爬到树上去睡；如果睡在地上，要么就在四周插上一道木桩，要么就把木桩插在两颗树之间。这样，野兽不惊醒我，就不可能到我身边。

　　我一来到海边，看到我住的那边是岛上最糟的地方，就吃了一惊，因为这里的海岸边有数不清的海龟；而在我住的那个海边一年半才找到了三只。这里还有无数种类繁多的飞禽；有些我曾见过，有些以前从未见过。许多飞禽的肉都很好吃。

　　我承认这边比我住的地方舒适得多，但我一点儿也不想搬家，因为我在那边定居了下来，渐渐习以为常了，在这里总像在旅行，不像是在家里。

　　我沿着海岸向东走，估计走了大约 12 英里，然后在岸上竖了一根大柱子作为标志，决定回家。我下次旅行要从岛的另一边出发，往东绕一圈，再回到这里立柱子的地方。

　　我回家时没走老路，而是走了另一条路，认为既然我能轻而易举地看到全岛，就不会找不到我原先的住所。但我发现自己错了，因为走了大约两三英里后，我发现自己进入了一个非常大的山谷，四周群山环抱，山上树林密布，除了太阳的方位，我分不清东西南北，但此刻看太阳也无济于事，除非我非常熟悉当时太阳的方位。

It happened to my farther misfortune, that the weather proved hazy for three or four days, while was in this valley; and not being able to see the sun, I wandered about very uncomfortably, and at last was obliged to find out the seaside, look for my post, and come back the same way I went; and then by easy journeys I turned homeward, the weather being exceeding hot, and my gun, ammunition, hatchet, and other things very heavy.

In this journey my dog surprised a young kid, and seized upon it, and I running in to take hold of it, caught it, and saved it alive from the dog.

I had a great mind to bring it home if I could; for I had often been musing, whether it might not be possible to get a kid or two, and so raise a breed of tame goats, which might supply me when my powder and shot should be all spent.

I made a collar to this little creature, and with a string which I made of some rope yarn, which I always carried about me, I led him along, though with some difficulty, till I came to my bower, and there I enclosed him and left him; for I was very impatient to be at home, from whence I had been absent above a month.

I reposed myself here a week, during which most of the time was taken up in making a cage for my poll, who began now to be a mere domestic, and to be mighty well acquainted with me. Then I began to think of the poor kid, and resolved to go and fetch it home; accordingly I went, and found it where I left it; for indeed it could not get out, but almost starved for want of food. I went and cut bows of trees and branches of such shrubs as I could find, and having fed it, I tied it as I did before, to lead it away; and as I continually fed it, the creature became so loving, so gentle and so fond that it would never leave me afterwards.

The rainy season of the autumnal equinox[1] was now come, and I kept the 30th of September in the same solemn manner as before, being the anniversary of my landing on the island, having now been there two years, and no more prospect of being delivered than the first day I came there. I spent the whole day in humble and thankful acknowledgments[2] of the many wonderful mercies of God.

---

[1] autumnal equinox 秋分
[2] acknowledgment *n.* 承认，承认书，感谢

更倒霉的是，在山谷里的三、四天中，雾气蒙蒙，不见阳光，我局促不安地四处乱走，最后只好回到海边，寻找那根柱子，顺原路返回，这时一路顺畅向家走去。因为天气非常热，所以我身上带的枪、弹药、短柄斧和其他东西显得很重。

这次回家途中，我的狗袭击了一只小山羊，并捉住了它。我连忙跑过去抓住小山羊，把它从狗嘴里救了下来。

如果可能的话，我很想把它带回家，因为我经常考虑逮一两只小山羊，繁殖出一群驯羊。到我弹尽粮绝时，可以供我充饥。

我给这只小山羊做了一个颈圈，又用我总带在身边的一些麻绳搓了一根绳子牵着它，费了一番劲儿才把它牵回我的乡间茅屋。我把它圈在里面，就离开了，因为我迫不及待想回家，离开家已经一个多月了。

我在家里休息了一个星期。在这期间，我大部分时间都用在了为那只鹦鹉做笼子上。这时，这只鹦鹉渐渐变得驯顺，和我非常亲热起来。随后，我想起了那只可怜的小山羊，决定去把它带回家来。于是，我就去了。它还在原来的地方，它确实不可能逃出来，因为没有东西吃，它差不多快饿死了。我去尽可能砍了一些树枝和灌木。喂过它后，我像原先那样拴住它牵着它走。随着我不断喂养它，它变得是那样温顺可爱，从那以后再也没有离开我。

秋分的雨季现在来临。我像以前一样非常庄重地度过了 9 月 30 日，因为这是我上岛的纪念日，我到这里现在已经两年了。和两年前这一天刚上岛时一样，毫无获救的希望。整整一天，我都怀着恭顺的心情感激上帝的种种奇妙的恩惠。

Before, as I walked about, either on my hunting or for viewing the country, the anguish[1] of my soul at my condition would break out upon me on a sudden. But now I began to exercise myself with new thoughts; I daily read the word of God. One morning being very sad, I opened the Bible upon these words, "I will never leave thee, nor forsake thee."

From this moment my very soul within me blessed God for directing my friend in England, without any order of mine, to pack the Bible up among my goods and for assisting me afterwards to save it out of the wreck of the ship.

---

[1] anguish *n.* 痛苦，苦恼

以前我四处打猎或观察地形时，一想到自己的处境，我的灵魂就会突然痛苦不堪。但现在，我开始用新的思想来修炼自己。我每天读上帝的语言。一天早上，我很伤心，便打开《圣经》，读到了这段话："我绝不会撇下你，也绝不会抛弃你。"

　　从这时起，我总是在内心深处赞美上帝，是他引导我在英国的朋友把《圣经》放在了我的货物中，虽然我没有吩咐他。我也赞美上帝，是他后来又协助我把《圣经》从破船里取了出来。

XII

In this disposition[1] of mind, I began my third year; and though I have not given the reader the trouble of so particular account of my works this year as the first, yet in general it may be observed that I was very seldom idle; but having regularly divided my time, according to the several daily employments that were before me, such as, first, my duty to God, and the reading the Scriptures, which I constantly set apart some time for thrice every day. Secondly, the going abroad with my gun for food, which generally took me up three hours in every morning, when it did not rain. Thirdly, the ordering, curing, preserving, and cooking what I had killed or caught for my supply; these took up great part of the day; also it is to be considered that the middle of the day when the sun was in the zenith, the violence of the heat was too great to stir out; so that about four hours in the evening was all the time I could be supposed to work in; with this exception, that sometimes I changed my hours of hunting and working, and went to work in the morning, and abroad with my gun in the afternoon.

For want of tools, want of help, and want of skill, everything I did took up many of my time. For example, I was full two and forty days making me a board for a long shelf, which I wanted in my cave; whereas two sawyers[2] with their tools and a saw-pit would have cut six of them out of the same tree in half a day.

But notwithstanding[3] this, with patience and labour I went through many things; and indeed everything that my circumstances made necessary to me to do.

---

1 disposition   *n.* 性情，素质，脾气
2 sawyer   *n.* 锯木匠
3 notwithstanding   *prep.* 虽然，尽管

12

　　我以这种心情开始了第三年的生活。尽管我没有像第一年那样不厌其烦地把自己的工作给读者一一叙述，但一般来说我很少空闲。我根据眼前的几项日常工作，定期划分时间。比如，首先履行对上帝的职责，总是抽出时间每天三次阅读《圣经》；其次，带枪外出寻找食物，如不下雨，一般每天上午占用我三个小时；其三，处理打死或捕获的猎物，或晒、或腌、或煮，以作为我的食品。这些占去了每天大部分时间。同时还要考虑到，每天中午太阳到天顶时，酷热难当，无法出门。因此，我能用来工作的所有时间就晚上四个小时左右。此外，有时我也把打猎和工作的时间调换，上午工作，下午带枪外出。

　　因为缺乏工具、缺乏帮手和缺乏经验，所以做每件事都要占用我许多时间。比如，我的洞里缺少一个长架子，我就花了整整 42 天才做成一块木板，而两个锯木工在锯坑里用锯子锯，半天就能从同一棵树上锯出六块木板。

　　不过，尽管如此，由于耐心和劳动，我做成了许多东西，而且确实都是我当时的处境必不可少的东西。

I was now, in the months of November and December, expecting my crop of barley and rice. The ground I had dug up for them was not great; for my seed of each was not above the quantity of half a peck; for I had lost one whole crop by sowing in the dry season; but now my crop promised very well, when on a sudden I found I was in danger of losing it all again by enemies of several sorts; at first, the goats, and wild creatures which I called hares who, tasting the sweetness of the blade[1], lay in it night and day, as soon as it came up, and ate it so close that it could get no time to shoot up into stalk.

This I saw no remedy for, but by making an enclosure about it with a hedge. However, as my arable[2] land was small, I got it totally well fenced in about three weeks' time; and shooting some of the creatures in the daytime, I set my dog to guard it in the night, tying him up to a stake at the gate, where he would stand and bark all night long; so in a little time the enemies forsook the place, and the corn grew very strong and well, and began to ripen apace[3].

But as the beasts ruined me before, while my corn was in the blade; so the birds were as likely to ruin me now, when it was in the ear; for going along by the place to see how it throve, I saw my little crop surrounded with fowls of I know not how many sorts, who stood, as it were, watching till I should be gone. I immediately let fly among them I had no sooner shot, but there rose up a little cloud of fowls, which I had not seen at all, from among the corn itself.

This touched me sensibly, for I foresaw, that in a few days they would devour all my hopes, that I should be starved, and never be able to raise a crop at all, and what to do I could not tell. However, I resolved not to lose my corn, if possible, though I should watch it night and day. In the first place, I went among it to see what damage was already done, and found they had spoiled a good deal of it, but that as it was yet too green for them, the loss was not so great, but that the remainder was like to be a good crop if it could be saved.

---

[1] blade   *n.* 草叶，（谷类等的）叶片
[2] arable   *adj.* 可耕的，适于耕种的
[3] apace   *adv.* 快速地，急速地

现在是 11 月和 12 月之间，我盼望着收获大麦和稻子。我耕种的那块地不大，因为我的种子每样都不超过半配克，又因为第一次是在旱季播种，把播下去的种子全毁了，但这次丰收在望时，我突然发现庄稼受到了好几种天敌的威胁，又有全部损失的危险。首先，就是山羊和我称为野兔的野物。它们尝到了禾苗的甜味后，就昼夜守在那里，等禾苗一长出来，就把它一下吃光，禾苗根本来不及长出茎秆。

　　除了用栅栏把庄稼地围起来，我想不出其他办法。不过，因为我的耕地面积不大，所以不到三星期我就把庄稼地完全围了起来。白天，我打死了几只动物；夜里，我把狗拴在大门口的一根柱子上，狗站在那里整夜吠叫，看守庄稼。所以没有多久，那些天敌就放弃了这块地方。庄稼长得又壮又好，开始很快成熟了起来。

　　但在庄稼长出禾苗时野兽过来祸害，现在庄稼结穗时那些小鸟又来祸害。因为有一天，我到地里去看庄稼的长势，却看到无数飞禽围住了那块小小的庄稼地，我不知道有多少种飞禽。它们好像就站在那里等着我走。我马上朝鸟群开了一枪。枪声一响，立刻又有一群飞禽纷纷从庄稼地里腾空而起，我刚才根本没有看到它们。

　　这显然让我伤心，因为我预见它们要不了几天就会吃光我所有的希望，我会饿死，再也无法种一粒庄稼，我不知道该怎么办。然而，我决心不让庄稼白白损失，如有可能，就是整天整夜看守也行。首先，我走进庄稼地去看看已经损失了多少，发现那些飞禽已经糟蹋了好多庄稼，但因为庄稼还发青，所以损失不算很大。如果我能把剩余的保住，还可能会有一个好收成。

I stayed by it to load my gun, and then coming away I could easily see the thieves sitting upon all the trees about me, as if they only waited till I was gone away, and the event proved it to be so; for as I walked off as if I was gone, I was no sooner out of their sight but they dropped down one by one into the corn again. I was so provoked that I could not have patience to stay till more came on, knowing that every grain that they ate now was a peck-loaf to me in the consequence; but coming up to the hedge, I fired again and killed three of them. I took them up and hanged them in chains; it is impossible to imagine that the fowls would not only not come at the corn but they forsook all that part of the island.

This I was very glad of, and about the latter end of December, which was our second harvest of the year, I reaped my crop. I was sadly put to it for a scythe[1] to cut it down, and—all I could do was to make one as well as I could out of one of the cutlasses[2], which I saved among the arms out of the ship. However, as my first crop was but small I had no great difficulty to cut it down; in short, I reaped it my way, for I cut nothing off but the ears, and carried it away in a great basket which I had made, and so rubbed it out with my hands; and at the end of all my harvesting, I found that out of my half peck of seed I had near two bushels of rice, and above two bushels and half of barley.

However, this was a great encouragement to me. I resolved not to taste any of this crop but to preserve it all for seed against the next season.

But first I was to prepare more land, for I had now seed enough to sow above an acre of ground. Before I did this, I had a week's work at least to make me a spade, and sowed my seed in two large flat pieces of ground, as near my house as I could find them to my mind, and fenced them in with a good hedge. I knew it would grow. This work was not so little as to take me up less than three months, because great part of that time was of the wet season, when I could not go abroad.

---

[1] scythe　*n.* 长柄镰刀，镰（古兵器）
[2] cutlass　*n.* 短剑，弯刀

我守在庄稼地边，给枪装上弹药。我走开时，清楚地看到那些飞贼都卧在我周围的树上，好像它们只等我走开似的。事实也的确是这样。因为我装着走开，它们一看见我走，就又立刻纷纷飞进庄稼地。我勃然大怒，等不及让更多的鸟飞下来，就走到栅栏边又开了一枪，一下子打死了三只，因为我知道它们现在吃掉的每一颗谷粒几年后对我来说就是一配克粮食。我把打死的鸟拾起来，用锁链吊起来。让人难以想像的是，那些飞禽不仅不再到庄稼地来，而且放弃了岛上这边所有的地方。

我对此非常高兴。到了一年中的第二个收获季节，大约 12 月底，我收割庄稼。让我伤心的是，要收割庄稼，就得用镰刀——而我所能做的就是尽可能用一把水手刀，这是我从船上的武器中取出来的。不过，第一次收成不多，所以没费多大周折就割完了。总之，我收割的方法很独特，因为我只割穗子。我把穗子装进自制的大筐子里搬回家，然后双手搓下谷粒。收获完后，我发现原来的半配克种子差不多打了两蒲式耳的稻米和两蒲式耳半多的大麦。

然而，这对我是一个极大的鼓励。我决定不吃这次收获的庄稼，而是全部留作下一季的种子。

但首先，我要多准备一些土地，因为我现在有了足够的种子，可以播种一英亩多的土地。在耕地前，我至少花了一个星期才做成一把铁锹，然后在我的房子附近找了两大片平地播下种子，并修了一道结实的栅栏把地围起来。我知道这种树篱一定会生长。这个工作花了我三个多月时间，因为这期间大部分都是雨季，我无法出门。

When it rained, and I could not go out, I had a great employment upon my hands, as follows, viz., I had long studied by some means or other, to make myself some earthen vessels, which indeed I wanted sorely, but knew not where to come at them. However, considering the heat of the climate, I did not doubt but if I could find out any such clay, I might botch up[1] some such pot, as might, being dried in the sun, be hard enough and strong enough to bear handling.

How after having laboured hard to find the clay, to dig it, to temper it, to bring it home and work it, I made two large earthen ugly jars, in about two months' labour.

However, as the sun baked these two very dry and hard, I lifted them very gently up, and set them down again in two great wicker-baskets which I had made on purpose for them, that they might not break, and as between the pot and the basket there was a little room to spare, I stuffed it full of the rice and barley straw, and these two pots being to stand always dry, I thought would hold my dry corn, and perhaps the meal, when the corn was bruised.

Though I miscarried[2] so much in my design for large pots, yet I made several smaller things with better success, such as little round pots, flat dishes, pitchers and pipkins[3], and the heat of the sun baked them strangely hard.

But all this would not answer my end, which was to get an earthen pot to hold what was liquid and bear the fire, which none of these could do. It happened after some time, making a pretty large fire for cooking my meat, when I went to put it out after I had done with it, I found a broken piece of one of my earthen-ware vessels in the fire, burnt as hard as a stone, and red as a tile. I was agreeably surprised to see it and said to myself that certainly they might be made to burn whole if they would burn broken.

---

[1] botch up　（由于不注意、不小心等）搞坏，弄糟
[2] miscarry　*vi.* 失败，被误送
[3] pipkin　*n.* 小瓦罐，小汲桶

下雨不能出门时，我着手如下一件重要工作，也就是，我早就研究想采用某种方法制作一些陶器，我确实非常需要，但不知道从哪里下手。不过，因为这里气候炎热，所以我敢肯定，只要能找到粘土，就能做一些罐子，然后放到太阳下晒，一定能晒得坚硬结实、经久耐用。

　　我费了很大劲儿找到了粘土，然后把土挖出来，调和好，运回家，揉捏，做成了两只难看的大陶罐，前后用了大约两个月的功夫。

　　不管怎样，当太阳把这两只大陶罐晒得又干又硬时，我把它们轻轻地搬起来，放进两只特意编织的大柳条筐里，以防它们破裂。我在陶罐和筐子之间的空隙处塞满了稻草和麦秸。因为这两只陶罐总是保持干燥，所以我想可以用来装粮食，说不定还可以装粮食磨出来的面粉。

　　尽管我做的大陶罐不很成功，但像小圆罐、盘子、水罐和小瓦锅这几样小东西做得都比较成功，而且炎热的太阳把它们晒得非常坚硬。

　　不过，这都没有达到我的最终目的，我的目的是搞一个能用来装液体、能经得起火烧的陶罐，而这些东西一个也做不到。过了一段时间，一次我偶然生起相当一大堆火烤肉，烤完后，我去灭火，发现火堆里有一块陶器碎片，被火烧得像石头一样硬，像砖一样红。看到这情形，我又惊又喜，对自己说，破陶器能烧，整只陶器肯定也可以烧。

This set me to studying how to order my fire, so as to make it burn me some pots. I placed three large pipkins, and two or three pots in a pile one upon another and placed my firewood all round it with a great heap of embers[1] under them, I plied the fire with fresh fuel round the outside, and upon the top, till I saw the pots in the inside red hot quite through, and observed that they did not crack at all; when I saw them clear red, I let them stand in that heat about 5 or 6 hours, till I found one of them, though it did not crack, did melt, for the sand which was mixed with the clay melted by the violence of the heat, and would have run into glass if I had gone on, so I slacked my fire gradually till the pots began to abate of the red colour; and watching them all night, that I might not let the fire abate too fast, in the morning I had three very good, I will not say handsome, pipkins and two other earthen pots, as hard burnt as could be desired; and one of them perfectly glazed with the running of the sand.

No joy at a thing of so mean a nature was ever equal to mine, when I found I had made an earthen pot that would bear the fire; and I had hardly patience to stay till they were cold, before I set one upon the fire again, with some water in it, to boil me some meat; and with a piece of a kid, I made some very good broth.

My next concern was to get me a stone mortar to stamp some corn in. I spent many a day to find out a great stone big enough to cut hollow and make fit for a mortar[2], and could find none at all, except what was in the solid rock, and which I had no way to dig or cut out; nor indeed were the rocks in the island of hardness sufficient, but were all of a sandy crumbling stone, which neither would bear the weight of a heavy pestle[3] or would break the corn without filling it with sand; so after a great deal of time lost in searching for a stone, I gave it over, and resolved to look out for a great block of hard wood, which I found indeed much easier; and getting one as big as I had strength to stir, I rounded it, and formed it in the outside with my axe and hatchet, and then made a hollow place in it with the fire. After this, I made a great heavy pestle of the ironwood.

---

[1] ember   *n.* 灰烬，余烬
[2] mortar   *n.* 臼，研钵
[3] pestle   *n.* 乳钵，槌，杵

这使我开始研究起怎样掌握火候，给自己烧出几只锅来。我把三只大罐和两三只锅一个个堆起来，四面架上木柴，在泥罐和泥锅下放了一大堆燃屑，然后在四周和顶上点起火，直到我看见里面的罐子红透为止，同时细心观察不让它们烧裂。我看到陶器烧得红透后，又让它们烧了五、六个小时。后来，我发现其中一只虽然没有破裂，但确实已经熔化，因为掺在粘土里的沙土被熊熊烈火烧化了，如果再烧下去，它就会化为玻璃。于是，我渐渐撤火，那些锅逐渐退去了红色。我整夜守着，不让火撤得太快。第二天早上，我便烧成了三只很好的瓦罐和两只瓦锅，虽然谈不上美观，但烧的硬度令人满意，其中一只因沙土被烧化而闪着漂亮的釉光。

我发现自己烧成了一只耐火的锅子，真是快乐无比，简直等不及让锅子冷下来，就把其中一只放到了火上，倒了一些水，煮起肉来，并用一块小山羊肉煮了一些可口的肉汤。

下一个问题是我需要一个舂粮食的石臼。我花了好多天时间想找一块大得可以挖空、适合做石臼的大石头，却怎么也无法找到，岛上只有实心岩石，根本无法挖凿，而且岩石的硬度确实不够，都是一些一碰就碎的沙石，既经不住重锤去舂，而且即使能捣碎谷物，也会从石臼里舂出许多沙子来。因此，当我花了许多时间找不到一块石头时，就放弃了，决定找一大块硬木头。这确实要容易得多。我找到了一块大得我勉强能搬动的木头，然后用长斧和短斧把木头砍圆，砍出了外形，然后用火在上面烧一个槽，终于做成了臼。之后，我又用硬木做了一个又大又重的杵。

My next difficulty was to make a sieve[1], to dress my meal and to part it from the bran[2] and the husk, without which I did not see it possible I could have any bread. This was a most difficult thing, so much as but to think on; for to be sure I had nothing like the necessary thing to make it; I mean fine thin canvas, or stuff, to search the meal through. And here I was at a full stop for many months. All the remedy that I found for this was that at last I did remember I had among the seamen's clothes which were saved out of the ship, some neckcloths of muslin[3]; and with some pieces of these, I made three small sieves, but proper enough for the work; and thus I made shift for some years.

The baking part was the next thing to be considered and how I should make bread when I came to have corn; for first I had no yeast[4]; as to that part, as there was no supplying the want, so I did not concern myself much about it. But for an oven, I was indeed in great pain; at length I found out an experiment for that also, which was this; I made some earthen vessels very broad, but not deep; that is to say, about two feet diameter[5], and not above nine inches deep; these I burnt in the fire, as I had done the other; and when I wanted to bake, I made a great fire upon my hearth, which I had paved with some square tiles of my own making and burning also.

When the firewood was burnt pretty much into live coals, I drew them forward upon this hearth, so as to cover it all over, and there I let them lie, till the hearth[6] was very hot, then sweeping away all the embers, I set down my loaves[7], and whelming[8] down the earthen pot upon them, drew the embers all round the outside of the pot, to keep in, and add to the heat; and thus, as well as in the best oven in the world, I baked my barley loaves.

---

[1] sieve　*n.* 筛，滤网
[2] bran　*n.* 糠，麸
[3] muslin　*n.* 一种薄细的棉布
[4] yeast　*n.* 酵母，发酵粉
[5] diameter　*n.* 直径
[6] hearth　*n.* 壁炉地面，炉边，炉膛
[7] loaf　*n.* (*pl.* loaves)大块烤过的食物，长方形的大块
[8] whelm　*v.* 淹没

我的下一个问题是做一个筛子，筛面粉，把面粉和麸皮分开。没有筛子，我看就无法做面包。做筛子想一想都是一件非常困难的事儿，因为我没有任何必要的材料可以用来做筛子，我是说那种细薄的帆布，或者是可以把面粉筛出来的布料。这使我好几个月都完全停了下来。最后，我突然想起一个补救办法，那就是在从船上搬下来的那些水手衣服里有几块薄细棉布围巾。我拿了几块做成三个小筛子，总算凑合着能用，这样将就了好几年。

　　要考虑的下一件事是烘烤和有了粮食后如何做面包的问题，因为首先我没有发酵粉，这是绝对满足不了需求的，所以我也就不去多想它了。至于烤炉，我费了很大劲儿，最后总算想出了一个试验的办法。具体做法如下：我先做了一些很宽的陶器，但不太深，也就是说，直径两英尺，深不超过九英寸。像上次烧制陶器那样，我把它们也放在火里烧过。当我想烤面包时，先用自己烧制的一些方砖在地上砌一个大炉子。

　　当木柴几乎全部烧成火炭时，我就把它们取出来放在炉子上，以便盖满炉子，让炉子烧得很热，然后扫掉所有的灰烬，把面包放进去，再把陶罐扣在炉子上，陶罐上再盖满灰烬。这不但能保热，还能加热。这样，我烤出来的大麦面包就像世界上最好的炉子烤出来的面包一样。

All these things took me up most part of the third year of my abode[1] here; and in the intervals of these things, I had my new harvest and husbandry[2] to manage; I reaped my corn in its season, and carried it home as well as I could, and laid it up in the ear, in my large baskets, till I had time to rub it out; for I had no floor to thrash it on, or instrument to thrash it with.

And now indeed my stock of corn increasing, I really wanted to build my barns bigger. I wanted a place to lay it up in; for the increase of the corn now yielded me so much that I had of the barley about twenty bushels[3], and of the rice as much or more; insomuch that now I resolved to begin to use it freely; also I resolved to see what quantity would be sufficient for me a whole year, and to sow but once a year.

Upon the whole, I found that the forty bushels of barley and rice was much more than I could consume in a year; so I resolved to sow just the same quantity every year that I sowed the last, in hopes that such a quantity would fully provide me with bread, etc.

All the while these things were doing, you may be sure my thoughts ran many times upon the prospect of land which I had seen from the other side of the island, and I was not without secret wishes that I were on shore there, fancying the seeing the mainland and an inhabited country, I might find some way or other to convey myself farther, and perhaps at last find some means of escape.

But all this while I made no allowance for the dangers of such a condition, and how I might fall into the hands of savages; for I had heard that the people of the Caribbean coast were cannibals; and I knew by the latitude that I could not be far off from that shore.

Now I wished for my boy Xury and the longboat, with which I sailed above a thousand miles on the coast of Africa; but this was in vain. Then I thought I would go and look at our ship's boat, which, as I have said, was blown up upon the shore, a great way in the storm, when we were first cast away. She lay almost where she did at first, but was turned by the force of the waves and the winds almost bottom upward, against a high ridge of beachy rough sand; but no water about her as before.

---

[1] abode   n. 住所，住处
[2] husbandry   n. 管理
[3] bushel   n. 蒲式耳（容量等于 8 加仑）

这些事占去了我在岛上第三年的大部分时间。在做这些事的间歇，我还要收庄稼和耕作管理。我按时收获，把谷物尽可能运回家。我把穗子放在大筐子里，有空时就用双手搓出来，因为我既没有打谷场，也没有打谷的工具。

现在，因为我的粮食库存确实越来越多，所以我的确需要扩建谷仓。我需要有一个地方来存放粮食，因为我的粮食已经增加到大约 20 蒲式耳大麦和 20 多蒲式耳大米，所以决定开始慷慨大方地使用。同时，我决定看看我一年需要多少粮食，然后一年只播种一次。

大体算来，我发现 40 蒲式耳的大麦和大米够我吃一年还要多。因此，我决定每年播种同样数量的种子，并希望收获的粮食完全供我做面包等用。

可以肯定，在做这些事的同时，我常想到我在岛上另一边所看到的陆地景色。我心里暗暗怀着一种愿望，希望能在那里上岸，并幻想着自己在找到大陆和有人烟的地方后，可能会设法走得更远一些，也许最终能找到逃生的办法。

但那时，我没有考虑到这种情况的危险性、我会怎样落入野人的手里，因为我曾听说加勒比海沿岸的人都是吃人族。从纬度来看，我知道我离那个海岸不会很远。

这时，我真想见到男仆苏利和那只大艇；我和苏利曾驾着那只大艇沿非洲海岸航行了 1000 多英里，但这无济于事。于是，我要去看看我们大船上的那只小艇，前面我曾说过，这只小艇是在我们最初遇难时被风暴一路刮到岸上的。它差不多还躺在原先的地方，但被风浪掀翻，船底几乎朝天，搁浅在一道高高的粗砾滩脊上，像以前一样四面无水。

If I had had hands to have refitted[1] her, and to have launched her into the water, the boat would have done well enough, and I might have gone back into Brazil with her easily enough; but I might have foreseen that I could no more turn her and set her upright upon her bottom than I could remove the island. However, I went to the woods and cut levers[2] and rollers and brought them to the boat, resolved to try what I could do.

I spared no pains, indeed, in this piece of fruitless toil[3], and spent three or four weeks about it; at last finding it impossible to heave it up with my little strength, I fell to digging away the sand, to undermine it and so to make it fall down, setting pieces of wood to thrust and guide it right, in the fall.

But when I had done this, I was unable to stir it up again, or to get under it, much less to move it forward towards the water; so I was forced to give it over; and yet, though I gave over the hopes of the boat, my desire to venture over for the main increased, rather than decreased, as the means for it seemed impossible.

This at length put me upon thinking, whether it was not possible to make myself a canoe, such as the natives of those climates make. This I not only thought possible, but easy, and pleased myself extremely with the thoughts of making it. But on my second thought, what was it to me that when I had chosen a vast tree in the woods, I might with much trouble cut it down, if after I might be able with my tools to hew[4] and dub[5] the outside into the proper shape of a boat, and burn or cut out the inside to make it hollow, so to make a boat of it—if after all this, I must leave it just there where I found it, and was not able to launch it into the water?

One would have thought, I could not have had the least reflection upon my mind of my circumstance, while I was making this boat; but I should have immediately thought how I should get it into the sea; but my thoughts were so intent upon my voyage over the sea in it, that I never once considered how I should get it off of the land; and it was really in its own nature more easy for me to guide it over forty-five miles of sea, than about forty-five fathom of land, where it lay, to set it a float in the water.

---

[1] refit   v. 整修，改装
[2] lever   n. 杆，杠杆
[3] toil   n. 辛苦，苦工
[4] hew   v. 砍
[5] dub   vt. 打击

如果我有帮手们整修，然后把小艇放到水里，它一定运行不错，那我驾着它就会轻松自如地返回巴西。但我早该预见到，要把这小艇翻过个，让它船底朝下，除非我能移动这座岛。然而，我还是走进树林，砍了一些做杠杆和滚木的木材，然后把它们运到小艇边，决定尽我所能试试看。

　　我真是不遗余力，最后却白费功夫，花了我三、四个星期时间，最后发现自己的力量微不足道，不可能抬起小艇。于是，我开始着手挖小艇下面的沙子，把下面挖空，让小艇落下来，同时用一些木头从下面插进去，让小艇落下来时摆正位置。

　　但当我做到这一步时，却再也无法移动它，也无法从船底下插入木头，更不要说把它移到水里去了。于是，我只得放弃。不过，尽管我放弃了使用小艇的希望，但我要冒险去岛对面大陆上的愿望，不仅没有因为种种方法都无法实现而减退，反而更加强烈了。

　　最后，我想到，是不是能像那些热带地区的土人那样做一只独木舟。我认为这不但可能，而且非常容易。做独木舟的想法使我非常高兴。但我转念又一想：当我在树林里选一棵大树，费了很大劲儿把树砍倒，再用我的工具把树的外部砍成小舟形状，然后把里面烧空或挖空，做成一只小船——如果这些都做完后，我仍然必须把小船留在原地而无法让它下水，那对我又有什么用呢？

　　有人也许会想到，我在做这小船时，不可能一点儿也想不到自己的处境；我应该马上想到我怎样让小船下海。但我当时一心只想驾船航行，从来没有考虑过怎样使小船离开陆地。其实，对我来说，驾船在海上航行45英里，要比在陆地上使它从原地移动45浔让它下水漂浮容易。

But the eagerness of my fancy prevailed, and to work I went. I felled a cedar tree. It was five feet ten inches diameter at the lower part next the stump[1], and four feet eleven inches diameter at the end of twenty-two feet, after which it lessened for a while, and then parted into branches. It was not without infinite labour that I felled this tree. I was twenty days hacking and hewing at it at the bottom. I was fourteen more getting the branches and limbs, and the vast spreading head of it cut off. After this, it cost me a month to shape it to something like the bottom of a boat. It cost me near three months more to clear the inside, and work it out so, as to make an exact boat of it. This I did indeed without fire, by mere mallet[2] and chisel[3], and by the dint[4] of hard labour, till I had brought it to be a very handsome canoe, and big enough to have carried six and twenty men, and consequently big enough to have carried me and all my cargo.

When I had gone through this work, I was extremely delighted with it. There remained nothing but to get it into the water.

But all my devices to get it into the water failed me; though they cost me infinite labour too. It lay about one hundred yards from the water. But the first inconvenience was, it was uphill towards the creek; to take away this discouragement, I resolved to dig into the surface of the earth, and so make a declivity[5]. And this difficulty managed, I could no more stir the canoe.

Then I measured the distance of ground, and resolved to cut a dock, or canal, to bring the water up to the canoe, seeing I could not bring the canoe down to the water. When I began to enter into it, and calculate how deep it was to be dug, how broad, how the stuff to be thrown out, I found, that by the number of hands I had, being none but my own, it must have been ten or twelve years before I should have gone through with it; for the shore lay high, so that at the upper end, it must have been at least twenty feet deep; so at length, though with great reluctancy, I gave this attempt over also.

In the middle of this work, I finished my fourth year in this place.

1　stump　*n.*　树桩，残余部分
2　mallet　*n.*　槌棒
3　chisel　*n.*　凿子
4　dint　*n.*　凹痕；力量，作用
5　declivity　*n.*　倾斜，下坡

然而，我想船想得心急，便开始着手行动。我砍倒了一棵雪松树。靠近树根的低层部分的直径达 5 英尺 10 英寸，在 22 英尺末梢的直径达 4 英尺 11 英寸，再向上才渐渐细了一些，然后开始长出分枝。砍倒这棵树，我真是费了九牛二虎之力。我用了 22 天时间砍伐根部，又用了 14 天多时间砍掉枝枝杈杈和蓬蓬勃勃的巨大树冠。之后，我又用了一个月时间砍出了船底的形状。接着，我又花了将近三个月时间挖空内部，把它做得完全像一只小船。我在挖空树干时，不用火烧，仅用楻子和凿子一点一点地凿空，直到最后成为一只非常漂亮的独木舟，大得足以乘 26 个人，因此可以把我和我所有的货物都装进去。

这项工作完成后，我非常高兴。现在只剩下让小船下水了。

尽管我想尽一切办法、费了九牛二虎之力，却无法把船移进水里。小船离水只有大约 100 码远。第一个不便之处就是，从小船到小河边是向上的坡地。为了排除这个障碍，我决定掘进地面，掘出一个向下的斜坡。而解决了这个困难后，我还是无法移动独木舟。

由于我无法让独木舟下水，因此就丈量了一下现场的距离，决定开辟一个船坞或一条运河，把水引到独木舟边。当我开始这项工作，并估算了一下，看运河要挖多深、多宽，怎样把挖出来的土运走时，我发现，如果只靠我一双手，肯定需要 10 到 12 年才会完成。因为河岸很高，所以从顶端到下面至少有 20 英尺深。就这样，尽管心里极不愿意，但我最后还是放弃了这个努力。

在进行这项工作过程中，我结束了在这个地方的第四年的生活。

XIII

I had now been here so long.

My ink had been gone some time.

The next thing to my ink's being wasted was that of my bread, I mean the biscuit which I brought out of the ship; this I had husbanded to the last degree, allowing myself but one cake of bread a day for above a year, and yet I was quite without bread for near a year before I got any corn of my own.

My clothes began to decay, too, mightily. As to linen, I had had none a good while, except some chequered shirts which I found in the chests of the other seamen, and which I carefully preserved, because many times I could bear no other clothes on but a shirt; and it was a very great help to me that I had among all the men's clothes of the ship almost three dozen of shirts. There were also several thick watch coats of the seamen, but they were too hot to wear; and though it is true that the weather was so violent hot that there was no need of clothes, yet I could not go quite naked; no, though I had been inclined to it, which I was not, nor could not abide[1] the thoughts of it, though I was all alone.

The reason why I could not go quite naked was, I could not bear the heat of the sun so well when quite naked, as with some clothes on; nay[2], the very heat frequently blistered[3] my skin; whereas with a shirt on, the air itself whistled under that shirt was twofold cooler than without it; no more could I ever bring myself to go out in the heat of sun, without a hat; the heat of the sun beating with such violence as it does in that place, would give me the headache presently, by darting so directly on my head, without a hat on, so that I could not bear it; whereas, if I put on my hat, it would presently go away.

---

[1] abide   *vt.* 忍受，容忍
[2] nay   *adv.* 不仅如此，而且
[3] blister   *vt.* （使）生出水泡

13

我到这里现在已经好久了。

墨水已经用完一段时间了。

除了墨水用完，面包也吃完了，我是说我从船上拿出来的饼干。我对饼干吃得非常节省，一天只吃一块，维持了一年多时间。然而，在收获自己种的粮食前，我还是将近一年都没有吃上面包。

我的衣服也开始破烂不堪了。至于亚麻布衬衣，我好一阵子就已经没有了，剩下的就是从其他水手的箱子里找到的几件方格衬衫，我小心翼翼地保存着这些衬衫，因为很多时候只能穿衬衫。船上的水手服里差不多三打衬衫帮了我的大忙，另外还有水手值更穿的几件厚外套，但穿起来太热。尽管这里天气确实非常酷热，不必穿衣服，但我总不能完全赤身裸体。即使我曾有这种倾向，我也不会这样做，我也受不了自己会有这种念头，纵然岛上只有我一个人。

我不能完全赤身裸体的理由是：当我完全赤身裸体时不能像穿有衣服那样忍受炎炎烈日；不仅如此，炎炎烈日经常把我的皮肤晒得起泡。而穿上衬衣，空气可以在衬衣下吹拂，这比不穿衣服要凉爽两倍。不戴帽子也不能到太阳地去，因为这里的太阳非常强烈，直接照在头上，马上就会晒得我头疼；而戴上帽子，头疼就马上消失了。

So I began to consider about putting the few rags I had into some order; I had worn out all the waistcoats I had, and my business was now to try if I could not make jackets out of the great watch coats which I had by me, and with such other materials as I had, so I set to work a-tailoring, or rather indeed a-botching, for I made most piteous work of it. However, I made shift to make two or three new waistcoats, which I hoped would serve me a great while; as for drawers, I made but a very sorry shift indeed till afterward.

I have mentioned that I saved the skins of all the creatures that I killed, I mean four-footed ones, and I had hung them up stretched out with sticks in the sun, by which means some of them were so dry and hard that they were fit for little but others it seems were very useful. The first thing I made of these was a great hat for my head, with the hair on the outside to shoot off the rain; and this I performed so well that after this I made me a suit of clothes wholly of these skins, viz., a waistcoat, and breeches open at knees, and both loose, for they were rather wanting to keep me cool than to keep me warm. I must not omit to acknowledge that they were wretchedly made.

After this I spent a great deal of time and pains to make me an umbrella; I was indeed in great want of one, and had a great mind to make one; I had seen them made in Brazil, where they are very useful in the great heats which are there. And I felt the heats every jot as great here, and greater too, being nearer the equinox[1]; besides, as I was obliged to be much abroad, it was a most useful thing to me, as well for the rains as the heats. The main difficulty I found was to make it let down. I could make it spread, but if it did not let down too and draw in, it was not portable for me any way but just over my head, which would not do. However, at last, as I said, I made one to answer, and covered it with skins, the hair upwards, so that it cast off the rains like a penthouse, and kept off the sun so effectually, that I could walk out in the hottest of the weather with greater advantage than I could before in the coolest, and when I had no need of it, could close it and carry it under my arm.

---

[1] equinox   *n.* 昼夜平分点，春分或秋分

于是，我开始考虑整理那些破衣服。所有的背心都已经穿破了，我现在要做的事就是设法用手边的水手值更的大衣和其他一些布料改成几件短上衣。于是，我就做起了裁缝，或者更准确地说，其实是胡乱缝合，因为我的手艺是再糟不过了。然而，我还是凑合做成了两三件新背心，我希望能穿一大段时间。至于短裤，我直到后来才可怜巴巴地做出来。

我曾提到过，我把打死的所有野兽（我指的是四足动物）的毛皮都保存起来，将毛皮摊开，用棍子支在太阳下晒干，有的被晒得又干又硬，简直无法使用，但有的看上去非常有用。我首先用这些毛皮做了一顶大帽子，把毛翻在外面，以便挡雨。帽子做得不错。之后，我又用一些毛皮做了一套衣服，也就是一件背心和一条在膝盖处开口的马裤。背心和马裤都很宽松，因为它们与其说是为了保暖，不如说是为了凉爽。我不得不承认它们做得都很不像样。

之后，我又花了大量时间和精力做了一把伞。我确实非常需要一把伞，也非常想做一把。我在巴西时曾见别人做过伞。巴西天气炎热，伞非常有用。这里的天气和巴西一样热，而且因更靠近赤道，比巴西还热。此外，由于我不得不经常外出，因此伞对我是一件非常有用的东西，既能挡雨又能遮阳。我发现做伞的主要困难是让伞能收起来。我可以把它撑开，但如果不能放下来、收进去，那就只能撑在头顶，根本无法携带，那可不行。不过，最后，正如我说的那样，总算做成了一把能放下来、收进去的伞。伞顶覆盖着毛皮，绒毛朝上，可以像雨篷一样有效地挡雨遮阳。这样，即使在最热的天气，我也能外出，比以前最凉爽的天气外出还要便利。我不需要伞时，就可以收起来，夹在腋下。

XIV

I cannot say that after this, for five years, any extraordinary thing happened to me, but I lived on in the same course, in the same posture and place, just as before; the chief things I was employed in, besides my yearly labour of planting my barley and rice, and curing my raisins, of both which I always kept up just enough to have sufficient stock of one year's provisions beforehand. I say, besides this yearly labour and my daily labour of going out with my gun, I had one labour to make me a canoe. So that by digging a canal to it of six feet wide, and four feet deep, I brought it into the creek, almost half a mile.

Now I had a boat, I thought of nothing but sailing round the island. For this purpose, that I might do everything with discretion and consideration, I fitted up a little mast to my boat, and made a sail to it, out of some of the pieces of the ship's sail, which lay in store.

Having fitted my mast and sail and tried the boat, I found she would sail very well. Then I made little lockers, or boxes, at either end of my boat, to put provisions, necessaries and ammunition, etc. into, to be kept dry, either from rain, or the spray of the sea; and a little long hollow place I cut in the inside of the boat, where I could lay gun, making a flap to hang down over it to keep it dry.

I fixed my umbrella also in a step at the stern, like a mast, to stand over my head, and keep the heat of the sun off of me like an awning[1]; and thus I every now and then took a little voyage upon the sea, but never went far out, nor far from the little creek.

---

[1] awning　*n.* 遮阳篷，雨篷

14

之后五年，没有发生什么特别的事儿，我还是在老地方，以同样的心境继续像以前那样，一成不变地生活着。我从事的主要工作就是，每年除了按时种大麦和稻子、晒葡萄干，还总是把它们预先储藏起来，够我一年吃用。除了每年的工作和每天带枪外出打猎，此外就是给自己又造了一只独木舟。于是，我挖了一条六英尺宽、四英尺深的运河，把独木舟引入差不多半英里外的那条小河。

既然有了小船，我就只想着环岛航行。为了达到这个目的，我要把每件事做得慎重周到。我在小船上安装了一根小小的桅杆，并用储藏的大船上的帆布做了一面帆。

安装好了桅杆和帆，我试航了一次，发现小船运行良好。于是，我在船两头都做了一些小存物柜或箱子，以便放粮食、日用品和弹药等，以免雨水或海浪打湿。另外，我又在船内挖了一道摆放枪支的小长槽，并做了一个可以垂下来盖住长槽的口盖，以防枪支受潮。

我又将那把伞安放在船尾的一个桅座上。伞像桅杆一样竖在我的头顶，又像遮阳篷一样挡住了炎炎烈日。于是，我就不时地到海面上航行一会儿，但从不走远，也不远离小河。

But at last being eager to view the circumference[1] of my little kingdom, I resolved upon my tour and accordingly I victualled[2] my ship for the voyage, putting in two dozen of my loaves of barley bread, an earthen pot full of parched[3] rice, a little bottle of rum, half a goat, and powder and shot for killing more, and two large watch coats, of those which I had saved out of the seamen's chests; these I took, one to lie upon, and the other to cover me in the night.

It was the sixth of November, in the sixth year of my reign or my captivity that I set out on this voyage, and I found it much longer than I expected; for though the island itself was not very large, yet when I came to the east side of it, I found a great ledge[4] of rocks lie out above two leagues into the sea, some above water, some under it; and beyond that, a shoal of sand, lying dry half a league more; so that I was obliged to go a great way out to sea to double the point.

When first I discovered them, I was going to give over my enterprise, and come back again, not knowing how far it might oblige me to go out to sea; and above all, doubting how I should get back again; so I came to an anchor; for I had made me a kind of an anchor with a piece of a broken grappling[5], which I got out of the ship.

Having secured my boat, I took my gun, and went on shore, climbing up upon a hill, which seemed to overlook that point, where I saw the full extent of it, and resolved to venture.

In my viewing the sea from that hill where I stood, I perceived a most furious current, which ran to the east, and even came close to the point; and I took the more notice of it, because I saw there might be some danger; that when I came into it, I might be carried out to sea by the strength of it, and not be able to make the island again; and indeed, had I not gotten first up upon this hill, 1 believe it would have been so; for there was the same current on the other side of the island, only that it set off at a farther distance; and I saw there was a strong eddy under the shore; so I had nothing to do but to get in out of the first current, and I should presently be in an eddy.

---

[1] circumference *n.* 圆周，周围
[2] victual *vt.* 给…供应储备食物
[3] parch *vt.* 烤（干），烘（干）
[4] ledge *n.* 暗礁；矿层
[5] grappling =grapnel grappling iron （打捞用的）抓机，爪钩

而最后，我急于想看看自己这个小小王国的边界，就决定绕岛航行一周。为此，我先往船上装粮食，装了两打大麦面包，又装了满满一罐炒米、一小瓶朗姆酒、半只山羊肉，还有一些火药和子弹，准备用来打更多的山羊。另外，我还拿出了两件水手值更大衣，那是我在水手箱里找到的。这两件衣服放到船上，一件用来铺，另一件我夜里用来盖。

　　我成为国王或流落到此的第六年的 11 月 6 日，开始了这次环岛航行。我发现这次航行比我预料的要长得多，因为岛本身尽管不大，但当我航行到东边时，只见一大堆岩石向海里延伸了两里格以上，这些礁石有的露出水面，有的藏在水下，礁石外面还有一片沙滩，有一里格半多宽。因此，我不得不把船开到远处的海面上，急速绕过这个尖岬。

　　我最先发现这些礁石时，准备放弃这次冒险计划，调头往回走，因为我不知道要向外海走多远；最重要的是，我怀疑自己能不能回到岛上。于是，我就下了锚，因为我用从大船上取下来的一只破铁钩做了一个锚。

　　我把船停稳后，就带枪走上岸，爬上一座可以俯视那个尖岬的小山。我在山顶上看清了尖岬的全貌，决定冒一下险。

　　我自己站在小山上眺望大海，察觉到有一股极其狂暴的涌流向东流去，甚至贴近了尖岬。我比较留意这股急流，因为我看到这股急流可能隐藏着某种危险。如果我把船开进去，就会被它冲到外海去，再也不能回到岛上。确实，如果我事先没有爬上这座山，我相信一定会是这样，因为岛那边也有一股同样的急流，只是离海岸较远，而且我看到在海岸下还有一股猛烈的涡流。所以，即使我躲过第一股急流，也会马上被卷入涡流中去。

I lay here, however, two days; because the wind blowing pretty fresh at east-southeast and that being just contrary to the said current, made a great breach of the sea upon the point; so that it was not safe for me to keep too close to the shore for the breach, nor to go too far off because of the stream.

The third day in the morning, the wind having abated overnight, the sea was calm, and I ventured; but I am a warning piece again, to all rash and ignorant pilots; for no sooner was I come to the point, when even I was not my boat's length from the shore, but I found myself in a great depth of water, and a current. It carried my boat along with it with such violence that all I could do could not keep her so much as on the edge of it; but I found it hurried me farther and farther out from the eddy, which was on my left hand. There was no wind stirring to help me, and all I could do with my paddlers signified nothing, and now I began to give myself over for lost; for as the current was on both sides of the island, I knew in a few leagues distance they must join again, and then I was irrecoverably[1] gone; nor did I see any possibility of avoiding it; so that I had no prospect before me but of perishing; not by the sea, for that was calm enough, but of starving for hunger. I had indeed found a turtle on the shore, as big almost as I could lift, and had tossed it into the boat; and I had a great jar of fresh water; but what was all this to being driven into the vast ocean, where to be sure, there was no shore, no mainland, or island, for a thousand leagues at least?

It is scarce possible to imagine the consternation[2] I was now in, being driven from my beloved island into the wide ocean, almost two leagues, and in the utmost despair of ever recovering it again. However, I worked hard, till indeed my strength was almost exhausted, and kept my boat as much to the northward, that is, towards the side of the current which the eddy lay on, as possibly I could; when about noon, as the sun passed the meridian[3], I thought I felt a little breeze of wind in my face, springing up from the south-southeast. This cheered my heart a little, and especially when in about half an hour more, it blew a pretty small gentle gale.

---

[1] irrecoverably *adv.* 无可挽救地
[2] consternation *n.* 惊愕，恐怖，惊惶失措
[3] meridian *n.* 子午线，正午

然而，我还是在这里停了两天，因为那两天一直刮相当强劲的东南风，风向偏东，而且风向正好与我上面说的那股急流的方向相反，所以尖岬附近的海面波涛汹涌。这样，如果我太靠近海岸，就会碰到大浪，太远离海岸，又会碰到急流，怎么走都不安全。

　　第三天早上，因为一夜过后风已经减小，海上风平浪静。于是，我又冒险前进，但我又给所有鲁莽无知的舵手当了一次前车之鉴，因为船刚走近那个尖岬，离海岸还没有船的长度那么远，就开进了深水区，并碰上了一股涌流。这股涌流汹涌澎湃，让我的船一直向前冲去。我竭尽全力想让船沿着这股涌流的边沿前进，但我发现自己离左边的那股涡流越来越远。这时没有一点儿风，我只能拼命划桨，但无济于事。我开始感到自己没有希望了，因为岛两边都有一股急流，我知道它们必定会在几里格之外汇合。到那时，我就死定了，而且我也看不出有什么可以避开的可能性。现在，除了死亡，我没有任何希望，不是被大海吞没，而是会饿死，因为这时海面上风平浪静。我确实曾在岸上抓到一只海龟，重得我几乎拿都拿不动。我把海龟扔进了船里。我还有一大罐淡水。但如果我被冲进汪洋大海，至少上千里格没有海岸，没有大陆，也没有岛屿，我所有这东西又有什么用呢？

　　眼看自己被冲入茫茫大海，离开心爱的小岛有将近两里格，又看到自己陷入了回岛的绝望之中，我此刻的惊慌简直难以想像。然而，我还是竭力划桨，直到差不多筋疲力尽。我尽量把船朝北面划去，也就是尽可能向那股急流和涡流交汇的海面划去。大约到了正午，太阳过了子午线，我想我感到脸上有了一点儿微风，风向东南偏南。这使我的精神为之一振，尤其是大约半个多小时后，刮起了小小的温和的强风。

By this time I was gotten at a frightful distance from the island, and had the least cloud or hazy weather intervened, I had been undone another way too; for I had no compass on board, and should never have known how to have steered towards the island, if I had but once lost sight of it; but the weather continuing clear, I applied myself to get up my mast again, spread my sail, standing away to the north as much as possible, to get out of the current.

Just as I had set my mast and sail, and the boat began to stretch away, I saw even by the clearness of the water, some alteration[1] of the current was near; for where the current was so strong, the water was foul; but perceiving the water clear, I found the current abate, and presently I found to the east, at about half a mile, a breach of the sea upon some rocks; these rocks I found caused the current to part again, and as the main stress of it ran away more southerly, leaving the rocks to the northeast; so the other returned by the repulse of the rocks, and made a strong eddy, which ran back again to the northwest, with a very sharp stream.

This eddy carried me about a league in my way back again directly towards the island, but about two leagues more to the northward than the current which carried me away at first; so that when I came near the island, I found myself open to the northern shore of it, that is to say, the other end of the island, opposite to that which I went out from.

When I had made something more than a league of way by the help of this eddy, I found it was spent and served me no farther. However, I found that being between the two great currents, viz., that on the south side which had hurried me away, and that on the north which lay about a league on the other side. I say between these two, in the wake of the island, I found the water at least still and running no way, and having still a breeze of wind fair for me, I kept on steering directly for the island, though not making such fresh way as I did before.

---

[1] alteration *n.* 变更，改造

此时，我离岛已经很远，让人感到可怕。如果这时再出现哪怕一点乌云或雾天，我就会毁灭，因为我船上没有带罗盘。如果我看不到海岛，就会永远不知道如何划回那座小岛。不过，因为天气持续晴朗，所以我马上又竖起桅杆，张开帆，尽可能向北驶去，以便躲过那股急流。

　　我刚竖起桅杆、张好帆，船开始向前行驶，就根据海水的清晰度看到了那股急流马上就要发生变化，因为水流猛的地方，水很浑浊。我察觉到水变清，急流缓和了下来。不久，我还发现，在东边大约半英里外，海浪打在一些岩石上。我发现这些岩石把这股急流又一分为二，主流继续向南方流去，另一股被这些岩石挡回，形成了一股猛烈的涡流，又流回了西北方，水流非常湍急。

　　这股涡流又直接把我朝小岛的方向冲了大约一里格远，但比起先把我冲走的那股急流又向北冲了大约两里格多。因此，当接近小岛时，我发现自己正驶向小岛北岸，也就是说，到了岛的另一端，和我出发时的方向刚好相反。

　　我借着这股涡流又走了一里格多后，发现它的力量已经用尽，再也不能把船向前推进了。我发现自己正处在两股激流之间，也就是处在把我冲走的南面那股急流和相距大约一里格的北面的急流之间。我是说，我处在紧随小岛后面的两股急流之间。这里海面至少平静，海水没有流动，而且还有一股顺风。我一直向岛上开去，尽管没有像以前走得那样快。

About four o'clock in the evening, being then within about a league of the island, I found the point of the rocks stretching out to the southward, and casting off the current more southwardly, had of course made another eddy to the north, and this I found very strong, but not directly setting the way my course lay which was due west, but almost full north. However having a fresh gale, I stretched across this eddy slanting northwest, and in about an hour came within about a mile of the shore, where it being smooth water, I soon got to land.

When I was on shore I fell on my knees and gave God thanks for my deliverance, resolving to lay aside all thoughts of my deliverance by my boat, and refreshing myself with such things as I had, I brought my boat close to the shore in a little cove that I had spied under some trees, and laid me down to sleep.

I was now at a great loss which way to get home with my boat. I had run so much hazard, and knew too much the case to think of attempting it by the way I went out, and what might be at the other side (I mean the west side) I knew not, nor had I any mind to run any more ventures; so I only resolved in the morning to make my way westward along the shore and to see if there was no creek where I might lay up my frigate[1] in safety, so as to have her again if I wanted her; in about three mile or thereabout coasting the shore, I came to a very good inlet about a mile over, which narrowed till it came to a very little rivulet[2], where I found a very convenient harbour for my boat and where she lay as if she had been in a little dock made on purpose for her. Here I put in, and having stowed my boat very safe, I went on shore to look about me and see where I was.

I soon found I had but a little past by the place where I had been before, when I travelled on foot to that shore; so taking nothing out of my boat but my gun and my umbrella, for it was exceeding hot, I began my march. The way was comfortable enough after such a voyage as I had been upon, and I reached my old bower in the evening.

---

[1] frigate   n.   三帆快速战舰，护卫舰
[2] rivulet   n.   小河，小溪，溪流

下午大约 4 点，在离小岛不到一里格的地方，我发现了伸向南方的尖岬。尖岬把急流进一步逼向南方，当然另一股涡流则向北方流去。我发现这股涡流很猛，但不是直接流向我要航行的正西方向，而是差不多正北方向。然而，由于风很大，因此我就斜向西北方向，穿过了这股涡流。大约一小时后，离岛只有一英里左右了，这里海面平静，我不久便上了岸。

上岸后，我跪在地上，感谢上帝的搭救，决心抛开坐小船离开孤岛的所有念头。我吃了一些所带的东西，将小船划进岸边藏在树阴下的一个小湾。随后，我就躺下来睡着了。

我现在对该从哪条路划船回家一无所知。我曾遭遇了这么多危险，非常清楚试图按出发时的原路回去是何种情形；而对小岛的另一边（我是说西边）可能是什么情况，我也一无所知，更没有心思再去冒什么险。所以，我只好决定第二天早上沿海岸向西航行，看有没有一条小河可以安全停泊我的帆船，以便我需要时再来取它。我驾船沿岸行驶了大约 3 英里，来到了一个非常不错的小湾，大约一英里长，小湾越来越窄，最后变成了一条非常小的小河。我发现这对我的小船来说是一个非常方便的港口，好像是特意为它建立的一个小船坞。我把小船划进去，安全可靠地停好后，便上岸环顾四周，看看自己身在何处。

我很快就发现，这里离我以前徒步旅行到过的地方不远。于是，我仅仅从船里拿出了枪和伞就出发了，因为天气非常炎热。经过这次航行后，我感到这段路走得真够轻松自在的。傍晚，我便到了自己原来的茅屋。

I got over the fence, and laid me down in the shade to rest my limbs; for I was very weary, and fell asleep. But I was waked out of my sleep by a voice calling me by my name several times, "Robin, Robin, Robin Crusoe, poor Robin Crusoe, where are you Robin Crusoe? Where are you? Where have you been?"

I was so dead asleep at first, being fatigued with rowing, the first part of the day and with walking the latter part that I did not wake thoroughly, but dozing between sleeping and waking, thought I dreamed that somebody spoke to me. But as the voice continued to repeat "Robin Crusoe, Robin Crusoe," at last I began to wake more perfectly, and was at first dreadfully frightened, and started up in the utmost consternation. But no sooner were my eyes open, but I saw my poll sitting on the top of the hedge.

However, even though I knew it was the parrot, and that indeed it could be nobody else, it was a good while before I could compose myself. First, I was amazed how the creature got thither, and then, how he should just keep about the place, and nowhere else. But as I was well satisfied it could be nobody but honest poll, I got it over; and holding out my hand, and calling him by his name, "Poll," the sociable creature came to me, and sat upon my thumb, as he used to do, and continued talking to me, "Poor Robin Crusoe!" and how did I come here? And where had I been? Just as if he had been overjoyed to see me again; and so I carried him home along with me.

我爬过围墙，躺在树阴下休息，因为非常疲惫，我躺下就睡着了。但我却被一个声音从睡梦中惊醒，那个声音反复叫着我的名字："鲁滨，鲁滨，鲁滨·克罗索！可怜的鲁滨·克罗索！你在哪里，鲁滨·克罗索？你在哪里？你到哪里去了？"

　　开始我睡得很死，因为前半天划船、后半天走路，又困又乏，所以我还没有完全清醒过来，只是处在半睡半醒之间，以为在睡梦中有人在跟我说话。但随着那声音不断地叫着"鲁滨·克罗索！鲁滨·克罗索！"我终于完全清醒过来，起先吓得胆战心惊，惊惶失措，一跃而起。但我睁眼一看，发现是我那只鹦鹉卧在树篱顶上。

　　然而，即使知道是那只鹦鹉，确实不可能是别人，我还是过了好一会儿才镇定下来。首先，我对这小鸟怎么飞到这里来感到吃惊。其次，为什么它总守在这个地方，不到别处去。但当我完全确信不是别人，而是忠实的鹦鹉时，恢复了常态。我伸出手，叫着它的名字"波尔"，这只友善的小鸟像往常一样，飞到我身边，落在我的大拇指上，继续对我说着"可怜的鲁滨·克罗索！"并说我怎么到了这里？我到哪里去了？好像非常高兴再次见到我似的。于是，我就带着它一道回家去了。

XV

I had now had enough of rambling to sea for some time, and had enough to do for many days to sit still and reflect upon the danger I had been in. I would have been very glad to have had my boat again on my side of the island; but I knew not how it was practicable to get it about. As to the east side of the island, which I had gone round; I knew well enough there was no venturing that way; my very heart would shrink, and my very blood run chill but to think of it. And as to the other side of the island, I did not know how it might be there; but supposing the current ran with the same force against the shore at the east as it passed by it on the other, I might run the same risk of being driven down the stream; so with these thoughts I contented myself to be without any boat, though it had been the product of so many months' labour to make it, and of so many more to get it unto the sea.

In this government of my temper, I remained near a year and lived a very sedate[1] retired life.

I improved myself in this time in all the mechanic exercises which my necessities put me upon applying myself to.

Besides this, I arrived at an unexpected perfection in my earthenware, and contrived well enough to make them with a wheel, which I found infinitely easier and better. But I think I was never more vain of my own performance, or more joyful for anything I found out, than for my being able to make a tobacco-pipe.

In my wickerware also I improved much, and made abundance of necessary baskets. Also large deep baskets were my receivers for my corn.

---

[1] sedate   *adj.* 安静的，稳重的

15

　　我现在受够了在海上漂流的那段时间，也受够了多日静坐在那里细想经历过的危险。我很乐意把小船弄回岛这边来，但我不知道切实可行的办法。至于岛的东边，我已经去过，心里明白不能再去那样冒险了。一想到这件事，我就胆战心惊、不寒而栗。至于岛的另一边，我也不知道是怎么回事。假如那边也有像东边那样的急流猛冲海岸，我可能会碰到同样的被卷进急流的危险。所以，想到这些，我便不再要那小船了，尽管我辛劳了好几个月才把它做成，又花了好几个月把它引到海里。

　　将近一年，我都压制着自己的性子，过着一种恬静悠闲的生活。

　　在这段时间，为了应付日常所需，我的所有手艺都有了长进。

　　此外，我的陶器也做得意想不到的完美。我想出了一个不错的方法，用一只磨轮来做陶器，我发现这样轻松好看得多。但我认为，在我自己的工作中，最得意、最高兴的是，我居然能做成一只烟斗。

　　在编藤器方面，我也有很大长进，编了很多自己需要的篮子，还做了一些又大又深的筐子来盛谷物。

I began now to perceive my powder abated considerably, and this was a want which it was impossible for me to supply; and I began seriously to consider what I must do when I should have no more powder; that is to say, how I should do to kill any goat. I had, as is observed in the third year of my being here, kept a young kid, and bred her up tame, and I was in hope of getting a he-goat, but I could not by any means bring it to pass, till my kid grew an old goat.

Now in the eleventh year of my residence, I set myself to study some art to trap and snare[1] the goats, to see whether I could not catch some of them alive, and particularly I wanted a she-goat great with young.

To this purpose I made snares to hamper them, and I do believe they were more than once taken in them, but my tackle[2] was not good, for I had no wire, and I always found them broken, and my bait devoured.

At length I resolved to try a pitfall, so I dug several large pits in the earth, in places where I had observed the goats used to feed, and over these pits I placed hurdles of my own making too, with a great weight upon them; and several times I put ears of barley and dry rice, without setting the trap, and I could easily perceive that the goats had gone in and eaten up the corn, for I could see the mark of their feet. At length I set three traps in one night, and going the next morning I found them all standing, and yet the bait eaten and gone. This was very discouraging.

However, I altered my trap, and, not to trouble you with particulars, going one morning to see my trap, I found in one of them a large old he-goat, and in one of the other, three kids, a male and two females.

As to the old one, I knew not what to do with him, for he was so fierce I durst not go into the pit to go about to bring him away alive. I could have killed him, but that was not my business, nor would it answer my end. So I let him out. Then I went to the three kids, and taking them one by one, I tied them with strings together, and with some difficulty brought them all home.

---

[1] snare *v.* 诱捕
[2] tackle *n.* 工具，用具，装备

我现在开始发现火药已经大大减少，这是我无法补充的一种必需品。于是，我开始认真考虑，我没有弹药时该怎么办，也就是说，我用什么办法去捕杀山羊。前面曾提到过，我到这里的第三年捉到了一只小母山羊，并把它驯养了起来。后来，我一直希望活捉一只公山羊。但我想尽办法也没有能捉到一只，直到小山羊变成了老山羊。

现在已经在岛上住了 11 年，我开始研究如何用陷阱诱捕那些山羊，看能不能活捉一些。我尤其想捉到一只怀孕的母羊。

为了达到这个目的，我做了几个捕具来捕捉它们。我确信它们不止一次被捕具夹住，但我的捕具不好，因为我没有铁丝，我总是发现捕具被挣断、诱饵被吃掉。

最后，我决定挖陷阱试试看。于是，我在山羊经常吃草的地方挖了好几个大深坑，并在这些坑上盖上了几块自制的活动栅栏，再在栅栏上压上一些很重的东西。有几次，我不设圈套，放了一些大麦穗和干稻。我可以轻易地看到那些山羊曾走进去吃完了谷物，因为我看到了它们的蹄印。终于，有一天夜里，我设了三个圈套。第二天早上，我过去一看，发现三个圈套都原封未动，诱饵却都吃光了。这真是令人扫兴。

不过，我还是把圈套做了一些改进，具体细节就不说了。有一天早上，我去看设的圈套，发现其中一个套着一只老公羊，另一个套着三只小羊，一公两母。

至于那只老公羊，我不知道该怎么对付它，因为它非常凶猛，我不敢下坑去活捉它。尽管我可以把它杀死，但那不是我份内的事儿，那也达不到我的目的，所以我就放了它。接着，我走到三只小山羊身边，把它们一一捉住，用绳子拴在一起，又费了一些劲儿把它们都牵回了家。

It was a good while before they would feed, but throwing them some sweet corn, it tempted them and they began to be tame; and now I found that if I expected to supply myself with goat-flesh when I had no powder or shot left, breeding some up tame was my only way.

But then it presently occurred to me that I must keep the tame from the wild, or else they would always run wild when they grew up, and the only way for this was to have some enclosed piece of ground, well fenced either with hedge, to keep them in so effectually that those within might not break out, or those without break in.

This was a great undertaking for one pair of hands, yet as I saw there was an absolute necessity of doing it, my first piece of work was to find out a proper piece of ground, viz., where there was likely to be herbage[1] for them to eat, water for them to drink, and cover to keep them from the sun.

Those who understand such enclosures will think I had very little contrivance, when I pitched upon a place very proper for all these, being a plain open piece of savanna, which had two or three little drills' of fresh water in it, and at one end was very woody. I say they will smile at my forecast when I shall tell them I began my enclosing of this piece of ground in such a manner that my hedge must have been at least two mile about. I did not consider that my goats would be as wild in so much compass as if they had had the whole island, and I should have so much room to chase them in that I should never catch them.

My hedge was begun and carried on about fifty yards, when this thought occurred to me, so I presently stopped short, and for the first beginning I resolved to enclose a piece of about 150 yards in length and 100 yards in breadth.

This answered my end, and in about a year and half I had a flock of twelve goats, kids and all; and in two years more I had three and forty, besides several that I took and killed for my food. And after that I enclosed five several pieces of ground to feed them in, with little pens[2] to drive them into, to take them as I wanted, and gates out of one piece of ground into another.

---

[1] herbage *n.* 草本，草
[2] pen *n.* 钢笔；围栏，围圈

好一阵子，它们都不肯吃东西，但我给它们扔了一些甜玉米穗，循循善诱，它们才开始驯顺起来。现在我发现，如果弹药用尽后我还想吃山羊肉，唯一的办法就是驯养一些山羊。

但紧接着，我又想到，我必须把驯养的山羊和野山羊隔离开来，否则它们长大时，就会跑野。唯一的办法就是找一块空地，用树篱牢牢围住，把它们有效地圈在里面。这样，里面的驯羊冲不出来，外面的野羊也闯不进去。

对我一双手来说，这是一项大工程。但我明白这样做绝对必要，所以我首先要做的工作是找到一块合适的地方，也就是，那里既要有青草供山羊吃，又要有水供它们喝，还要有遮阳的阴凉地。

我找到了一个符合这三个条件的非常合适的地方。这是一大片平坦的草原。草原上有两三条清水小溪，小溪的一头树木茂密。而那些懂得圈地的人一定会认为我这样做缺少计划。我敢说，我把自己开始建围栏的方法告诉他们，他们一定会笑话我，因为我的树篱围起来至少有两英里。我没有考虑到，山羊在这么大的范围内，一定会到处乱跑，就像它们在整个岛上跑一样。要在这么大的空间里捕捉它们，我根本无法捉到。

我开始动手修栅栏，而且完成了大约 50 码时，才想到了这一点。于是，我马上停了下来，并决定先圈一块大约长 150 码、宽 100 码的地方。

我这个目的总算达到了。大约不到一年半，我就有了大大小小 12 只山羊。又过了两年，除了被我宰杀吃掉的几只，我已有了 43 只山羊。之后，我又圈了五块地方养羊。这些圈地上都做了小围栏。我要捉羊时，就把它们赶进去，而且各块地之间还有门彼此相通。

Now I not only had goat's flesh to feed on when I pleased, but milk too.

Then to see how like a king I dined too all alone, attended by my servants; Poll, as if he had been my favourite, was the only person permitted to talk to me. My dog who was now grown very old and crazy, and had found no species to multiply his kind upon, sat always at my right hand, and two cats, one on one side the table, and one on the other, expecting now and then a bit from my hand, as a mark of special favour.

But these were not the two cats which I brought on shore at first, for they were both of them dead, and had been interred near my habitation by my own hand; but one of them having multiplied by I know not what kind of creature, these were two which I had preserved tame, whereas the rest ran wild in the woods, and became indeed troublesome to me at last; for they would often come into my house, and plunder[1] me too, till at last I was obliged to shoot them, and did kill a great many; at length they left me, and in this plentiful manner I lived.

I was something impatient, as I have observed, to have the use of my boat, though very loath to run any more hazards; and therefore sometimes I sat contriving ways to get her about the island, and at other times I sat myself down contented enough without her. But I had a mind to go down to the point of the island, where, in my last ramble, I went up the hill to see how the shore lay, and how the current set, that I might see what I had to do. This inclination increased upon me every day, and at length I resolved to travel thither by land, following the edge of the shore.

I travelled first along the seashore, directly to the place where I first brought my boat to an anchor, to get up upon the rocks; and having no boat now to take care of, I went over the land a nearer way to the same height that I was upon before, when looking forward to the point of the rocks which lay out, and which I was obliged to double with my boat, I was surprised to see the sea all smooth and quiet.

---

[1] plunder   v. 抢劫

现在我不仅随时有羊肉吃，而且还有羊奶喝。

然后再看看我是怎样像国王一样由仆人们伺候着独自用餐的吧。鹦鹉波尔好像是我的宠臣，只有它才允许和我说话。我的狗现在又老又蠢，找不到可以繁殖的物种，总是卧在我右首；那两只猫则各卧一边，不时地希望从我手里得到一点吃的，把这作为一种特殊的恩宠。

但这不是我最初带上岸的两只猫，因为那两只已经死了，我亲手把它们葬在了我的住所附近，但其中一只不知同哪种动物交配，生下了许多小猫。这两只就是我从那些小猫中留下来驯养的，而其余的都跑进树林，成了野猫。那些野猫后来确实让我讨厌，因为它们经常跑到我的家里抢东西。最后，我不得不向它们开枪，而且的确杀了很多，它们终于离开了我。我现在生活得很富裕。

我曾说过，我很想使用那只小船，但又很不情愿再冒任何风险。因此，有时我会坐在那里千方百计想把船弄到小岛这边来；有时我又会安下心来，认为没有它也行。但我总想到岛那边的尖岬去，因为上次出游时我正是在那里登上小山，远眺海岸的走向、急流的流向，然后看我该怎么办。这个念头我在心里一天比一天强烈。最后，我决定沿着海岸边从陆地走到那边去。

我先沿海岸径直走到我上次抛锚登上小山的地方。现在我不用照管小船，抄近路登上了上次登过的那座小山。我远眺伸入海里的尖岬时，吃惊地看到，上次我不得不驾船绕行的海面现在却风平浪静。

But I was presently convinced how it was, viz., that the tide of ebb setting from the west and joining with the current of waters from some great river on the shore must be the occasion of this current; and that according as the wind blew more forcibly from the west, or from the north, this current came nearer, or went farther from the shore; for waiting thereabouts till evening, I went up to the rock again, and then the tide of ebb being made, I plainly saw the current again as before, only, that it ran farther off, being near half a league from the shore; whereas in my case, it set close upon the shore, and hurried me and my canoe along with it, which at another time it would not have done.

This observation convinced me that I had nothing to do but to observe the ebbing and the flowing of the tide, and I might very easily bring my boat about the island again. But when I began to think of putting it in practice, I had such a terror upon my spirits at the remembrance of the danger I had been in, that I could not think of it again with any patience; but on the contrary, I took up another resolution which was more safe, though more laborious[1]; and this was, that I would make me another canoe; and so have one for one side of the island, and one for the other.

Now I had two plantations in the island; one my little fortification or tent, with the wall about it under the rock, with the cave behind me, which by this time I had enlarged into several apartments, or caves, one within another. One of these, which was the driest, and largest, and had a door out beyond my wall or fortification; that is to say, beyond where my wall joined to the rock, was all filled up with the large earthen pots, and with fourteen or fifteen great baskets, which would hold five or six bushels of provision each.

As for my wall made with long piles, those piles grew all like trees, and were by this time grown so big and spread so very much that there was not the least appearance to anyone's view of any habitation behind them.

Near this dwelling of mine, but a little farther within the land, and upon lower ground, lay my two pieces of corn-ground, which I kept duly cultivated and sowed, and which duly yielded me their harvest in its season.

---

[1] laborious *adj.* （指工作）艰苦的，费力的

但不久，我就明白了是怎么回事，也就是，从西边退下来的潮水和岸上一条大河的水流汇合，形成了那股急流；随着时而西风烈、时而北风紧，这股急流就离岸时近时远。等到傍晚时分，我又登上小山顶。当时正值退潮，我又清楚地看到了那股急流，还是像以前一样，不过这次离岸较远，差不多有半里格；而我上次来时，急流离岸很近，所以就把我和独木舟冲走了。而在其他时候，它不会这样。

这次观察使我确信，只要注意潮水涨落，我就可以轻而易举地把小船重新弄到岛那边。但开始想行动时，我又想起了上次经历的危险，禁不住胆战心惊，所以吓得连想都不敢想了。相反，我又作出了一个更安全却更费力的决定，也就是，我要再造一只独木舟。这样，我在岛这边有一只，岛那边也有一只。

现在我在岛上有了两个庄园。一个是我那个小小的城堡或帐篷，在小山脚下四周建起了围墙，后面是岩洞，到现在我已经把岩洞扩大成了好几个房间或洞室，一个套着一个。其中有一间最干最大，并有一个门通到围墙或城堡外面，也就是说，通到了围墙和山石的连接处。我在这一间里放满了陶土烧成的大瓦缸，还放了十四五只大筐子，每只大筐子能装五、六蒲式耳粮食。

至于我用长树桩垒的那堵围墙，那些树桩都长成了树，现在长得又大又密，谁都根本看不出来后面会住有人。

在我这个住所附近，往岛里再走一点儿，在地势较低的地方，有我的两块庄稼地。我按时耕种，按季收获。

Besides this, I had my country seat, and I had now a tolerable plantation there also; for first, I had my little bower, which I kept in repair; that is to say, I kept the hedge which circled it in, constantly fitted up to its usual height, the ladder standing always in the inside; I kept the trees which at first were no more than my stakes, but were now grown very firm and tall; I kept them always so cut that they might spread and grow thick and wild. In the middle of this I had my tent always standing; and under this I had made me a squab[1], with the skins and with other soft things, and a blanket laid on them, and a great watch-coat to cover me; and here, whenever I had occasion to be absent from my chief seat, I took up my country habitation.

Adjoining to this I had my enclosures for my goats. And as I had taken an inconceivable deal of pains to fence and enclose this ground and stuck the outside of the hedge so full of small stakes. Afterwards, those stakes grew in the next rainy season, making the enclosure strong like a wall, indeed stronger than any wall.

In this place also I had my grapes growing, which I principally depended on for my winter store of raisins; and which I never failed to preserve very carefully, as the best and most agreeable dainty[2] of my whole diet.

As this was also about half way between my other habitation and the place where I had laid up my boat, I generally stayed, and lay here in my way thither; for I used frequently to visit my boat, and I kept all things about or belonging to her in very good order; sometimes I went out in her to divert myself, but no more hazardous voyages would I go, nor scarce ever far from the shore. But now I come to a new scene of my life.

---

[1] squab　*n.*　（坐或靠的）厚垫子
[2] dainty　*n.*　适口的食物，美味

此外，我还有乡间别墅，现在那里也是一座尚好的庄园，因为首先我有一间小茅屋。这间茅屋我不断修缮。也就是说，我经常修剪周围的树篱，使其总是保持平常的高度。梯子总是靠在里面。那些树起初不过是一些树桩，现在长得又壮又高。我总是不断修剪它们，所以它们长得枝繁叶茂、蓬蓬勃勃。树篱中央总是搭着一顶帐篷。我在帐篷下放了一张睡垫，那是我用兽皮和其他一些柔软材料做成的。睡垫上还铺了一条毛毯；另外还有一件值更大衣放自己盖。每当我有事离开主宅时，就住在乡间别墅。

和别墅相邻，我给那些山羊圈了地。为了圈这块地，我曾历尽艰辛，在栅栏外面插满了小木桩。后来，在下一个雨季中，这些小木桩都长大了，长得像一堵坚固的围墙似的，其实比围墙还坚固。

在这块地方，我还种了葡萄，我每年冬天储藏的葡萄干，主要是从自己葡萄园里收获的葡萄晒制而成的。这些葡萄干我都非常小心地保藏，因为这是我所有食物中最营养、最可口的美味。

乡间别墅大约处在我停船的地方和海边住所的中途，我每次去泊船处总要在这里停留，因为我常去看看那只独木舟，并把船里的东西整理得井井有条。有时，我也划着独木舟出去消遣，但再也不敢冒险航行，也不敢再远离海岸。而这时，我的生活出现了一幕新的情景。

XVI

It happened one day about noon going towards my boat, I was exceedingly surprised with the print of a man's naked foot on the shore, which was very plain to be seen in the sand. I stood like one thunder-struck, or as if I had seen an apparition[1]; I listened, I looked round me, I could hear nothing, nor see anything; I went up to a rising ground to look farther, I went up the shore and down the shore, but it was all one, I could see no other impression but that one. I went to it again to see if there were any more, and to observe if it might not be my fancy; but there was no room for that, for there was exactly the very print of a foot; how it came thither, I knew not, nor could in the least imagine. I came home to my fortification, not feeling the ground I went on, but terrified to the last degree, looking behind me at every two or three steps, mistaking every bush and tree and every stump at a distance to be a man.

When I came to my castle, I fled into it like one pursued. I slept none that night. Thus my fear banished[2] all my religious hope.

These thoughts took me up many hours, days; nay, I may say, weeks and months; and one particular effect of my cogitations[3] on this occasion, I cannot omit, viz., one morning early, lying in my bed, and filled with thought about my danger from the appearance of savages, I found it discomposed[4] me very much, upon which those words of the Scripture came into my thoughts, "Call upon me in the day of trouble, and I will deliver, and thou shalt glorify me."

---

[1] apparition　*n.* 离奇出现的东西，（尤指）鬼怪，幽灵
[2] banish　*vt.* 流放，驱逐，消除
[3] cogitation　*n.* 沉思，思考
[4] discompose　*vt.* 使不安

16

　　有一天，大约是在中午时分，我正向那只小船走去，突然在沙滩上发现了一个人的光脚印，清晰可见，我大吃一惊。我站在那里，像遭到了晴天霹雳，又像见到了鬼。我侧耳倾听，又环顾四周，但一无所闻，也一无所见。我走上一个坡地，向远处眺望。我又在海边来回跑了几次，但就见一个脚印，再也看不到其他脚印。我又走到脚印前，看看还有没有其他脚印，看看它是不是我的幻觉。但毫无疑问，因为确实是一个脚印。这脚印是怎么来的，我不得而知，也根本无法想像。我脚不沾地、惊恐万分地跑到自己的城堡，一路上每跑两三步就回一次头，错把远处的每个矮树丛、每棵树和每个树桩都当成了一个人。

　　我一跑到城堡，就逃了进去，好像真有人追赶似的。我一夜都没有合眼。因此，恐惧驱走了我所有的宗教希望。

　　这些想法占去了我许多时日，而且不止于此，我可以说，占去了我几个星期、几个月。思考的结果当时对我产生了一种特殊的影响，我绝不能遗漏，也就是，一天早晨，我正躺在床上满脑子想着野人出现的危险，感到心神不安。这时，我想起了《圣经》上的话："患难之时请求我，我将拯救你，你一定会赞美我。"

Upon this, rising cheerfully out of my bed, my heart was not only comforted, but I was guided and encouraged to pray earnestly to God for deliverance. When I had done praying, I took up my Bible, and opening it to read, the first words that presented to me were, "Wait on the Lord, and be of good cheer, and he shall strengthen thy heart; wait, I say, on the Lord." It is impossible to express the comfort this gave me. In answer, I thankfully laid down the book, and was no more sad, at least, not on that occasion.

It came into my thought one day that all this might be a mere chimera[1] of my own; and that this foot might be the print of my own foot, when I came on shore from my boat. This cheered me up a little too, and I began to persuade myself it was all a delusion[2]; that it was nothing else but my own foot; for I could by no means tell for certain where I had trod, and where I had not.

But I could not persuade myself fully of this, till I should go down to the shore again, see this print of a foot, measure it by my own, and see if there was any similitude[3] or fitness, that I might be assured it was my own foot. But when I came to the place, first, it appeared evidently to me, that when I laid up my boat, I could not possibly be on shore anywhere thereabout. Secondly, when I came to measure the mark with my own foot, I found my foot not so large by a great deal; so that I shook with cold, like one in an ague. And I went home again, filled with the belief that some man or men had been on shore there; or in short, that the island was inhabited, and I might be surprised before I was aware.

The first thing I proposed to myself was to throw down my enclosures, and turn all my tame cattle wild into the woods, that the enemy might not find them and then frequent the island in prospect of the like booty[4]. Then to the simple thing of digging up my two cornfields, that they might not find such a grain there, and still be prompted to frequent the island; then to demolish[5] my bower and tent, that they might not see any vestiges[6] of habitation, and be prompted to look farther, in order to find out the persons inhabiting.

---

[1] chimera   n.   妖怪，狂想
[2] delusion   n.   错觉
[3] similitude   n.   相似，外表
[4] booty   n.   战利品，获得之物
[5] demolish   vt.   毁坏，破坏
[6] vestige   n.   遗迹，痕迹

于是，我愉快地从床上爬起来，不仅心里得到了安慰，而且得到了指引和鼓舞，虔诚地向上帝祈祷，恳求他拯救我。做完祈祷，我就拿起《圣经》，打开读了起来，首先呈现在我眼前的下面这句话："追随上帝，要精神振奋，他会增强你的信心，所以要追随上帝。"这几句话给我的安慰真是难以言表。于是，我放下《圣经》，心里充满了感激，不再忧愁，至少当时不再难过了。

有一天，我想到这一切也许仅仅是自己的幻觉。这只脚印可能是我下船上岸时自己留在沙滩上的脚印。这也使我稍稍高兴了点儿。我开始说服自己，那都是一种错觉，那只不过是自己留下的脚印，因为我根本搞不清哪里我曾走过、哪里没有走过。

不过，我还不能完全使自己相信这一点，我应该再到海滨去一次，看看那个脚印，用自己的脚去量一下，看是不是大小一样，这样我才能确信那就是自己的脚印。但当我来到那个地方时，首先在我看来，我当初停放小船时，显然不可能在那一带的任何地方上岸；其次，当我用自己的脚去量那个脚印时，发现我的脚没有那样大。所以，我像发疟疾似的不寒而栗。我又回到家里，信誓旦旦地认为有人在那里上过岸。总之，岛上住有了人，说不定什么时候还等我明白是怎么回事会对我突然袭击。

我计划做的第一件事就是拆掉那些围墙，把所有驯养的山羊放生树林，以免敌人发现它们，然后经常上岛掠夺更多类似的战利品；其次，我打算挖掉那两块粮田，以免他们在那里发现这种粮食，再常常到岛上劫掠。接下来，我打算毁掉茅屋和帐篷，以免他们会发现住人的任何痕迹，然后进一步向前搜寻，找出住在这里的人。

This confusion of my thoughts kept me waking all night; but in the morning I fell asleep; I slept very soundly, and woke much better composed than I had ever been before; and now I began to think sedately; and I concluded that this island, which was so exceeding pleasant, fruitful, and no farther from the mainland than as I had seen, was not so entirely abandoned as I might imagine. That although there were no stated inhabitants who lived on the spot; yet that there might sometimes come boats off from the shore, who either with design or perhaps never, but when they were driven by cross winds, might come to this place. That I had lived here fifteen years now, and had not met with the least shadow or figure of any people yet; and that if at any time they should be driven here, it was probable they went away again as soon as ever they could, seeing they had never thought fit to fix there upon any occasion, to this time.

That the most I could suggest any danger from was from any such casual accidental landing of straggling[1] people from the main, who, as it was likely if they were driven hither, were here against their wills; so they made no stay here, but went off again with all possible speed, seldom staying one night on shore, lest they should not have the help of the tides and daylight back again; and that therefore I had nothing to do but to consider of some safe retreat, in case I should see any savages land upon the spot.

Now I began sorely to repent that I had dug my cave so large, as to bring a door through again, which door came out beyond where my fortification joined to the rock; upon maturely considering this therefore, I resolved to draw me a second fortification, in the same manner of a semicircle[2], at a distance from my wall, just where I had planted a double row of trees, about twelve years before. These trees having been planted so thick before, they wanted but a few piles to be driven between them, that they should be thicker and stronger, and my wall would be soon finished.

---

[1] straggling *adj.* 脱离队伍的，落后的
[2] semicircle *n.* 半圆形

这样胡思乱，想使我彻夜未眠。但到第二天早上，我倒头睡去。我睡得很香，醒来后，比以前镇定多了。我开始心平气和地思考，最后得出结论：这个小岛风景宜人，物产丰富，而且离大陆不远，不可能像我想像的那样完全没有人迹。尽管岛上没有固定居住的居民，但对面大陆上的船有时可能来岛上靠岸。那些上岛的人有些可能有一定的目的，有些则可能是被逆风刮过来的。我现在已在岛上住了 15 年，但从未见过一个人影或鬼影，因为即使他们偶尔被逆风刮到这里，也总是尽快离开，看来到现在为止他们仍然一直认为这座岛不宜久留。

我能想起的最大危险，就是那边大陆上偶尔在此登岸的零零散散的居民，因为他们很可能是被逆风刮到了这里，上岛是迫不得已，所以他们绝不愿呆在这里，而是尽可能快地再次离开，很少在岛上过夜，惟恐他们不能借助潮水的力量白天再返回去。因此，我只需要考虑一个安全的退路，以防野人在这里上岸。

现在，我开始非常后悔把山洞挖得太大了，还在围墙和岩石连接处开了一个门。因此，经过深思熟虑后，我决定在围墙外边——也就是我大约 12 年前种两行树的地方——再筑起一道同样的半圆形防御工事。这些树原来就种得很密，所以只在树干之间再打几个木桩，它们就会更加紧密坚固。我很快就完成了这道围墙。

So that I had now a double wall, and my outer wall was thickened with pieces of timber, old cables, and everything I could think of, to make it strong; having in it seven little holes, about as big as I might put my arm out at. In the inside of this, I thickened my wall to above ten foot thick, with continual bringing earth out of my cave, and laying it at the foot of the wall, and walking upon it; and through the seven holes, I contrived to plant the muskets[1], of which I got seven on shore out of the ship; these, I say, I planted like my cannon, and fitted them into frames that held them like a carriage[2], that so I could fire all the seven guns in two minutes' time. This wall I was many a weary month a-finishing, and yet never thought myself safe till it was done.

When this was done, I stuck all the ground without my wall, for a great way every way, as full with stakes of the osier-like wood, which I found so apt to grow. I might set in near twenty thousand of them, leaving a pretty large space between them and my wall, that I might have room to see an enemy, and they might have no shelter from the young trees, if they attempted to approach my outer wall.

Thus in two years' time I had a thick grove and in five or six years' time I had a wood before my dwelling, growing so monstrous thick and strong that it was indeed perfectly impassable[3]; and no men of what kind soever[4] would ever imagine that there was anything beyond it, much less a habitation. As for the way which I proposed to myself to go in and out, for I left no avenue; it was by setting two ladders, one to a part of the rock which was low, and then broke in, and left room to place another ladder upon that; so when the two ladders were taken down, no man living could come down to me without mischieving himself; and if they had come down, they were still on the outside of my outer wall.

---

[1] musket   *n.* 步枪
[2] carriage   *n.* 马车；（机械）车架
[3] impassable   *adj.* 不能通行的，无路可通的
[4] soever   *adv.* 无论，不论何种

这样，我现在就有了双层围墙。我在外墙上用了一些木料、旧锚索以及我能想到的一切东西加厚加固，并在墙上开了七个小洞，大小刚好能伸过我的手臂。在围墙内，我不断从山洞里搬了不少泥土，倒在墙脚，并用脚在上面踩实，把墙加厚到了 10 多英尺。这七个小洞我计划放那些火铳。我从大船上拿了七支火铳。我把这些枪安置得像加农炮，并用架子装好，像炮架似的托住。这样，我两分钟内能连开七枪。这道墙，我辛苦了好几个月才完成。而在没有完成前，我一直认为自己不安全。

这个完成后，我在墙外四面八方插满了杞柳似的树桩，因为我发现它们非常容易生长。我可能插了有将近两万个，同时在那些树桩和围墙之间留出了一块相当大的空地，以便我可以有看到敌人的空间。如果敌人企图靠近外墙，他们就不可能有遮挡的小树了。

这样，不到两年时间，我就有了一片浓密的小树林，不到五、六年时间，我的住所前就长成了一大片森林，浓密粗壮，确实难以通行。任何人无论怎样也不会想到树林那边会有什么东西，更不会想到会有人住。至于我为自己安排的进出口，则是靠两个梯子，因为我没有留路。一个梯子靠在地势低的岩石上，然后进去后，给第二个梯子留出了空档。所以，撤掉两架梯子后，任何人不受到伤害，不可能下到我身边。就是他们下来，也只能落在我的外墙外面。

Now I had a great concern upon me for my little herd of goats; they were not only a present supply to me upon every occasion without the expence of powder and shot; but also without the fatigue of hunting after the wild ones, and I was loath to lose the advantage of them, and to have them all to nurse up over again.

To this purpose, after long consideration, I could think of but two ways to preserve them; one was to find another convenient place to dig a cave underground, and to drive them into it every night; and the other was to enclose two or three little bits of land, remote from one another and as much concealed as I could, where I might keep about half a dozen young goats in each place. So that if any disaster happened to the flock in general, I might be able to raise them again with little trouble and time. And this, though it would require a great deal of time and labour, I thought was the most rational[1] design.

Accordingly I spent some time to find out the most retired parts of the island; and I pitched upon one which was as private indeed as my heart could wish for; it was a little damp piece of ground in the middle of the hollow and thick woods, where I almost lost myself once before, endeavouring to come back that way from the eastern part of the island. Here I found a clear piece of land near three acres, so surrounded with woods that it was almost an enclosure by Nature.

I immediately went to work with this piece of ground, and in less than a month's time, I had so fenced it round that my flock, who were not so wild now as at first they might be supposed to be, were well enough secured in it. So, without any farther delay, I removed ten young she-goats and two he-goats to this piece; and when they were there, I continued to perfect the fence till I had made it as secure as the other.

All this labour I was at the expence of, purely from my apprehensions on the account of the print of a man's foot which I had seen; for as yet I never saw any human creature come near the island, and I had now lived two years under these uneasinesses, which indeed made my life much less comfortable than it was before.

---

[1] rational   *adj.* 理性的，合理的

现在，我非常关心那一小群山羊，它们不仅可以随时满足我的需要，不必浪费任何火药和子弹，而且也不用费劲儿去追捕那些野山羊。再说，我也不愿失去驯养山羊提供的便利，再从头开始驯养它们。

为了达到这个目的，我考虑了好长时间，认为只能有两个办法保全羊群。一是另找一个方便的地方，挖一个地洞，每天晚上把羊赶进去；另一个办法是再圈两三块小地方，彼此相隔很远，尽可能隐蔽点儿，我可以在每个地方养大约六、七只羊。这样，如果大羊群发生什么不幸，我还能费点儿时间和精力把它们再养起来。尽管这个办法需要很多时间和劳力，但我认为是一个最合理的计划。

于是，我就花了一些时间去寻找岛上最幽静的地方。我选定了一块非常隐蔽、合我心意的地方。那是一小片湿洼地，处在一片密林的中央。我以前尽力从岛的东部回家时差点儿在这里迷路。我在这里找到了一片空地，将近三英亩大，四周到处都是密林，几乎成了天然篱墙。

我马上在这块地上干了起来。不到一个月时间，我就围好了篱墙，羊群现在不像以前那样野了，关在那里相当安全。因此，我一点儿也不敢耽搁，马上将 10 只小母羊和两只公羊移到了那里。山羊移过去后，我继续加固篱墙，直至做得和第一个圈地的篱墙一样牢固。

我这样不辞辛劳，纯粹是因为我看到那只脚印而产生了种种忧虑。其实，我至今还没有看到任何人靠近这座岛。我现在已经在这种种不安中又生活了两年。这种不安的心情确实使我的生活远远不像以前那样轻松自在了。

XVII

After I had thus secured one part of my little living stock, I went about the whole island, searching for another private place, to make such another deposit; when wandering more to the west point of the island, than I had ever done yet, and looking out to sea, I thought I saw a boat upon the sea, at a great distance; I had found a prospective glass or two, in one of the seamen's chests, which I saved out of our ship; but I had it not about me, and this was so remote that I looked at it till my eyes were not able to hold to look any longer; whether it was a boat or not, I do not know; but as I descended from the hill, I could see no more of it, so I gave it over; only I resolved to go no more out without a prospective glass in my pocket.

When I came down the hill, to the end of the island, where indeed I had never been before, I was presently convinced that the seeing the print of a man's foot was not such a strange thing in the island as I imagined; and but that it was a special Providence that I was cast upon the side of the island, where the savages never came. I should easily have known that nothing was more frequent than for the canoes from the main, when they happened to be a little too far out at sea, to shoot over to that side of the island for harbour; likewise, as they often met and fought in their canoes, the victors having taken any prisoners, would bring them over to this shore, where according to their dreadful customs, being all cannibals, they would kill and eat them; of which hereafter.

When I came down the hill to the shore, being the southwest point of the island, I was perfectly confounded[1] and amazed; nor is it possible for me to express the horror of my mind at seeing the shore spread with skulls, hands, feet, and other bones of human bodies; and particularly I observed a place where there had been a fire made, and a circle dug in the earth, like a cockpit, where it is supposed the savage wretches had sat down to their inhuman feastings upon the bodies of their fellow-creatures.

---

[1] confounded *adj.* 糊涂的，困惑的

17

　　这样，我把其中一小部分牲畜安置好后，便走遍了全岛，想再找一片幽僻的地方，再建一个这样的圈羊地。我一直往岛的西部走，到了一个我以前从未到过的地方。我向海上眺望，我想我看到海上很远处有一只船。我曾从大船上一个水手的箱子里找到了一两副望远镜，却没有带在身上。而且距离太远，我望着它，直望得我的眼睛无法再坚持望下去。我不知道那是不是一只船。我从山上下来时，再也无法看到它了，于是就不再看了。但我决定以后出门口袋里一定要带一副望远镜。

　　我走下小山，来到我以前确实从未到过的小岛尽头时，马上明白，在岛上看到人的脚印并不像我原来想像的那样奇怪，而是老天爷特意安排，让我漂流到了岛上野人从来不到的那边。我早就应该毫不费力地知道，那些大陆上来的独木舟有时在海上走得有点儿太远，会划到岛这边来寻找港口停泊。同样，他们的独木舟经常在海上相遇，相互拼杀，打胜的部落就把抓到的俘虏带到岛这边来。按照吃人部落的可怕习俗，他们把俘虏杀死并吃掉。这事儿，我以后再谈。

　　我从小山上下来，来到位于西南角的岛边，吓得惊惶失措、目瞪口呆，也难以形容我看到海岸上满地都是人的头骨、手骨、脚骨和人体其他部分的骨头的恐怖心情。我尤其注意到有一个地方曾生过火，地上挖了一个斗鸡场似的圆圈，我想那些野蛮的坏人就是围坐在那里，举行残忍的宴会，饕餮自己同类的肉体。

I was so astonished with the sight of these things that I entertained no notions of any danger to myself from it for a long while; all my apprehensions were buried in the thoughts of such a pitch of inhuman, hellish[1] brutality, and the horror of the degeneracy[2] of human nature; which though I had heard of often, yet I never had so near a view of before. I turned away my face from the horrid spectacle. So I gat[3] me up the hill again, with the speed I could, and walked on towards my own habitation.

I knew I had been here now almost eighteen years, and never saw the least footsteps of human creature there before; and I might be here eighteen more, as entirely concealed as I was now, if I did not discover myself to them, unless I found a better sort of creatures than cannibals to make myself known to.

Yet I entertained such an abhorrence[4] of the savage wretches and the wretched inhuman custom of their devouring and eating one another up that I continued pensive and sad, and kept close within my own circle for almost two years after this. When I say my own circle, I mean by it, my three plantations, viz., my castle, my country seat and my enclosure in the woods; nor did I so much as go to look after my boat in all this time; but began rather to think of making me another; for I could not think of ever making any more attempts to bring the other boat round the island to me, lest I should meet with some of these creatures at sea, in which, if I had happened to have fallen into their hands, I knew what would have been my lot.

So that for two years after this, I never fired my gun once off, though I never went out without it; and which was more, as I had saved three pistols out of the ship, I always carried them out with me, or at least two of them, sticking them in my goat-skin belt; also I furbished up one of the great cutlasses[5] that I had out of the ship, and made me a belt to put it on also.

Things going on thus for some time, I seemed, excepting these cautions, to be reduced to my former calm, sedate way of living.

---

[1] hellish   *adj.* 地狱般的

[2] degeneracy   *n.* 堕落，退化

[3] gat   *vbl.* get 的过去式(古代用法)

[4] abhorrence   *n.* 痛恨，憎恶

[5] cutlass   *n.* 短剑，弯刀

看到这些东西，我万分惊讶，好一阵子都没有注意到对我自己的任何危险。我所有的忧虑都用在了对这种极端野蛮凶恶的残忍行为和人性堕落到这样可怕地步的沉思上。尽管我以前经常听说过吃人的事儿，但我从来没有这样近地看到过。我转过脸，不再看这可怕的景象。于是，我又飞快地跑上小山，向自己的住所奔去。

我知道我到这里已经快 18 年了，从未见过以前人类到过的脚印。只要我像现在这样完全隐蔽起来，只要我不向他们暴露自己，我可能会再住上 18 年。除非我发现比吃人族更好的人，才和他们认识。

我对这伙野蛮的坏人和他们互相吞吃的野蛮恶俗深恶痛绝。所以，从那以后，我差不多有两年时间整天郁郁寡欢、愁眉不展，紧紧守在自己的活动范围内。我说的活动范围就是指我的三处庄园，也就是我的城堡、别墅和森林里的圈地。在此期间，我甚至也没有去照看过那只小船，而是宁愿开始想另造一只，因为我连想都不敢再想把那只小船设法弄回岛这边，惟恐在海上碰到那些野人。如果碰巧落到他们手里，我知道自己会是什么样的命运。

所以，此后的两年，我从来没有开过一次枪，尽管我每次出门时总带着枪。此外，因为我曾从大船上弄了三把手枪，所以每次出门总带着它们，我至少带两把，挂在腰间的羊皮带上。我还把从船上拿下来的一把大腰刀磨快，也系了一条带子挂在腰间。

这样过了一段时间，除了这些预防措施，我仿佛又恢复了以前那种平静、沉着的生活方式。

As in my present condition there were not really many things which I wanted; and I had dropped a good design, which I had once bent my thoughts too much upon; and that was, to try if I could not make some of my barley into malt[1], and then try to brew[2] myself some beer. This was really a whimsical[3] thought, and I reproved[4] myself often for the simplicity of it; for I presently saw there would be the want of several things necessary to the making my beer that it would be impossible for me to supply; as first, casks to preserve it in, which was a thing, that as I have observed already, I could never compass[5]. In the next place, I had no hops to make it keep, no yeast[6] to make it work, no copper or kettle to make it boil.

But my invention now ran quite another way; for night and day, I could think of nothing but how I might destroy some of these monsters in their cruel bloody entertainment, and if possible, save the victim they should bring hither to destroy.

Sometimes I contrived to dig a hole under the place where they made their fire, and put in five or six pound of gunpowder, which when they kindled their fire, would consequently take fire, and blow up all that was near it; but as in the first place I should be very loath to waste so much powder upon them, my store being now within the quantity of one barrel; so neither could I be sure of its going off at any certain time, when it might surprise them; and at best, that it would do little more than just blow the fire about their ears and fright them, but not sufficient to make them forsake the place; so I laid it aside, and then proposed that I would place myself in ambush[7], in some convenient place, with my three guns all double-loaded; and in the middle of their bloody ceremony, let fly at them, when I should be sure to kill or wound perhaps two or three at every shoot; and then falling in upon them with my three pistols and my sword, I made no doubt but that if there was twenty I should kill them all.

---

[1] malt   *n.* 麦芽
[2] brew   *v.* 酿造，酝酿
[3] whimsical   *adj.* 反复无常的，古怪的
[4] reprove   *v.* 责备
[5] compass   *vt.* 围绕…而行；包围
[6] yeast   *n.* 酵母，发酵粉
[7] ambush   *n.* 埋伏，伏兵

就我目前的境况来说，其实我想要的东西并不多。我放弃了一个煞费苦心的好计划，也就是，想试一下能不能把大麦制成麦芽，再试一下用麦芽酿一些啤酒。这确实是一个异想天开的想法，连我都经常责备自己思想太简单，因为我不久就看到自己缺乏酿造啤酒必需的几样东西，也不可能搞到手。首先，没有存放啤酒的木桶，前面已经说过，这是一件我怎么也箍不好的东西。其次，我没有使酒保持不变的啤酒花，没有发酵的酵母，也没有煮沸用的铜锅或水壶。

不过，我的发明创造现在转向了另一方面，因为我日夜都只想着怎样能在这伙食人恶魔在进行血腥的人肉宴时消灭他们一些；而且如果可能的话，救出他们带过来准备吃掉的俘虏。

有时我又想设法在他们生火的地方下面挖一个洞，然后在里面放进五、六磅火药。等他们生火时，肯定会引爆火药，把附近的一切都炸毁。但我首先很不情愿在他们身上浪费这么多火药，因为现在我储存的火药量不到一桶了。再说，我也不能确定火药能在某个特定时间爆炸，对他们突然袭击。最多也不过是把火星溅到他们的耳朵四周，吓他们一跳，但不足以使他们放弃这个地方。于是，我把这个计划放到了一边，然后又想了一个办法，那就是给自己找一个适当地方埋伏起来，把三支枪装上双倍弹药，在他们举行血腥的仪式时，向他们开火，我一枪肯定能打死或打伤两三个，然后带上我的三支手枪和一把腰刀向他们冲去，如果他们只有一二十人，我肯定能把他们杀光。

At length I found a place in the side of the hill, where I was satisfied I might securely wait till I saw any of their boats coming, and might then, even before they would be ready to come on shore, convey myself unseen into thickets[1] of trees, in one of which there was a hollow large enough to conceal me entirely; and where I might sit and observe all their bloody doings, and take my full aim at their heads, when they were so close together.

Then I resolved to fix my design, and accordingly I prepared two muskets and my fowling piece; I also loaded my pistols; and I was well provided with ammunition for a second and third charge.

After I had laid the scheme of my design, and in my imagination put it in practice, I continually made my tour every morning up to the top of the hill, which was from my castle about three miles or more, to see if I could observe any boats upon the sea, coming near the island, or standing over towards it; but I began to tire of this hard duty, after I had for two or three months constantly kept my watch; but came always back without any discovery, there having not in all that time been the least appearance, not only on or near the shore; but not on the whole ocean, so far as my eyes or glasses could reach every way.

So my opinion of the action itself began to alter, and I began with cooler and calmer thoughts to consider what it was I was going to engage in. It is certain these people either do not commit this as a crime. They do not know it be offence, and then commit it in defiance of divine justice.

In the next place it occurred to me that this really was the way not to deliver myself, but entirely to ruin and destroy myself; for unless I was sure to kill every one that not only should be on shore at that time, but that should ever come on shore afterwards, if but one of them escaped to tell their country people what had happened, they would come over again by thousands to revenge the death of their fellows, and 1 should only bring upon myself a certain destruction.

Upon the whole I concluded that neither in principle or in policy I ought one way or other to concern myself in this affair. That my business was by all possible means to conceal myself from them.

---

[1] thicket *n.* 灌木丛

最后，我在小山坡上找到了一个地方，我确信可以安全地等在那里，监视他们的船过来。然后，在他们准备上岸之前，我就可以藏身在丛林里，因为那里有一个坑，大得足够让我完全藏身。我可以坐在那里，观察他们所有的残忍行为。等他们扎成堆时，我就完全对准他们的脑袋开枪。

接下来，我决定在这里实施自己的计划。我先准备好两支火铳和一支鸟枪。每支手枪也装上子弹，而且还带足了弹药，以供第二次和第三次射击。

计划安排好后，我在自己的想像中将它付诸实施，每天上午都要不断地跑上山顶去巡视，看看海上有没有小船驶近小岛或从远处向小岛驶来。小山离我的城堡大约有三英里多。但一连守望了两三个月，我开始厌倦了这件苦差事，因为每天总是一无所获，不仅海岸上或海岸附近没有小船出现，就连我用眼睛或望远镜向四面八方了望，也不见整个海面上有小船的影子。

于是，我对自己的计划也改变了看法，并开始冷静考虑自己的行动。毫无疑问，这些人并不把这看作是一种犯罪。他们并不是知道这是违背天理的罪行而故意去犯罪。

其次，我又想到，这其实不是拯救自己的方法，而是会完全毁灭自己，因为除非我有把握杀死当时上岸的每个人，还能杀死以后上岸的每个人。否则，如果有一个人逃回去，把这里发生的一切告诉自己的同胞，他们就会有成千上万的人过来报仇，那我只会自取灭亡。

总之，我得出结论，无论在原则上还是策略上，我都不应该介入这件事；我的任务就是采取一切可能的办法隐藏自己，不让他们发现。

XVIII

In this disposition[1] I continued for near a year after this; and so far was I from desiring an occasion for falling upon these wretches, that in all that time I never once went up the hill to see whether there were any of them in sight, or to know whether any of them had been on shore there or not; only this I did I went and removed my boat, which I had on the other side of the island, and carried it down to the east end of the whole island, where I ran it into a little cove which I found under some high rocks, and where I knew, by reason of the currents, the savages durst[2] not, at least would not come with their boats upon any account whatsoever.

With my boat I carried away everything that I had left there belonging to her.

Besides this, I kept myself more retired than ever, and seldom went from my cell, other than upon my constant employment, viz., to milk my she-goats and manage my little flock in the woods; which as it was quite on the other part of the island, was quite out of danger; for certain it is, that these savage people who sometimes haunted this island, never came with any thoughts of finding anything here; and consequently[3] never wandered off from the coast.

---

[1] disposition   *n.* 性情，脾气
[2] durst   *vbl.* dare 的过去分词
[3] consequently   *adv.* 从而，因此

18

之后，我在这种心情下又过了将近一年。这段时间，我不再想寻找攻击这些坏蛋的机会，也没有再上小山去看他们是不是出现在海面上，不想知道他们有没有人上岸，只是去把停放在岛另一边的小船移到了整个岛的东边。我在一些高高的岩石下发现了一个小湾，就把小船划了进去。因为那里有急流，我知道那些野人无论如何也不敢、至少不愿坐小船过来。

我把放在船上的所有东西都搬了下来。

此外，我比以前更加隐居。除了日常的工作，也就是挤羊奶、照管树林里的羊群，很少外出。因为羊群完全在岛的另一边，所以没有什么危险。这些有时上岛的野人从来没有想在岛上找到什么东西，因此从不离开海岸。

I had the care of my safety more now upon my hands than that of my food. I cared not to drive a nail, or chop a stick of wood now, for fear the noise I should make should be heard; much less would I fire a gun, for the same reason; and above all, I was intolerably uneasy at making any fire, lest the smoke, which is visible at a great distance in the day, should betray me; and for this reason I removed that part of my business which required fire, such as burning of pots and pipes, etc., into my new apartment in the woods, where after I had been some time, I found a mere natural cave in the earth, which went in a vast way, and where, I dare say, no savage, had he been at the mouth of it, would be so hardy as to venture in, nor indeed, would any man else but one who, like me, wanted nothing so much as a safe retreat.

The mouth of this hollow, was at the bottom of a great rock. While I was cutting down some wood here, I perceived that behind a very thick branch of low brushwood, there was a kind of hollow place; I was curious to look into it, and getting with difficulty into the mouth of it, I found it was pretty large; that is to say, sufficient for me to stand upright in it, and perhaps another with me; but I must confess to you, I made more haste out than I did in, when looking farther into the place, and which was perfectly dark, I saw two broad shining eyes of some creature, whether devil or man I knew not, which twinkled like two stars, the dim light from the cave's mouth shining directly in and making the reflection.

However, after some pause, I recovered myself, and began to call myself a thousand fools, and tell myself that he that was afraid to see the Devil was not fit to live twenty years in an island all alone; upon this, plucking up[1] my courage, I took up a great firebrand[2], and in I rushed again, with the stick flaming in my hand; I had not gone three steps in, but I was almost as much frightened as I was before; for I heard a very loud sigh, like that of a man in some pain, and it was followed by a broken noise, as if of words half expressed, and then a deep sigh again. I stepped back and was indeed struck with such a surprise that it put me into a cold sweat.

---

[1] pluck up 振作；拔起
[2] firebrand *n.* 火把，燃烧的木柴

我现在对安全的关心胜于对食物的关心。我现在不喜欢钉钉子、劈柴火，惟恐声音被人听见；由于同样的原因，我更不喜欢开枪。尤其是我一生火就感到忐忑不安，惟恐烟火在白天大老远被人看见而暴露自己。因此，我把需要生火的事儿（如用锅子煮东西或抽烟斗等）都转移到了林间新居。我在那里呆了一段时间后，发现了一个纯天然地洞。地洞非常大。我敢说，就是有野人来到洞口，也绝不敢进去。其他人确实也不敢进去，除了像我这样一心只想要安全藏身之地的人。

地洞口在一块大岩石的底部。我在这里砍柴时，察觉到在一片非常浓密的矮灌木丛后面有一个凹地。我好奇地向里面瞧了瞧，然后吃力地走进洞口，发现里面相当大，也就是说，足够我在里面直立起来，也许还能再站一个人。但我必须向你们承认，我一进去就赶快出来了。我朝地洞深处一看，只见里面漆黑一片，有两只闪闪发亮的大眼睛，我不知道是鬼是人，在洞口直射进去的微光的反射下，那双眼睛像两颗星星似的闪闪发光。

然而，停了一会儿后，我又恢复了常态，开始连声骂自己笨蛋，对自己说，谁怕魔鬼，谁就不适合孤身一人在一个岛上住20年。于是，我又鼓起勇气，点起一个大火把，手持熊熊燃烧的火把又冲进洞去。但我刚走出三步，又几乎像先前那样吓了一跳，因为我听到了一声非常响亮的叹息，就像一个人在痛苦中发出的叹息。接着是一阵时断时续的声音，仿佛是吞吞吐吐的说话声，然后又是一声深深的叹息。我向后退去，确实吓出了一身冷汗。

But still plucking up my spirits as well as I could, I stepped forward again, and by the light of the firebrand, holding it up a little over my head, I saw lying on the ground a most monstrous frightful old he-goat, gasping for life.

I stirred him a little to see if I could get him out, and he essayed to get up, but was not able to raise himself; and I thought with myself, he might even lie there; for if he had frightened me so, he would certainly fright any of the savages, if any of them should be so hardy as to come in there, while he had any life in him.

I was now recovered from my surprise, and began to look round me, when I found the cave was but very small, that is to say, it might be about twelve feet over, but in no manner of shape, either round or square, no hands having ever been employed in making it, but those of mere Nature. I observed also that there was a place at the farther side of it that went in farther, but was so low that it required me to creep upon my hands and knees to go into it, and whither I went I knew not; so having no candle, I gave it over for some time; but resolved to come again the next day, provided with candles and a tinderbox[1], which I had made of the lock of one of the muskets, with some wildfire in the pan.

Accordingly the next day, I came provided with six large candles of my own making; for I made very good candles now of goat's tallow[2]; and going into this low place, I was obliged to creep upon all fours almost ten yards; which I thought was a venture bold enough, considering that I knew not how far it might go, nor what was beyond it.

When I got through the strait, I found the roof rose higher up, I believe near twenty feet; but never was such a glorious sight seen in the island, I dare say, as it was, to look round the sides and roof of this cave; the walls reflected hundred thousand lights to me from my two candles; what it was in rock, whether diamonds, or any other precious stones or gold, I knew not.

---

[1] tinderbox   *n.* 火绒箱，易燃物
[2] tallow   *n.* 牛脂，动物脂

不过，我还是尽可能鼓起勇气，将火把稍微举过头顶，又向前走去。我借着火光一看，原来地上躺着一只大得吓人的老公山羊，正在那里苟延残喘。

我稍微动了动它，看能不能把它赶出去；它想站起来，但无法站起来。于是，我就暗自想道，就让它躺在那里吧。既然它吓了我一跳，只要它还有一口气，也肯定会把胆敢走进来的野人吓一跳。

这时，我从惊愕中恢复过来，开始环顾四周，发现洞很小，也就是说，可能大约 12 英尺，不方也不圆，不成什么形状，没有经过任何人手加工，而是纯天然洞穴。我还观察到，在地洞深处那边还有一个地方，但很低，需要我俯身才能爬进去。我不知道这洞通向哪里。我没有蜡烛，只好暂不进去，但决定第二天带上蜡烛和火绒盒再来。火绒盒是我用一支火铳上的枪机做成的。另外还得再带一盘火种。

于是，第二天，我带上六支自己做的大蜡烛去了，因为我现在已经能用羊脂做出很好的蜡烛。我钻进这个低矮的地方时，不得不匍匐在地爬了将近 10 码。我想这是一个足够大胆的冒险，因为我既不知道洞有多深，也不知道洞那边是什么。

钻过这段狭窄的通道后，我发现洞顶高了起来，我相信有将近 20 英尺。我环顾地洞四周和顶上，我敢说，在这岛上，好像还从来没有见过这样壮丽的景象。洞壁反射着我的两支烛光，光芒四射。这里的岩石里含有什么，是钻石、宝石还是金子，我不得而知。

The place I was in was a most delightful grotto[1] of its kind, though perfectly dark; the floor was dry and level and had a sort of small loose gravel upon it, neither was there any damp on the sides or roof. The only difficulty in it was the entrance, which, however, as it was a place of security, and such a retreat as I wanted, I thought that was a convenience; so that I was really rejoiced at the discovery, and resolved without any delay to bring some of those things which I was most anxious about to this place; particularly, I resolved to bring hither my magazine of powder, and all my spare arms, viz., two fowling-pieces, for I had three in all; and three muskets, for of them I had eight in all; so I kept at my castle only five, which stood ready mounted like pieces of cannon, on my outmost[2] fence; and were ready also to take out upon any expedition.

Upon this occasion of removing my ammunition, I took occasion to open the barrel of powder which I took up out of the sea and which had been wet; and I found that the water had penetrated about three or four inches into the powder on every side, which caking and growing hard, had preserved the inside like a kernel[3] in a shell; so that I had near sixty pound of very good powder in the center of the cask, and this was an agreeable discovery to me at that time; so I carried all away thither, never keeping above two or three pounds of powder with me in my castle, for fear of a surprise of any kind. I also carried thither all the lead I had belt for bullets.

I was now in my twenty third year of residence in this island, and was so naturalized[4] to the place and to the manner of living that could I have but enjoyed the certainty that no savages would come to the place to disturb me, I could have been content to have capitulated[5] for spending the rest of my time there, even to the last moment, till I had laid me down and died, like the old goat in the cave.

---

[1] grotto   *n.* 洞穴，岩穴，人工洞室
[2] outmost   *adj.* 最外面的，最远的
[3] kernel   *n.* （硬壳果）仁；核心
[4] naturalize   *vt.* 使归化；使加入···国籍
[5] capitulate   *vi.* 有条件投降，认输，停止抵抗

尽管我所在的地方一片漆黑，却是一个非常可爱的洞穴，地面干燥平坦，上面有一种细碎的砂砾。洞壁和洞顶也不潮湿。洞里唯一的困难就是入口。然而，这正是一个安全的地方和我想要的隐退处，所以我认为这是一个有利条件。我对自己的发现真是欣喜万分，马上决定把我最担心的一部分东西搬到这个地方，尤其是决定把我的火药库和所有备用的武器——也就是两支鸟枪（因为我共有三支）和三支火铳（因为我共有八支）——搬到这里。于是，我在城堡里只留下五支，像大炮一样架在外墙上，作战需要时也可以随时拿下来。

　　在这次转移弹药时，我顺便打开了从海上捞起来的那桶受潮的火药，发现水渗进火药四周大约三、四英寸，结成了一层硬块，保护着里面的火药，就像果壳里的仁似的。所以，我从木桶中央搞到了差不多 60 磅上好的火药，这在当时对我来说是一个可喜的发现。于是，我统统搬到了洞里，在城堡里放的火药绝不超过两三磅，惟恐发生什么意外。我还把做子弹的铅也都搬了过去。

　　我现在在岛上已经住了 23 年，而且对这个地方和这种生活方式已经习以为常了。如果能肯定没有野人到这个地方打搅我，我会心甘情愿在此度过余生，直到生命的最后一刻，就像洞里的那只老山羊那样躺下死去。

I had also arrived to some little diversions[1] and amusements, which made the time pass more pleasantly with me a great deal, than it did before; as first, I had taught my Poll, as I noted before, to speak; and he lived with me no less than six and twenty years. How long he might live afterwards, I know not. My dog was a very pleasant and loving companion to me for no less than sixteen years of my time and then died of mere old age; as for my cats, they multiplied so excessively that I was obliged to shoot several of them at first, to keep them from devouring me and all I had; but at length, when the two old ones I brought with me were gone, and after some time continually driving them from me and letting them have no provision with me, they all ran wild into the woods, except two or three favourites, which I kept tame. Besides these, I always kept two or three household kids about me, who I taught to feed out of my hand; and I had two more parrots which talked pretty well and would all call "Robin Crusoe"; but none like my first. I had also several tame seafowls[2], whose names I know not, who I caught upon the shore and cut their wings; and the little stakes which I had planted before my castle wall being now grown up to a good thick grove, these fowls all lived among these low trees and bred there, which was very agreeable to me; so that as I said above, I began to be very well contented with the life I led, if it might but have been secured from the dread of the savages.

It was now the month of December; and this being the southern solstice[3], for winter I cannot call it, was the particular time of my harvest and required my being pretty much abroad in the fields; when going out pretty early in the morning, even before it was thorough daylight, I was surprised with seeing a light of some fire upon the shore, at a distance from me, of about two mile towards the end of the island, where I had observed some savages had been as before; but not on the other side; but to my great affliction, it was on my side of the island.

---

[1] diversion   *n.* 转移；解闷，娱乐
[2] seafowl   *n.* (=seabird)海鸟
[3] solstice   *n.* 至，至日，至点

同时，我还想出了一些小小的消遣和娱乐，这使我打发起时间来比以前愉快多了。首先，我前面也提到过，教会了鹦鹉波尔说话。它和我一起生活了不下 26 年。我不知道它后来又活了多久。我的狗也是一个友善可爱的伴侣，跟了我不下 16 年，后来老死了。至于我那些猫，由于它们繁殖太多，我不得不开枪先打死了好几只，免得它们把我所有的东西都吃光。但最后，我从船上带下来的两只老猫都死了。过了一段时间，我又不断驱逐那些小猫，不给它们吃东西，结果它们都跑进树林，变成了野猫。只有两三只我最喜欢的小猫，我驯养了起来。此外，我身边总是养两三只小山羊，教会它们在我手里吃东西。我还养了两只鹦鹉，它们说得相当好，都会叫鲁滨·克鲁索，但都比不上第一只。我还养了几只海鸟，我不知道它们的名字。我在海边抓住了它们，剪去了翅膀。我以前在城堡围墙外打下去的那些小树桩现在已长成了一片浓密的小树林。这些鸟都栖息在矮树丛中，并生出了小鸟，这在我看来非常惬意。所以，正如我前面所说，只要能不担心那些野人的袭击，我对自己的这种生活渐渐感到心满意足。

　　现在是 12 月冬至。这里的 12 月根本不能称为冬天，这是我收获的特殊时节，需要我经常出门到田里去。一天清晨，天还没有完全亮，我就出门了。突然，我吃惊地看到小岛尽头的海岸上有一片火光，那里离我大约有两英里远。我以前曾看到一些野人到过那里。但让我大为痛苦的是，火光不是在岛那边，而是在我这边。

I was indeed terribly surprised at the sight and stepped short within my grove, not daring to go out, lest I might be surprised; and yet I had no more peace within, from the apprehensions I had that if these savages in rambling over the island, should find my corn standing, or cut, or any of my works and improvements, they would immediately conclude that there were people in the place and would then never give over till they had found me out. In this extremity[1] I went back directly to my castle, pulled up the ladder after me, and made all things without look as wild and natural as I could.

Then I prepared myself within, putting myself in a posture of defence; I loaded all my muskets and all my pistols, and resolved to defend myself to the last gasp and earnestly prayed to God to deliver me out of the hands of the barbarians; and in this posture I continued about two hours; but began to be mighty impatient for intelligence abroad.

After sitting a while longer, and musing what I should do in this case, I was not able to bear sitting in ignorance any longer; so setting up my ladder to the side of the hill where there was a flat place and then pulling the ladder up after me, I set it up again, and mounted to the top of the hill; and pulling out my perspective glass, which I had taken on purpose, I laid me down flat on my belly on the ground, and began to look for the place; I presently found there was no less than nine naked savages, sitting round a small fire they had made, not to warm them; for they had no need of that, the weather being extreme hot.

They had two canoes with them, which they had haled up upon the shore; and as it was then tide of ebb, they seemed to me to wait for the return of the flood to go away again; it is not easy to imagine what confusion this sight put me into, especially seeing them come on my side the island, and so near me too; but when I observed their coming must be always with the current of the ebb, I began afterwards to be more sedate in my mind, being satisfied that I might go abroad with safety all the time of the tide of flood, if they were not on shore before. And having made this observation, I went abroad about my harvest work with the more composure[2].

---

[1] extremity   *n.* 末端；穷困，绝境
[2] composure   *n.* 镇静，沉着

看到这个情景，我确实大吃一惊，马上在小树林里停住脚步，不敢再往外走，惟恐自己受到突然袭击。然而，我心里怎么也无法平静，因为我怕这些野人万一在岛上走动，发现我的庄稼有些已经收割，有些还没有收割，或者发现我的生活设施，他们马上会断定岛上有人，那他们不找到我是绝不会罢休的。在这危机关头，我马上跑回城堡，收起梯子，并把围墙外的所有东西尽可能都弄成荒芜自然的样子。

随后，我在城堡内做好了防御袭击的准备，把所有的火铳和手枪都装好了弹药，决心自卫到最后一口气，同时郑重其事地祈求上帝把我从那些野人的手里拯救出来。我以这种心情持续了大约两小时，就开始急不可耐地想知道外面的消息。

我又坐了一会儿，沉思着自己在这种情况下该怎么办。最后，我再也无法忍受这样一无所知地坐下去了。于是，我把梯子靠在山边的平地上，然后再把梯子抽上来靠在山坡上，登上山顶。我匍匐在地，掏出特意带在身边的望远镜，开始寻找那个地方。我马上发现那里有不下九个赤身裸体的野人，围坐在一小堆火边。他们生火不是为了取暖，因为天气很热，他们根本不需要。

他们有两只独木舟，已经拖到了岸上。那时正好退潮，在我看来他们好像要等潮水回来后再走。难以想像这情景使我陷入了多么慌乱的境地；尤其是看到他们到了我这边的小岛，而且还离我这么近。但当我后来注意到他们总是必须在退潮时过来，才开始安下心来。只要他们没有先上岸，我相信我在涨潮期间外出就平安无事。既然观察到这一点，我就可以更加从容地外出收获庄稼了。

As I expected, so it proved; for as soon as the tide made to the westward, I saw them all take boat, and row all away. Before they went off, they went to dancing for an hour and more, and I could easily discern their postures and gestures by my glasses. But whether they were men or women, that I could not distinguish.

As soon as I saw them shipped and gone, I took two guns upon my shoulders and two pistols at my girdle[1] and my great sword by my side, without a scabbard[2], and with all the speed I was able to make, I went away to the hill, where I had discovered the first appearance of all; and as soon as I gat thither, which was not less than two hours (for I could not go apace, being so loaden with arms as I was) I perceived there had been three canoes more of savages on that place; and looking out farther, I saw they were all at sea together, making over for the main.

This was a dreadful sight to me, especially when going down to the shore, I could see the marks of horror, which the dismal work they had been about had left behind it, viz., the blood, the bones, and part of the flesh of human bodies, eaten and devoured by those wretches, with merriment[3] and sport. I was so filled with indignation at the sight that I began now to premeditate[4] the destruction of the next that I saw there, let them be who or how many soever.

It seemed evident to me that the visits which they thus make to this island are not very frequent; for it was above fifteen months before any more of them came on shore there again. As to the rainy seasons, they are sure not to come abroad, at least not so far; yet all this while I lived uncomfortably, by reason of the constant apprehensions I was in of their coming upon me by surprise.

---

[1] girdle *n.* 带，腰带
[2] scabbard *n.* 鞘
[3] merriment *n.* 欢喜，嬉戏
[4] premeditate *v.* 预谋，预先考虑

果然不出所料。因为当潮水一开始西流，我就看到他们都上船划桨而去。在离开前，他们还跳了一个多小时的舞。通过望远镜，我可以轻松地看到他们手舞足蹈的样子。然而，是男是女，我辨别不出来。

一见他们上船离去，我就肩扛两支枪，腰带上别了两把手枪，身边挎了一把无鞘长剑，尽可能快地向那座小山跑去，我就是在那里第一次发现了野人的踪迹。我用了至少两小时才到达那里，因为我带了那么多武器，不可能走得再快了。我一到那里就看到那个地方还有三只独木舟。再向远处望去，只见他们都聚到了海上，朝大陆方向驶去。

在我看来，这是一个可怕的景象，尤其是我下山走到岸边时，可以看到那一处处恐怖的痕迹，那是他们饕餮宴会后留下的可怕痕迹，也就是，那些坏蛋一边狼吞虎咽、一边寻欢作乐留下的血迹、人骨和部分人肉。见此情景，我义愤填膺，就马上开始盘算起来，下次再见到他们，不管他们是谁，也不管他们来多少人，我都要把他们消灭。

显然，在我看来，他们好像并不是经常到岛上来，因为他们 15 个多月后才又在那里上岸。至于雨季，他们肯定不会出门，至少不会跑这么远。然而，所有这段时间，我却生活得并不舒心，因为我不时担心他们会对我突然袭击。

XIX

I spent my days now in great perplexity and anxiety of mind, expecting that I should one day or other fall into the hands of these merciless creatures; and if I did at any time venture abroad, it was not without looking round me with the greatest care and caution imaginable.

However, I wore out a year and three months more before I ever saw any more of the savages. It is true they might have been there once or twice; but either they made no stay, or at least I did not hear them; but in the month of May in my four and twentieth year, I had a very strange encounter with them.

On the sixteenth day of May, it blew a very great storm of wind all day, with a great deal of lightning and thunder, and a very foul night it was after it; I know not what was the particular occasion of it; but as I was reading in the Bible, and taken up with very serious thoughts about my present condition, I was surprised with a noise of a gun, as I thought, fired at sea.

I started up in the greatest haste imaginable, and in a trice clapped my ladder to the middle place of the rock, and pulled it after me, and mounting it the second time, got to the top of the hill the very moment that a flash of fire bid me listen for a second gun, which accordingly, in about half a minute I heard; and by the sound, knew that it was from that part of the sea where I was driven down the current in my boat.

I immediately considered that this must be some ship in distress, and that they had or some other ship in company, and fired these guns for signals of distress, and to obtain help. I had this presence of mind at that minute, as to think that though I could not help them, it may be they might help me; so I brought together all the dry wood I could get at hand, and making a good handsome pile, I set it on fire upon the hill; the wood was dry and blazed freely; and though the wind blew very hard, yet it burnt fairly out; that I was certain, if there was any such thing as a ship, they must needs see it, and no doubt they did; for as soon as ever my fire blazed up, I heard another gun, and after that several others, all from the same quarter; I plied my fire all night long, till day broke.

19

我现在每天都生活在巨大的困惑和焦虑之中，料想着自己总有一天会落入这些残酷无情的人手里。就是什么时候冒险外出，我也总是尽可能小心翼翼左顾右盼。

然而，过了一年零三个多月，我才又见到了野人。他们确实可能到过那里一两次。但他们要么没有在岛上逗留，要么至少我没有听到他们的动静。但到了在岛上生活的第 24 年的 5 月，我和他们发生了一次非常奇特的遭遇。

5 月 16 日，整整一天都风雨大作、电闪雷鸣，而且直到夜里，仍是风雨交加。我不知道这是一个什么样的特殊日子，但当我正在读《圣经》，认真考虑自己当前的处境时，突然吃惊地听到一声枪响，我想是从海上打的枪。

我尽可能快地一跃而起，转眼间就把梯子靠在岩石中央，然后把梯子抽上去靠在那里，又登上去，爬到了山顶。就在此时，我看见火光一闪，明白第二枪又要响了。于是，半分钟后，我便听到了枪声。从声音，我知道枪声是从我上次坐船被急流冲走的那一带海上传来的。

我马上想到，这一定是有船遇险了，而且他们有其他船同行，就开枪发出了遇险信号，想获得帮助。此时此刻，我非常镇定，我想，尽管我无法帮助他们，但也许他们能帮助我。于是，我把附近所有的干柴都收集到一块，堆成一大堆，在山上点起了火。木柴干燥，火熊熊燃烧了起来。尽管风刮得很大，火还是相当旺。我确信，如果海上真有这样一只船，他们一定会看得见，而且他们确实看到了。因为我的火一燃烧起来，我就又听到了一声枪响，随后又是好几声枪响，都是从同一个方向传来的。我把火整整烧了一夜，一直烧到了天亮。

And when it was broad day, and the air cleared up, I saw something at a great distance at sea, full east of the island, whether a sail or a hull I could not distinguish, no, not with my glasses, the distance was so great, and the weather still something hazy also; at least it was so out at sea.

I looked frequently at it all that day, and soon perceived that it did not move; so I presently concluded that it was a ship at an anchor. I took my gun in my hand, and ran toward the south side of the island, to the rocks where I had formerly been carried away with the current, and getting up there, the weather by this time being perfectly clear, I could plainly see the wreck of a ship cast away in the night upon those concealed rocks which I found when I was out in my boat; and which rocks, as they checked the violence of the stream, and made a kind of eddy, were the occasion of my recovering from the most desperate hopeless condition.

It seems these men, being out of their knowledge, and the rocks being wholly under water, had been driven upon them in the night, the wind blowing hard at east and east-northeast. Had they seen the island, as I must necessarily suppose they did not, they must, as I thought, have endeavoured to have saved themselves on shore by the help of their boat; but their firing of guns for help, especially when they saw my fire, filled me with many thoughts. First, I imagined that upon seeing my light, they might have put themselves into their boat and have endeavoured to make the shore; but that the sea going very high, they might have been cast away; other times I imagined that they might have lost their boat before. Other times I imagined they had some other ship, or ships in company, who upon the signals of distress they had made, had taken them up, and carried them off. Other whiles I fancied they were all gone off to sea in their boat, and being hurried away by the current that I had been formerly in, were carried out into the great ocean.

I cannot explain by any possible energy of words what a strange longing or hankering[1] of desires I felt in my soul upon this sight, breaking out sometimes thus, "O that there had been but one or two; nay, or but one soul saved out of this ship, to have escaped to me, that I might but have had one companion, one fellow-creature to have spoken to me, and to have conversed with!" In all the time of my solitary life I never felt so earnest, so strong a desire after the society of my fellow-creatures, or so deep a regret at the want of it.

---

[1] hankering *n.* 渴望

214

天光大亮后，空气渐渐清朗。我看到，小岛正东方向很远处的海面上有什么东西，是帆还是船体，我分辨不清。我用望远镜也无济于事，因为距离太远，而且天气还是雾蒙蒙的；至少海面上是这样。

　　整整一天，我都经常望着那个东西，不久便发现它一动不动。于是，我马上断定，那是一条抛锚的大船。我拿起枪，朝岛南边跑去，跑到了我上次被急流冲走的那些岩石边。到了那里，天气此时已经完全放晴。我可以清楚地看到有一条大船夜里撞在暗礁上失事了。我上次驾船出游时，就发现了那些暗礁。正是那些暗礁挡住了汹涌的急流，形成了一股涡流，使我从那次最绝望的境地得以死里逃生。

　　这些人因不熟悉地形，那些暗礁又都在水下，昨晚的东北风刮得很大，所以船撞上了暗礁。如果他们看到这个小岛，我想他们一定会用船上的救生艇竭尽全力划到岸上来。不过，我想他们肯定没有看到小岛，而是鸣枪求救，尤其是他们看到我燃起的火光后。这使我充满了种种想法。首先，我想到他们看到我点燃的火光后，也许会下到救生艇里拼命向岸上划，但由于风大浪高，他们也许会被冲走。一会儿我又想，也许他们已经失去了救生艇。一会儿我又想，也许和他们同行的船看到他们发出遇险的信号后，已经把他们救起来带走了。一会儿我又想，他们都坐上救生艇出海去了，然后遇到了我上次自己碰上的那股急流，被冲进了汪洋大海。

　　看到这情景，我无法用语言来解释灵魂深处的一种莫名其妙的渴望，有时就这样脱口喊道：“噢，哪怕只有一两个人，不，就一个人能从船上得救，逃到我这里，我就有一个人作伴，就有一个人跟我说话，跟我交谈了啊！”在所有孤独的生活中，我从来没有这样坚决认真、这样强烈渴望和人交往，也从来没有这样深切感到没有伴侣的懊悔。

But till the last year of my being on this island, I never knew whether any were saved out of that ship or no; and had only the affliction some days after to see the corpse of a drowned boy come on shore at the end of the island which was next the shipwreck. He had on no clothes but a seaman's waistcoat, a pair of open-kneed linen drawers and a blue linen shirt; but nothing to direct me so much as to guess what nation he was of. He had nothing in his pocket but two pieces of eight and a tobacco pipe; the last was to me of ten times more value than the first.

It was now calm, and I had a great mind to venture out in my boat to this wreck; not doubting but I might find something on board that might be useful to me; but that did not altogether press me so much as the possibility that there might be yet some living creature on board, whose life I might not only save, but might, by saving that life, comfort my own to the last degree; and this thought clung so to my heart that I could not be quiet night or day, but I must venture out in my boat on board this wreck. The impression was so strong upon my mind that it could not be resisted.

Under the power of this impression, I hastened back to my castle, prepared everything for my voyage. And thus loading myself with everything necessary, I went down to my boat, got the water out of her, and got her afloat, loaded all my cargo in her. I rowed the canoe along the shore, at last to the utmost point of the island on that side, viz., northeast. And now I was to launch out into the ocean. I looked on the rapid currents which ran constantly on both sides of the island at a distance, and which were very terrible to me, from the remembrance of the hazard I had been in before, and my heart began to fail me; for I foresaw that if I was driven into either of those currents, I should be carried a vast way out to sea, and perhaps out of my reach, or sight of the island again; and that then, as my boat was but small, if any little gale of wind should rise, I should be inevitably lost.

These thoughts so oppressed my mind that I began to give over my enterprise, and having haled my boat into a little creek on the shore, I stepped out and sat me down upon a little rising bit of ground, very pensive and anxious, between fear and desire, about my voyage; when as I was musing, I could perceive that the tide was turned and the flood came on, upon which my going was for so many hours impracticable[1].

---

[1] impracticable   *adj.* 不可行的

但直到我在岛上的最后一年，也不知道那条船上有没有人得救。更不幸的是，几天后，我在靠近失事船的岛那端看到了一个淹死的小伙子的尸体冲到了岸边。他只穿了一件水手背心、一件亚麻蓝衬衣和一条开膝亚麻衬裤。但我根本无法猜出他是哪国人，他的口袋里只有两枚八里亚尔金币和一只烟斗。在我看来，烟斗的价值比金币要高10倍。

　　这时，风平浪静，我很想冒险坐小船到这个失事船上去。我相信也许会在船上找到一些对我可能有用的东西。但更使我要上那只船的是我希望船上可能还会有活人。这样，我不仅可以救他的命，而且如果我能救他的命，对我将是极大的安慰。这个想法紧紧地抓住我的心，所以我日夜不宁，我必须乘小船出去，到那条破船上看看。这种想法是那样强烈，所以我无法抗拒。

　　在这种想法的影响下，我匆匆跑回城堡，为出航准备所有的一切。随后，我把一切必需品都背在身上，走到小船边，先弄干船里的水，让船浮起来，接着把所有东西都放进船里。我沿海岸划着独木舟，最后划到了小岛最远处那边，也就是东北角。现在，我要把独木舟驶入大洋里去。我遥望着远处海岛两边奔腾不息的两股急流，回想起先前遭到的危险，感到非常可怕，开始丧失了信心。因为我预见到，只要我被卷入那两股急流中的任何一股，小船一定会被冲进外海。也许我就再也回不到小岛，再也看不到小岛了。到时候，我的船这么小，只要稍微起一阵风，我肯定会丧命。

　　这些念头压迫着我的思想，所以我开始放弃了自己的计划。我把小船拉进沿岸的一条小河后，迈步上岸，在一块小小的高地上坐下来，对这次航行沉思冥想、心事重重，一方面害怕前进，一方面又充满想望。我正在沉思冥想时，察觉到潮流发生了变化，潮水开始上涨，这样我好几个小时都走不了了。

Upon this presently it occurred to me that I should go up to the highest piece of ground I could find, and observe, if I could, how the sets of the currents lay, when the flood came in, that I might judge whether, if I was driven one way out, I might not expect to be driven another way home, with the same rapidness of the currents. This thought was no sooner in my head but I cast my eye upon a little hill which sufficiently overlooked the sea both ways and from whence I had a clear view of the currents; here I found that as the current of the ebb set out close by the south point of the island; so the current of the flood set in close by the shore of the north side, and that I had nothing to do but to keep to the north of the island in my return, and I should do well enough.

Encouraged with this observation, I resolved the next morning to set out with the first of the tide; and reposing myself for the night in the canoe, under the great watch-coat, I launched out. I made first a little out to sea full north, till I began to feel the benefit of the current, which set eastward and which carried me at a great rate, and yet did not so hurry me as the southern side current had done before, so I went at a great rate, directly for the wreck, and in less than two hours I came up to it.

It was a dismal sight to look at. The ship, which by its building was Spanish, stuck fast, jammed in between two rocks; all the stern and quarter of her was beaten to pieces with the sea; and as her forecastle[1], which stuck in the rocks, had run on with great violence, her mainmast and foremast were broken short off; but her bowsprit[2] was sound, and the head and bow appeared firm; when I came close to her, a dog appeared upon her, who seeing me coming, yelped and cried; and as soon as I called him, he jumped into the sea, to come to me, and I took him into the boat; but found him almost dead for hunger and thirst. I gave him a cake of my bread, and he ate it like a ravenous[3] wolf, that had been starving a fortnight[4] in the snow. I then gave the poor creature some fresh water.

---

[1] forecastle   *n.* 前甲板，船头的船楼
[2] bowsprit   *n.* 船首斜桅
[3] ravenous   *adj.* 贪婪的，渴望的，狼吞虎咽的
[4] fortnight   *n.* 两星期

这时，我突然想到，应该尽可能找一个最高的地方，上去观察一下，看潮水上涨时那两股急流的流向，我就可以判断出，如果我被一股急流冲入大海，是不是有可能被另一股急流冲回来。我刚想到这一点，就看到了一座小山。我从山上完全可以看到两边的海面，而且对两股急流的流向一目了然。到了山上，我发现退潮的急流是沿着小岛南部朝外流，涨潮的急流是沿着小岛北部向里流。这样，我回来时，只要贴着北部航行，就可以了。

这次观察使我大受鼓舞，我决定第二天早上乘第一次潮流出发。我把水手值更大衣盖在身上，在独木舟里睡了一夜后，就划船出发了。我一出海，就朝正北驶去，直至我开始得益于那股急流，那股急流向东奔流；小船在急流中飞速行驶，但流速没有上次岛南边那股急流那么大，所以我径直朝失事船飞驶而去。不到两小时，我就来到了破船边。

眼前的景象一片狼藉。从那条船的结构看，这是一条西班牙船，船身卡在两块礁石之间，夹得很紧。船尾和后舱都被海浪击得粉碎。夹在礁石中间的前舱因受到猛烈撞击，主桅和前桅都被折断，但船首斜桅完好无损，船头似乎非常坚固。当我靠近破船时，船上出现了一条狗。它见我驶来，就汪汪吠叫起来。我一喊它，它就跳进海里，游到我身边。我把它拽进小船里。它又饿又渴，快要死了。我给了它一块面包，它就像一只在雪地里一直饿了两周的狼一样吃了起来。随后，我又给这条可怜的狗喝了一些淡水。

After this I went on board; but the first sight. I met with was two men drowned, in the cook-room, or forecastle of the ship, with their arms fast about one another. I concluded, as is indeed probable, that when the ship struck, it being in a storm, the sea broke so high and so continually over her that the men were not able to bear it, and were strangled with the constant rushing in of the water, as much as if they had been under water.

Besides the dog, there was nothing left in the ship that had life; nor any goods that I could see but what were spoiled by the water. There were some casks of liquor, whether wine or brandy, I knew not, which lay lower in the hold; and which, the water being ebbed out, I could see; but they were too big to meddle with. I saw several chests; and I got two of them into the boat, without examining what was in them.

Had the stern of the ship been fixed, and the forepart[1] broken off, I am persuaded I might have made a good voyage; for by what I found in these two chests, I had room to suppose the ship had a great deal of wealth on board; and if I may guess by the course she steered, she must have been bound from the Buenos Ayres, or the Rio de la Plata, in the south part of America, beyond Brazil, to Havana, in the Gulf of Mexico, and so perhaps to Spain. She had no doubt a great treasure in her; but of no use at that time to anybody; and what became of the rest of her people, I then knew not.

I found, besides these chests, a little cask full of liquor, of about twenty gallons, which I got into my boat, with much difficulty; there were several muskets in a cabin and a great powder-horn, with about four pounds of powder in it; as for the muskets, I had no occasion for them; so I left them, but took the powder-horn. I took a fire shovel and tongs[2], which I wanted extremely; as also two little brass kettles, a copper pot to make chocolate, and a gridiron[3]; with this cargo and the dog I came away, the tide beginning to make home again; and the same evening, about an hour within night, I reached the island again.

---

[1] forepart *n.* 早期；最前部
[2] tongs *n.* 钳子，夹具
[3] gridiron *n.* 烤架，格状物

之后，我就上了大船，但我第一眼看到的是两个淹死的人，他们相互紧紧抱在一起，躺在前舱的厨房里。我推断，很有可能，船触礁时，又遇到了风暴，海浪不断打在船上，船上的人活像被埋在水下一样，实在无法忍受，窒息而死。

　　除了那条狗，船上没有剩下有生命的东西，我能看到的货物也都被海水泡坏了。船舱底部还有几桶酒，我不知道是葡萄酒还是白兰地，因海水退去，我可以看到，那些酒桶很大，我搬不动。我还看见了几只箱子。我把其中两只搬进了自己的小船，没有检查里面是什么东西。

　　如果是船尾触礁、船首撞碎，我相信我可能不虚此行，因为从两只箱子里发现的东西来看，我有理由认为，船上有很多财富。从这条船所走的航线，我可以猜出，它一定是从美洲南部地区巴西那边的布宜诺斯艾利斯或拉普拉塔河出发，开往墨西哥湾的哈瓦那，然后也许再从那里驶向西班牙。船上肯定会有大量财宝，但这些财宝此时对任何人都毫无用处。船上的其他人发生了什么情况，我当时也不知道。

　　除了这些箱子，我还找到了满满一小桶酒，大约有 20 加仑。我费了好大劲儿才把酒桶搬进小船。船舱里还有几支火铳和一只大火药角筒，里面大约有四磅火药。至于那些火铳，我用不上它们，就留了下来，只拿了火药角筒。我还拿了一把火炉铲和一把火钳，因为我特别需要它们。我又拿了两只小铜壶、一只做巧克力的铜锅和一个烤架。刚好这时潮水又开始往回流，我就带着这货物和那只狗离开了。当天晚上，天黑后大约不到一小时，我就到达了小岛。

I reposed that night in the boat, and in the morning I resolved to harbour what I had gotten in my new cave, not to carry it home to my castle. After refreshing myself, I got all my cargo on shore, and began to examine the particulars. The cask of liquor I found to be a kind of rum, but not such as we had in Brazil; and in a word, not at all good; but when I came to open the chests, I found several things of great use to me. For example, I found in one a fine case of bottles, of an extraordinary kind and filled with cordial[1] waters, fine and very good; the bottles held about three pints each and were tipped with silver. I found two pots of very good succades[2], so fastened also on top that the salt water had not hurt them; and two more of the same, which the water had spoiled. I found some very good shirts, which were very welcome to me; and about a dozen and half of linen white handkerchiefs, and coloured neckcloths; the former were also very welcome, being exceeding refreshing to wipe my face in a hot day; besides this, when I came to the till in the chest, I found there three great bags of pieces of eight, which held about eleven hundred pieces in all; and in one of them, wrapped up in a paper, six doubloons[3] of gold and some small bars of gold; I suppose they might all weigh near a pound.

The other chest I found had some clothes in it, but of little value; but by the circumstances it must have belonged to the gunner's mate. Upon the whole, I got very little by this voyage, that was of any use to me; for as to the money, I would have given it all for three or four pair of English shoes and stockings, which were things I greatly wanted, but had not had on my feet now for many years. I had indeed gotten two pair of shoes now, which I took off of the feet of the two drowned men, who I saw in the wreck; and I found two pair more in one of the chests; but they were not like our English shoes, either for ease or service. I found in this seaman's chest, about fifty pieces of eight in royals, but no gold.

However, I lugged[4] this money home to my cave, and laid it up as I had done that before.

---

[1] cordial   adj. 热忱的，诚恳的，兴奋的
[2] succade   n. 蜜饯
[3] doubloon   n. 从前西班牙金币的名称
[4] lug   vt. 使劲拉，用力拖

我在小船上睡了一夜。第二天早上，我决定把运回来的东西都藏到新发现的地洞里，而不是带到城堡里去。我吃了些东西后，把所有的货物都搬上岸，并开始仔细查看。我发现搬回来的那桶酒是一种朗姆酒，但与我们在巴西时的朗姆酒不一样，总之一点儿都不好喝。但我最终打开那两只大箱子时，找到了好几样对我非常有用的东西。比如，我在一只箱子里发现了一只精致的小酒箱，里面的酒瓶非常别致，装满了上等的提神酒，每瓶装大约三品脱，瓶口上包着一层银。我还发现两罐上好的蜜饯，因为封口很紧，所以海水没有泡坏它们。还有两罐蜜饯已经被海水泡坏了。我又找到一些很好的衬衫，这我非常欢迎。还有大约一打半亚麻白手帕和彩色围巾。亚麻手帕我也非常欢迎，热天拿来擦脸特别凉爽。此外，我检查到箱子里的钱匣时，发现有三大袋八里亚尔银币，总共有 1100 枚左右，其中一袋里有六枚西班牙金币和一些小金条，都裹在纸里，我想可能有差不多一磅重。

　　我在另一只大箱子里找到了一些衣服，但价值不大。看样子，这只箱子是属于船上副炮手的。总之，我这次出海弄到的东西有用的寥寥无几。至于那些钱，我愿意用来换三、四双英国鞋子和长袜，因为这些都是我非常需要的东西，我已经好多年没有穿过鞋袜了。我现在确实弄到了两双鞋，那是我从遇难船上见到的两个淹死的水手的脚上脱下来的。我还在一只大箱子里找到两双鞋。可是，这两双鞋都没有英国鞋子舒适耐穿。在这个船员的箱子里，我又找到了大约 50 枚八里亚尔银币，但没有金币。

　　不过，我还是把这钱搬回了洞里，像以前一样存好。

Having now brought all my things on shore and secured them, I went back to my boat and rowed her along the shore to her old harbour, where I laid her up, and made the best of my way to my old habitation, where I found everything safe and quiet; so I began to repose myself, live after my old fashion, and take care of my family affairs; and for a while, I lived easy enough; only that I was more vigilant than I used to be, looked out oftener and did not go abroad so much; and if at any time I did stir with any freedom, it was always to the east part of the island, where I was pretty well satisfied the savages never came, and where I could go without so many precautions and such a load of arms and ammunition as I always carried with me if I went the other way.

我把所有东西运到岸上妥善保管好后，回到小船上，沿着海岸划到原来的港口，把船停好，然后尽可能快地回到了老住所。到了那里，我发现一切都平安无事，就开始休息，像过去一样生活，照看家务。而且，有一阵子，我过得悠闲自在，只是比以前更加警惕，经常注意外面的动静，也不大外出。如果我什么时候确实要到外面自由活动，也总是到小岛东部去，因为我确信野人从未到过那里，我去那里可以不用那么多防范措施，也用不着带那么多武器弹药。如果到另一个方向去，总要随身带很多。

XX

I lived in this condition near two years more; but my head was all this two years filled with projects and designs how I might get away from this island; for sometimes I was for making another voyage to the wreck, though my reason told me that there was nothing left there worth the hazard of my voyage. Sometimes for a ramble one way, sometimes another; and I believe verily[1], if I had had the boat that I went from Sallee in, I should have ventured to sea, bound anywhere, I knew not whither.

I am now to be supposed retired into my castle, after my late voyage to the wreck, my frigate laid up and secured under water, as usual, and my condition restored to what it was before. I had more wealth indeed than I had before, but was not at all the richer; for I had no more use for it.

It was one of the nights in the rainy season in March, the four and twentieth year of my first setting foot in this island of solitariness; I was lying in my hammock awake. I came to reflect seriously upon the real danger I had been in, for so many years, in this very island.

My head was for some time taken up in considering the nature of these wretched creatures, I mean the savages; and how it came to pass in the world that the wise Governor of all things should give up any of His creatures to such inhumanity; but as this ended in some (at that time fruitless) speculations, it occurred to me to enquire what part of the world these wretches lived in; how far off the coast was from whence they came; what they ventured over so far from home for; what kind of boats they had; and why I might not order myself and my business so that I might be as able to go over thither as they were to come to me.

---

[1] verily   *adv.* 实在，真正地，肯定地

20

我在这种情况下又过了将近两年，但这两年来，我的头脑里充满了各种可能逃离小岛的计划和方案。有时，我还想再到那条破船上去一趟，尽管理智告诉我，船上没有留下什么值得我再次冒险出海的东西了。有时，我又想乘小船来回走走。我坚信，如果现在有我从萨利逃出来时坐的那条小船，我早就冒险出海，信马由缰，不知去向了。

最近从破船回来后，我应该说现在一直隐居在城堡里。我像往常一样把独木舟妥善沉入水下，恢复了以前那种生活状态。尽管我现在比以前更有钱了，但一点儿也不富有，因为金钱对我毫无用处。

我踏上这座孤岛已经 24 年了。现在是三月的雨季。一天夜里，我醒着躺在吊床上，认真考虑起了这么多年来自己在这座岛上面临的危险。

一时间，我又想到了这些坏蛋——我是说那些野人——的天性，主宰万物的英明上帝怎么会容忍自己的生灵沦落到这样没有人性的地步，但我想来想去，当时也不得其解。于是，我又想到另一些问题：这些坏蛋住在什么地方，他们来的地方离海岸有多远，他们冒险走这么远来干什么，他们乘的是哪一种船，既然他们能到我这边来，我为什么不能收拾一下到他们那边去呢。

I never so much as troubled myself to consider what I should do with myself when I came thither; what would become of me if I fell into the hands of the savages; or how I should escape from them if they attempted me. My mind was wholly bent upon the notion of my passing over in my boat to the mainland; that if I reached the shore of the main, I might perhaps meet with relief, or I might coast along, as I did on the shore of Africa, till I came to some inhabited country, and where I might find some relief.

When this had agitated my thoughts for two hours or more, with such violence that it set my very blood into a ferment[1], and my pulse beat as high as if I had been in a fever, merely with the extraordinary fervour of my mind about it, Nature, as if I had been fatigued and exhausted with the very thought of it, threw me into a sound sleep; one would have thought I should have dreamed of it. But I did not, nor of anything relating to it; but I dreamed that as I was going out in the morning as usual from my castle, I saw upon the shore two canoes and eleven savages coming to land, and that they brought with them another savage, who they were going to kill, in order to eat him; when on a sudden the savage that they were going to kill jumped away and ran for his life; and I thought in my sleep that he came running into my little thick grove[2], before my fortification, to hide himself; and that I, seeing him alone and not perceiving that the other sought him that way, showed myself to him, and smiling upon him, encouraged him; that he knelt down to me, seeming to pray me to assist him; upon which I showed my ladder, made him go up, and carried him into my cave, and he became my servant; and that as soon as I had gotten this man, I said to myself, "Now I may certainly venture to the mainland; for this fellow will serve me as a pilot, and will tell me what to do, and whither to go for provisions; and whither not to go for fear of being devoured; what places to venture into, and what to escape." I woke with this thought and was under such inexpressible impressions of joy at the prospect of my escape in my dream that the disappointments which I felt upon coming to myself and finding it was no more than a dream were equally extravagant the other way, and threw me into a very great dejection of spirit.

---

[1] ferment   *n.* 酵素，发酵；动乱
[2] grove   *n.* 小树林

我从来没有费神去考虑过到那边时我该怎么办，如果落入野人手里我会怎么样，也没有考虑过如果他们企图杀害我，我如何逃命。我一门心思想乘小船渡过海峡到大陆上去。我想，只要到达大陆岸边，我就可能遇到救星；要么，我可以像上次在非洲沿岸那样，让小船沿海岸航行，一直驶到有人居住的地方，在那里我可能会找到救星。

　　这让我的思想躁动了两个多小时，是那样猛烈，使我热血沸腾、脉跳加快，好像我得了热病一般，当然这只是我头脑发热。我就这样想啊想，想得筋疲力尽、沉沉睡去。有人会认为我会梦到这种情景。可是，我没有做，也没有做与这有关的梦，而是梦见自己像往常一样早上走出城堡，看到两只独木舟和 11 个野人靠岸登陆；他们还带了一个野人，准备把他杀吃。突然，他们要杀的那个野人跳起来，拼命奔逃。我想他在我的睡梦中很快就跑进城堡前面浓密的小树林躲了起来。我看到他是单独一人，没有看到其他野人朝那条路追来，便向他走去，一边朝他微笑，一边鼓励他。他向我跪倒在地，好像是恳求我帮他。于是，我指了指梯子，让他爬上去，并把他带进我的洞穴。他成了我的仆人。我一得到这个人，就对自己说："现在，我肯定可以冒险到大陆去了，因为这个人一定会做我的领航员，而且会告诉我该怎么做，到哪里搞到食物，哪里不能去，以免被吃掉，什么地方可以放心大胆地去，什么地方应该避开。"我这样想着就醒来了。我对自己梦中有逃脱的希望而高兴得难以言表。而等到我清醒过来，发现这不过是一场梦，这情景同样难以言表，让我万分沮丧。

Upon this, however, I made this conclusion that my only way to go about an attempt for an escape was, if possible, to get a savage into my possession; and if possible, it should be one of their prisoners, who they had condemned to be eaten and should bring thither to kill; but it was impossible to effect this thought without attacking a whole caravan of them and killing them all. My heart trembled at the thoughts of shedding so much blood, though it was for my deliverance.

The eager prevailing desire of deliverance at length mastered all the rest; and I resolved, if possible, to get one of those savages into my hands, cost what it would.

With this resolution in my thoughts, I set myself upon the scout as often as possible, and indeed so often till I was heartily tired of it, for it was above a year and half that I waited, and for great part of that time went out to the west end and to the southwest corner of the island almost every day to see for canoes, but none appeared. This was very discouraging, and began to trouble me much. But the longer it seemed to be delayed, the more eager I was for it; in a word, I was not at first so careful to shun[1] the sight of these savages and avoid being seen by them as I was now eager to be upon them.

Besides, I fancied myself able to manage one, nay, two or three savages, if I had them so as to make them entirely slaves to me, to do whatever I should direct them, and to prevent their being able at any time to do me any hurt. It was a great while that I pleased myself with this affair, but nothing still presented.

---

[1] shun *vt.* 避开，避免

然而，我由此得出了结论：我唯一能力图逃走的办法就是尽可能弄到一个野人；而且，如果可能，应该是一个被他们带来准备杀吃的俘虏。可是，要实现这个想法，不向一大队野人进攻，并把他们杀光，是不可能的事儿。一想到要流那么多血，我的心都颤抖，尽管这样做是为了让自己获救。

　　最后，要求获救的迫切愿望战胜了其他所有的一切。所以，我决定尽可能不惜代价从那些野人手里搞到一个野人。

　　这样决定后，我尽可能经常出去侦察。我一有空就出去，到后来又厌烦起来，因为我一等就是一年半多，差不多每天都要跑到小岛西头和西南角，看看有没有独木舟，但什么也没有出现。这真是让人扫兴，开始让我心烦意乱。但拖延的时间越长，我越迫不及待。总之，我没有像当初那样小心翼翼避开这些野人的视线，以免被他们看到，现在是迫不及待想碰到他们。

　　此外，我认为自己能对付一个野人，不，能对付两三个野人，只要能把他们弄到手，我可以叫他们完全成为我的奴隶，叫他们做什么就做什么，而且可以随时防止他们伤害我。我好一阵子都对这件事沾沾自喜，但还是什么也没有出现。

XXI

About a year and half later, I was surprised one morning early with seeing no less than five canoes all on shore together on my side of the island; and the people who belonged to them all landed, and out of my sight. The number of them broke all my measures, for seeing so many and knowing that they always came four or six, or sometimes more in a boat, I could not tell what to think of, or how to take my measures, to attack twenty or thirty men single-handed; so I lay still in my castle, having waited a good while, listening to hear if they made any noise; at length being very impatient, I set my guns at the foot of my ladder and clambered up to the top of the hill by my two stages as usual; standing so, however, that my head did not appear above the hill, so that they could not perceive me by any means; here I observed by the help of my perspective glass that they were no less than thirty in number, that they had a fire kindled, that they had had meat dressed. They were all dancing in many barbarous gestures and figures, their own way, round the fire.

While I was thus looking on them, I perceived by my perspective two miserable wretches dragged from the boats, where, it seems, they were laid by, and were now brought out for the slaughter[1]. I perceived one of them immediately fell, being knocked down, I suppose, with a club or wooden sword, and two or three others were at work immediately cutting him open for their cookery, while the other victim was left standing by himself, till they should be ready for him. In that very moment this poor wretch seeing himself a little at liberty, Nature inspired him with hopes of life, and he started away from them, and ran with incredible swiftness along the sands directly towards me, I mean towards that part of the coast where my habitation was.

---

[1] slaughter   *n.* 屠宰，残杀，屠杀

21

大约一年半后，一天早晨，我突然看到多达五只独木舟一起在小岛这边靠了岸，船上的人都已经登陆，不见了踪影。他们来的人数打破了我所有的计划，因为我看到这么多船，而且知道一只小船总是坐四到六个人，有时会更多，我不知道该怎么办，也不知道独自一人该采取什么措施进攻二三十个人。所以，我静静地守在城堡里，等了好久，侧耳倾听他们是不是有什么动静。最后，我等得很不耐烦，就把枪都放在梯子脚下，像往常那样分两步爬上小山顶。不过，我站在那里，头没有露出山顶，他们无论如何也不可能看到我。我在这里借助望远镜进行观察，发现他们多达 30 人，已经点起火，烤起了肉。这时，他们正以各种各样的野蛮姿势和独特方式围着火堆手舞足蹈。

我正在这样观望时，从望远镜里察觉到两个可怜的家伙被从小船上拖了出来。看样子，这两个人是被事先放在船上，现在拖上岸准备屠杀的。我发觉其中一个立刻倒了下来，我猜是被木棍或木刀打倒的。接着便又有两三个人马上动手把他开膛破肚，准备烧烤。另一个俘虏被撂在一边，站在那里等他们准备动手。就在此时，这个可怜的家伙看见自己稍微有了点儿自由，不由产生了逃生的希望。他突然从他们身边跑开，以惊人的速度沿着沙滩径直朝我这边奔来。我是说，朝我的住处所在的海岸这一带奔来。

I was dreadfully frightened when I perceived him to run my way; and especially when, as I thought, I saw him pursued by the whole body, and now I expected that part of my dream was coming to pass, and that he would certainly take shelter in my grove; but I could not depend by any means upon my dream for the rest of it, viz., that the other savages would not pursue him thither, and find him there. However, I kept my station, and my spirits began to recover when I found that there was not above three men that followed him; and still more was I encouraged when I found that he outstripped[1] them exceedingly in running, and gained ground of them, so that if he could but hold it for half an hour, I saw easily he would fairly get away from them all.

There was between them and my castle the creek which I mentioned often at the first part of my story, when I landed my cargoes out of the ship; and this I saw plainly he must necessarily swim over, or the poor wretch would be taken there. But when the savage escaping came thither, he made nothing of it, though the tide was then up, but plunging in, swam through in about thirty strokes or thereabouts[2], landed and ran on with exceeding strength and swiftness; when the three persons came to the creek, I found that two of them could swim, but the third could not, and that standing on the other side, he looked at the other, but went no further; and soon after went softly back again.

I observed that the two who swam were yet more than twice as long swimming over the creek as the fellow was that fled from them. It came now upon my thoughts that now was my time to get me a servant, and perhaps a companion, or assistant; I immediately ran down the ladders and fetched my two guns; and getting up again, with the same haste, to the top of the hill, I crossed toward the sea; and having a very short cut, and all down hill, clapped myself in the way between the pursuers and the pursued; hallowing[3] aloud to him that fled, who, looking back, was at first perhaps as much frightened at me as at them; but I beckoned with my hand to him to come back; and in the meantime, I slowly advanced towards the two that followed.

---

[1] outstrip *v.* 超过
[2] thereabouts *adv.* 在那附近，大约
[3] hallow *vt.* 使神圣；视为神圣

我发觉他朝我这边跑来，吓得心惊肉跳，尤其是以为会有一整队人马追赶他的时候。这时，我希望自己的一部分梦境就要实现了，他肯定会在我的小树林里躲起来，可是，梦境里的其余部分我却无论如何也无法相信，也就是说，其他野人不会来追他，也不会发现他躲在树林里。然而，我还是站在原地。当我发现追他的不超过三个人时，又渐渐恢复了勇气。而更让我鼓舞的是，我发现他跑得远远超过追他的那三个人，而且跟他们拉开了距离，只要他能再坚持半小时，我看他就能轻而易举完全逃出他们的手心。

　　在他们和我的城堡之间有一条小河。我在本书开头部分经常提到这条小河，我就是在那里把大船上的货物搬上岸的。我看得一清二楚，这个可怜的家伙一定要游过小河，否则他一定会被抓住。那个野人跑到河边，没有把小河当回事，就纵身跳了下去，尽管此时河水已经上涨。他划了 30 来下，就游过了河。他爬上岸，以惊人的力量和速度继续向前跑。那三个野人追到了河边。我发现其中两个会游泳，另一个不会。他站在对岸，看着其他两个，没有进一步行动。过了一会儿，他便又悄悄回去了。

　　我注意到，那两个会游泳的野人比那逃跑的野人游得慢，用了一倍多长的时间才游过了河。这时，我的脑海里想到，现在正是我要找一个仆人的时候；也许我还能找到一个侣伴或帮手呢。我马上跑下梯子，取来两支枪，然后又迅速爬上梯子，爬到山顶，向海边跑去。我抄了一条近路，跑下山去，马上跑到追踪者和逃跑者之间的路上，向那个逃跑的野人大声呼唤。他回头望了望，起初大概对我就像对追赶他的野人一样胆战心惊，但我招手让他回来，同时慢慢地向追上来的两个野人挺进。

Then rushing at once upon the foremost, I knocked him down with the stock of my piece; I was loath to fire, because I would not have the rest hear; though at that distance, it would not have been easily heard, and being out of sight of the smoke too, they would not have easily known what to make of it. Having knocked this fellow down, the other who pursued with him stopped, as if he had been frightened; and I advanced apace towards him; but as I came nearer, I perceived presently he had a bow and arrow and was fitting it to shoot at me; so I was then necessitated to shoot at him first, which I did, and killed him at the first shoot; the poor savage who fled, but had stopped; though he saw both his enemies fallen and killed, yet was so frightened with the fire and noise of my piece that he stood stock still and neither came forward or went backward, though he seemed rather inclined to fly still than to come on; I hallooed[1] again to him, and made signs to come forward, which he easily understood, and came a little way, then stopped again, and then a little further, and stopped again, and I could then perceive that he stood trembling, as if he had been taken prisoner, and had just been to be killed, as his two enemies were; I beckoned him again to come to me, and gave him all the signs of encouragement that I could think of, and he came nearer and nearer, kneeling down every ten or twelve steps in token of acknowledgement for my saving his life. I smiled at him, and looked pleasantly, and beckoned to him to come still nearer; at length he came close to me, and then he kneeled down again, kissed the ground, and laid his head upon the ground, and taking me by the foot, set my foot upon his head; this it seems was in token of swearing to be my slave for ever; I took him up, and made much of him, and encouraged him all I could. But there was more work to do yet, for I perceived the savage who I knocked down was not killed, but stunned with the blow, and began to come to himself; so I pointed to him, and showing him the savage, that he was not dead; upon this he spoke some words to me, and though I could not understand them, yet I thought they were pleasant to hear, for they were the first sound of a man's voice, that I had heard, my own excepted, for above twenty-five years.

---

[1] halloo *v.* 高呼，高声招呼喊叫

随后，我马上冲向最前面那个人跟前，用枪托把他打倒在地。我之所以不愿意开枪，是因为我不愿意让其余的野人听见，尽管距离这么远，枪声难以听到，而且也看不到硝烟，他们难以弄清是怎么回事。这个野人被打倒后，同他一起追来的那个野人就停住了脚步，好像他被吓住了。于是，我又迅速奔向他。但当离他越来越近时，我马上发觉他手里拿起弓箭正准备拉弓朝我放箭。所以，我当时不得不先向他开枪，一枪就把他打死了。那个逃跑的野人也停住了脚步。尽管他看到两个敌人都已经倒下被杀，但被我的枪火和枪声吓得站在了那里，一动不动，既不前进也不后退，看样子他很想逃跑，而不想走近我。我又向他大声招呼，招手让他过来。他很容易就明白了我的意思，向前走走停停，停停走走。这时，我可以看到他站在那里，浑身发抖，仿佛他已经被俘，就要像他的两个敌人那样被杀死。我又向他招招手，让他到我身边来，并想方设法做出种种鼓励他的姿势。他这才越走越近，每走一二十步便跪下来，以示感谢我对他的救命之恩。我向他微笑，作出友善的样子，并招呼他再靠近点儿。最后，他走到我跟前，再次跪下来，亲吻地面，把头贴在地上，将我的一只脚放到他的头上，好像是在发誓永远做我的奴隶。我把他扶起来，非常重视他，尽可能鼓励他。但事情还没有完，因为我发现我用枪托打倒的那个野人并没有死，只是被打昏了，渐渐苏醒过来。于是，我向他指了指那个野人，表示他没有死。见此情景，他对我说了几句话，尽管我不明白是什么意思，但我认为说听起来非常悦耳，因为这是 25 年多来，除了我自己的声音之外，我第一次听到人的声音。

But there was no time for such reflections now; the savage who was knocked down recovered himself so far, as to sit up upon the ground, and I perceived that my savage began to be afraid; but when I saw that, I presented my other piece at the man as if I would shoot him; upon this my savage, for so I call him now, made a motion to me to lend him my sword, which hung naked in a belt by my side; so I did. He no sooner had it, but he ran to his enemy, and at one blow cut off his head; when he had done this, he came laughing to me in sign of triumph, and brought me the sword again, and with abundance of gestures which I did not understand, laid it down with the head of the savage that he had killed, just before me.

But that which astonished him most was to know how I had killed the other Indian so far off; so pointing to him, he made signs to me to let him go to him, so I bade him go as well as I could; when he came to him, he stood like one amazed, looking at him, turned him first on one side, then onto other, looked at the wound the bullet had made, which, it seems, was just in his breast, where it had made a hole, and no great quantity of blood had followed, but he had bled inwardly, for he was quite dead; he took up his bow and arrows, and came back, so I turned to go away and beckoned to him to follow me, making signs to him that more might come after them.

Upon this he signed to me that he should bury them with sand, that they might not be seen by the rest if they followed; and so I made signs again to him to do so; he fell to work, and in an instant he had scraped[1] a hole in the sand with his hands big enough to bury the first in, and then dragged him into it and covered him, and did so also by the other; I believe he had buried them both in a quarter of an hour; then calling him away, I carried him not to my castle, but quite away to my cave, on the farther part of the island.

Here I gave him bread and a bunch of raisins to eat, and a draught of water; and I made signs for him to go lie down and sleep, pointing to a place where I had laid a great parcel of rice straw and a blanket upon it, which I used to sleep upon myself sometimes; so the poor creature laid down and went to sleep.

---

[1] scrape *vt.* 挖空；刮成；穿孔

不过，现在不是这样反思的时候。那个被打倒的野人已经清醒过来，在地上坐起来。我发觉被我救出的野人开始感到害怕。看到这一点，我举起另一支枪瞄准那个人，仿佛我要向他射击。这时，我那个野人（我现在这样叫他）做了个手势，要我把挂在腰间的那把无鞘剑借给他。于是，我就把剑借给了他。他一拿住剑，就奔向他的敌人，手起刀落，砍下了那个野人的头。做完后，他带着胜利的笑声来到我面前，先把剑还给了我，然后做了许多莫名其妙的手势，把他砍下来的野人的头放在了我正面前。

然而，他很惊讶，急切想知道从这么远的距离我是怎么打死另一个印第安人的。他用手指了指那个野人的尸体，做着手势要我让他过去看看。我也打着手势，竭力让他懂得我同意他过去。他走到去，好像目瞪口呆，望着那个死人，然后把尸体翻来翻去，看着子弹打的枪伤，看来子弹正好打中那人的胸部，在那里穿了个洞，血流得不多，因为人完全死了，血都流进了体内。他取下那个野人的弓箭，回到我跟前。于是，我转身离开，招手让他跟着我，同时打手势告诉他后面可能还会有更多的人追来。

于是，他向我示意应该把他们用沙土埋起来，这样就是其他野人追上来，也不会发现。我便又打手势让他这样做。他着手干了起来，转眼间就用双手在沙土里刨了一个坑，坑大得刚好埋第一个野人。他把尸体拖进去，用沙土盖好，另一个也如法炮制。我相信，他用了不到一刻钟就埋好了两具尸体。随后，我叫他跟我一起离开。我没有把他带到城堡去，而是带到了岛上更远处的洞穴里。

到了洞里，我给他吃了面包和一串葡萄干，又让他喝了一点儿水。之后，我指着一个地方，示意他躺下来睡觉。我在那里铺了一大堆稻草，上面还有一条毯子，我过去有时也在上面睡觉。于是，这个可怜的家伙躺下来就睡着了。

XXII

After about half an hour, he woke again, and came out of the cave to me; for I had been milking my goats. When he espied[1] me, he came running to me, laying himself down again upon the ground, and set my other foot upon his head, as he had done before; I understood him, and let him know I was very pleased with him; in a little time I began to speak to him and teach him to speak to me; and first, I made him know his name should be Friday, which was the day I saved his life; I called him so for the memory of the time; I likewise taught him to say Master, and then let him know that was to be my name; I likewise taught him to say Yes and No and to know the meaning of them; I gave him some milk in an earthen pot and let him see me drink it before him and sop my bread in it; and I gave him a cake of bread to do the like, which he quickly complied with, and made signs that it was very good for him.

I kept there with him all that night; but as soon as it was day, I beckoned to him to come with me, and let him know I would give him some clothes, at which he seemed very glad, for he was stark naked. As we went by the place where he had buried the two men, he pointed exactly to the place and showed me the marks that he had made to find them again, making signs to me that we should dig them up again and eat them; at this I appeared very angry, expressed my abhorrence of it, made as if I would vomit at the thoughts of it, and beckoned with my hand to him to come away, which he did immediately, with great submission. I then led him up to the top of the hill, to see if his enemies were gone; and pulling out my glass, I looked, and saw plainly the place where they had been, but no appearance of them or of their canoes; so that it was plain they were gone and had left their two comrades behind them, without any search after them.

---

[1] espy *vt.* 看到

22

　　大约半小时后，他又醒来，然后到洞外来找我，因为我一直在挤羊奶。他看到我，就向我跑来，又趴在地上，像先前那样把我的另一只脚放到他的头上。我明白了他的意思，并告诉他，我对他非常满意。过了一小会儿，我开始对他说话，并教他和我说话。首先，我让他知道他的名字应该叫星期五，因为我是在星期五这天救了他的命，我这样叫他是为了纪念这一天。我教他说"主人"，并告诉他这就是我的名字。我还教他说"是"和"不是"，并让他知道这两个词的意思。我将陶罐里的一些羊奶递给他，然后喝给他看，并把面包浸在羊奶里吃给他看。随后，我递给他一块面包，让他学我的样子吃。他马上服从，并向我做手势，表示非常好吃。

　　我和他在那里睡了一夜。但天一亮，我就招呼他跟我一起出来，并告诉他，我要给他一些衣服。他对此好像非常高兴，因为他一丝不挂。当我们走过他埋那两个人的地方时，他准确指着那个地方，并给我看他做的记号。他向我做着手势，表示我们要把尸体挖出来吃掉。我对此显得非常生气，深恶痛绝，做出一想到这事儿就要呕吐的样子，然后招手让他离开。他马上俯首听命。于是，我把他带到小山顶上，看看他的敌人走了没有。我拿出望远镜，一眼就看清了他们曾呆过的那个地方，但没有见那些野人和独木舟的踪影。显然，他们都已经走了，撇下了两个同伙，根本没有找他们。

But I was not content with this discovery; I took my man Friday with me, giving him the sword in his hand, with the bow and arrows at his back, which I found he could use very dexterously[1], making him carry one gun for me, and I two for myself, and away we marched to the place where these creatures had been; for I had a mind now to get some fuller intelligence of them. When I came to the place, my very blood ran chill in my veins and my heart sunk within me at the horror of the spectacle. Indeed it was a dreadful sight, at least it was so to me; though Friday made nothing of it. The place was covered with human bones, the ground dyed with their blood, great pieces of flesh left here and there, half eaten, mangled[2] and scorched; and in short, all the tokens of the triumphant feast they had been making there, after a victory over their enemies; I saw three skulls, five hands, and the bones of three or four legs and feet, and abundance of other parts of the bodies; and Friday, by his signs, made me understand that they brought over four prisoners to feast upon; that three of them were eaten up, and that he, pointing to himself, was the fourth. That there had been a great battle between them and their next king, whose subjects it seems he had been one of; and that they had taken a great number of prisoners, all which were carried to several places by those that had taken them in the fight, in order to feast upon them, as was done here by these wretches upon those they brought hither.

I caused Friday to gather all the skulls, bones, flesh, and whatever remained, and lay them together on a heap and make a great fire upon it and burn them all to ashes.

When we had done this, we came back to our castle, and there I fell to work for my man Friday; and first of all, I gave him a pair of linen drawers; then I made him a jerkin[3] of goat's skin; and I gave him a cap of hare-skin; and thus he was mighty well pleased to see himself almost as well clothed as his master.

---

[1] dexterously   adv. 巧妙地，敏捷地
[2] mangle   vt. 乱砍，撕裂，破坏
[3] jerkin   n. 男用无袖短上衣，短上衣

可是，我对这一发现并不满足。我带上奴隶星期五，给了他一把剑，让他拿在手里，他还背着弓箭，我发现他使用弓箭非常娴熟，同时还让他给我背一支枪，我自己则背了两支枪。之后，我们就向这些野人曾呆过的地方出发了，因为我现在想进一步了解他们的情况。我来到那个地方，看到那可怕的景象，浑身冰冷，心往下沉。那的确是一幅可怕的景象，至少在我看来是这样，尽管星期五根本不当回事儿。那里到处都是人骨头，地面上沾满了鲜血，各处留下了大片大片的人肉，有的吃了一半，有的被撕开并被烧焦。总之，到处都是他们战胜敌人后在那里一直举行人肉宴留下的痕迹。我看到有三个颅骨、五只手，三、四根腿骨和脚骨，还有很多人体的其他部分。星期五用手势使我明白，他们带过来四个俘虏来这里欢宴，其中三个已被吃掉。他指了指自己说，他是第四个。他又告诉我说，那些野人和他们的下一任国王之间发生了一场大战，看来他是新国王的臣民。新国王这边也抓了一大批俘虏，这些俘虏都被带到了不同的地方杀吃，就像这些坏蛋把他们带到这里杀吃那样。

　　我让星期五把所有的颅骨、人骨、人肉以及那些野人吃剩的东西收集在一起，堆成一堆，点起大火，把它们都烧成了灰烬。

　　做完这件事，我们就回到了城堡。一到那里，我就开始为我的随从星期五忙活起来。首先，我给了他一条亚麻衬裤，然后又给他做了一件无袖羊皮短上衣，还给了他一顶兔皮帽子。他看到自己和主人穿得差不多一样好，非常高兴。

The next day after I came home to my hutch with him, I began to consider where I should lodge him; and that I might do well for him and yet be perfectly easy myself; I made a little tent for him in the vacant place between my two fortifications, in the inside of the last, and in the outside of the first; and as there was a door or entrance there into my cave, I made a formal framed doorcase, and a door to it of boards, and set it up in the passage, a little within the entrance; and causing the door to open on the inside, I barred[1] it up in the night, taking in my ladders too; so that Friday could no way come at me in the inside of my innermost wall without making so much noise in getting over that it must needs waken me; for my first wall had now a complete roof over it of long poles, covering all my tent and leaning up to the side of the hill, which was again laid across with smaller sticks instead of laths, and then thatched over a great thickness with the rice straw, which was strong like reeds; and at the hole or place which was left to go in or out by the ladder, I had placed a kind of trapdoor, which, if it had been attempted on the outside, would not have opened at all, but would have fallen down, and made a great noise; and as to weapons, I took them all to my side every night.

But I needed none of all this precaution; for never man had a more faithful, loving, sincere servant than Friday was to me; his very affections were tied to me, like those of a child to a father; and I dare say he would have sacrificed his life for the saving mine upon any occasion whatsoever.

I was greatly delighted with him and made it my business to teach him everything, especially to make him speak and understand me when I spoke; and he was the aptest scholar that ever was, and particularly was so merry, so constantly diligent, and so pleased when he could but understand me or make me understand him that it was very pleasant to me to talk to him; and now my life began to be so easy that I began to say to myself that could I but have been safe from more savages, I cared not if I was never to remove from the place while I lived.

---

[1] bar *vt.* 阻挡；把门关住

跟星期五回家后第二天，我就开始考虑我应该让他住在什么地方，我既要让他住好，又要使自己完全放心。我便在两道围墙之间内墙外、外墙里的空地上给他搭了一顶小帐篷。因为内墙上有一个入口通到山洞，所以我在入口处做了一个正式门框和一扇木板门，安放在通道入口处，并让门朝里开。我夜里把门从里面闩上，同时把梯子也收进来。这样，星期五想翻过内墙向我袭击，不可能不弄出许多声响，这样一定会把我惊醒，因为我在内墙和山边之间用长木杆搭了一个完整的屋顶，把我的帐篷全都遮盖了起来。木杆上又横搭了许多较小的木棍，而不是木板条，然后在上面盖了厚厚一层像芦苇一样结实的稻草。我还在用梯子爬进爬出的地方装了一种活板门，谁要想从外面把门打开，是根本不可能的，这样活板门就会掉下来，发出巨大响声。至于武器，我则每天夜里都把它们放在身边。

　　可是，我根本不需要采取所有这防范措施，因为从来没有人有过比星期五对我更可靠、更忠实、更真诚的仆人。他对我的感情就像孩子对父亲的感情一样密不可分。我敢说，他任何时候都会为救我而牺牲自己的生命。

　　我对他非常高兴，并尽自己的职责教他做所有的一切，尤其是教他说话，并听懂我说的话。他学得比任何人都快，尤其是学习时兴高采烈、勤勤恳恳，每当他听懂我的话或让我听懂他的话时，他总是一副心满意足的样子，和他谈话对我来说非常有趣。现在，我的生活渐渐轻松起来，所以我开始对自己说，只要我能不遭到更多野人的袭击，就是永远不离开这个地方，我也不在乎。

After I had been two or three days returned to my castle, I thought that, in order to bring Friday off from his horrid way of feeding and from the relish[1] of a cannibal's stomach, I ought to let him taste other flesh; so I took him out with me one morning to the woods. I went indeed intending to kill a kid out of my own flock and bring him home and dress it. But as I was going, I saw a she-goat lying down in the shade and two young kids sitting by her; I caught hold of Friday. "Hold," said I, "stand still"; and made signs to him not to stir; immediately I presented my piece, shot and killed one of the kids. The poor creature who had at a distance, indeed, seen me kill his enemy, but did not know or could imagine how it was done, was sensibly surprised, trembled and shook, and looked so amazed that I thought he would have sunk down. He did not see the kid I shot at, or perceive I had killed it, but ripped up his waistcoat to feel if he was not wounded, and, as I found presently, thought I was resolved to kill him; for he came and kneeled down to me, and embracing my knees, said a great many things I did not understand; but I could easily see that the meaning was to pray me not to kill him.

I soon found a way to convince him that I would do him no harm, and taking him up by the hand laughed at him, and pointed to the kid which I had killed, beckoned to him to run and fetch it, which he did; and while he was wondering and looking to see how the creature was killed, I loaded my gun again, and by and by I saw a great fowl like a hawk sit upon a tree within shot; so to let Friday understand a little what I would do, I called him to me again, pointed at the fowl which was indeed a parrot, though I thought it had been a hawk, I say, pointing to the parrot and to my gun and to the ground under the parrot, to let him see I would make it fall, I made him understand that I would shoot and kill that bird; accordingly I fired and bade him look, and immediately he saw the parrot fall, he stood like one frightened again, notwithstanding all I had said to him; and I found he was the more amazed because he did not see me put anything into the gun; but thought that there must be some wonderful fund of death and destruction in that thing, able to kill man, beast, bird, or anything near or far off; and the astonishment this created in him was such as could not wear off for a long time.

---

[1] relish *n.* （常与 for 连用）喜欢；爱好

回到城堡两三天后，我认为，为了改掉星期五吃东西的可怕的样子和吃人的爱好，我应该让他尝尝别的肉的味道。所以，一天早上，我带他到树林里去，其实是想从自己的羊群里杀一只小羊，带回家烤烤吃。但正走着，我看到有一只母羊躺倒在树阴下，身边卧着两只小羊。我抓住星期五，说："站住，别动。"然后打手势，让他不要动。接着，我举枪瞄准，开枪打死了一只小羊。可怜的星期五确实曾在远处看到我用枪打死了他的敌人，但当时不知道、也无法想像是怎么回事，这次明显吃了一惊，他浑身颤抖，看上去目瞪口呆，我想他一定会瘫倒在地。他既没有看我开枪射击的那只小羊，也没有发觉我已经打死了小羊，而是撕开他自己的背心，在身上摸了一下，看自己有没有受伤。随后，我马上发现，他是以为我要决心杀死他，因为他走过来，向我跪倒，抱住我的膝盖，说了好多好多我听不懂的话，但我可以毫不费力地明白，他的意思是恳求我不要杀他。

　　我马上找到了一个方法，使他相信，我绝不会伤害他。我一边用手拉他起来，一边冲他大笑，并用手指着我打死的那只小羊，招手让他跑过去把它带回来。他就跑了过去。他觉得奇怪，在那里查看小山羊是怎样被打死的。这时，我又把枪装上了子弹。过了一会儿，我看见一只老鹰似的大鸟卧在我射程内的一棵树上。为了让星期五稍微明白我是怎样开枪的，便又把他叫到我跟前，用手指了指那只鸟，其实那是一只鹦鹉，我原以为是一只鹰。我用手指了指那只鹦鹉，然后指了指我的枪和鹦鹉下面的地面，让他看到我要让它掉下来，我让他明白我要开枪打死那只鸟。于是，我就开了枪，并吩咐他注意看。他马上看到那只鹦鹉掉了下来。他又吓得目瞪口呆站在那里，尽管我事先都已经对他说过。我发现他更加惊讶，因为他没有看到我往枪里放任何东西，他以为枪里一定藏有什么神奇的致命东西，能把人、兽、鸟或远远近近的任何生物都杀死。而且这东西在他身上产生的惊讶之情很长时间都不可能消失。

And I believe, if I would have let him, he would have worshipped me and my gun. As for the gun itself, he would not so much as touch it for several days after; but would speak to it and talk to it as if it had answered him, when he was by himself; which, as I afterwards learned of him, was to desire it not to kill him.

After his astonishment was a little over at this, I pointed to him to run and fetch the bird I had shot, which he did, but stayed some time; for the parrot not being quite dead, was fluttered away a good way off from the place where she fell; however, he found her, took her up, and brought her to me; and as I had perceived his ignorance about the gun before, I took this advantage to charge the gun again, and not let him see me do it, that I might be ready for any other mark that might present; but nothing more offered at that time; so I brought home the kid, and the same evening I took the skin off and cut it out as well as I could; and having a pot for that purpose, I boiled, or stewed some of the flesh, and made some very good broth; and after I had begun to eat some, I gave some to my man, who seemed very glad of it and liked it very well; but that which was strangest to him was to see me eat salt with it; he made a sign to me that the salt was not good to eat, and putting a little into his own mouth, he seemed to nauseate[1] it, and would spit and sputter at it, washing his mouth with fresh water after it; on the other hand, I took some meat in my mouth without salt, and I pretended to spit and sputter[2] for want of salt, as fast as he had done at the salt; but it would not do, he would never care for salt with his meat or in his broth; at least not a great while, and then but a very little.

Having thus fed him with boiled meat and broth, I was resolved to feast him the next day with roasting a piece of the kid; this I did by hanging it before the fire in a string as I had seen many people do in England, setting two poles up, one on each side the fire, and one cross on the top, and tying the string to the cross-stick, letting the meat turn continually. This Friday admired very much; but when he came to taste the flesh, he took so many ways to tell me how well he liked it that I could not but understand him; and at last he told me he would never eat man's flesh any more, which I was very glad to hear.

---

[1] nauseate   *vt.* 使厌恶，使恶心，使作呕
[2] sputter   *vt.* 喷出，飞溅出；气急败坏地说

我相信，如果我让他这样下去，他一定会把我和我的枪当神一样来敬。至于那支枪，过了好几天他连碰都不敢碰，总是一个人对枪说个没完，好像它答应了他什么似的。我后来才从他嘴里得知，他是在请求枪不要杀害他。

等他的惊讶之情过去了一点儿后，我用手指了指那只鸟掉下去的地方，让他跑过去把鸟拾来。他去了好半天才回来，因为那只鹦鹉还没有完全死，它落下来后又扑棱了好长一段路。不过，星期五还是找到了它，把它拾起来，递给了我。我发觉他对我的枪一无所知，就趁他去拾鸟的机会又装上了弹药，不让他看见我是怎样装的，以便为出现任何其他目标做好准备，但当时再也没有出现什么目标。于是，我便把那只小羊带回了家，当晚就把它剥皮，尽可能把肉切碎。因为我专门有一只罐子，所以就煮或炖了一些肉，熬成了非常鲜美的羊肉汤。我吃了一些后，也给他吃了一些。他好像非常高兴，吃得津津有味。但最让他感到奇怪的是，他看到我在里面放盐吃。他向我做了个手势，表示盐不好吃。他把一点儿盐放在自己的嘴里，好像恶心欲吐，呸呸吐了一阵，之后又用清水嗽了嗽口。而我也拿了一块没有放盐的肉放进嘴里，假装因为没有盐而呸呸吐了一阵，就像他有盐赶紧漱口一样。可是，这不顶用。他就是不喜欢在肉里或汤里放盐。至少他好长一段时间不喜欢，后来也只是放很少一点儿盐。

这样，吃过煮羊肉和喝羊肉汤后，我决定第二天请他吃烤羊肉。我采用在英国常见的烤法，在火的每一侧各插一根顶部有叉的木杆，上面架一根横杆，再把肉吊在横杆上，让肉不断转动。星期五对我这种烤法非常钦佩。他尝了烤羊肉后，用各种各样的方法告诉我他是多么喜欢，直到我明白他的意思。最后，他对我说，他再也不吃人肉了。听到这话，我非常高兴。

The next day I set him to work to beating some corn out and sifting[1] it in the manner I used to do, and he soon understood how to do it as well as I, especially after he had seen what the meaning of it was, and that it was to make bread of; for after that I let him see me make my bread and bake it too, and in a little time Friday was able to do all the work for me, as well as I could do it myself.

I begun now to consider that having two mouths to feed instead of one, I must provide more ground for my harvest and plant a larger quantity of corn than I used to do; so I marked out a larger piece of land and began the fence in the same manner as before, in which Friday not only worked very willingly and very hard, but did it very cheerfully.

This was the pleasantest year of all the life I led in this place; Friday began to talk pretty well and understand the names of almost everything I had occasion to call for, and of every place I had to send him to, and talked a great deal to me; so that I began really to love the creature; and, on his side, I believe he loved me more than it was possible for him ever to love anything before.

I had a mind once to try if he had any hankering[2] inclination to his own country again, and having learned his English so well that he could answer me almost any questions, I asked him whether the nation that he belonged to never conquered in battle, at which he smiled, and said, "Yes, yes, we always fight the better"; and so we began the following discourse:

"You always fight the better," said I, "How came you to be taken prisoner then, Friday?"

Friday: My nation beat much, for all that.

Master: How beat? If your nation beat them, how come you to be taken?

Friday: They more many than my nation in the place where me was; they take one, two, three, and me; my nation over beat them in the yonder place, where me no was; there my nation take one, two, great thousand.

Master: But why did not your side recover you from the hands of your enemies then?

---

[1] sift   v.   筛，筛分；过滤
[2] hankering   n. 渴望，切望

第二天，我派他去打谷，并像我过去那样把谷筛出来。不久，他就明白如何做得和我一样好了，尤其是他明白这样做的意思、明白是要做面包之后。因为等他打完谷后，我就让他看我做面包、烤面包。过了一会儿，他也能做面包、烤面包，做得和我一样好了。

这时，我开始考虑到，现在既然有了两张嘴而不是一张嘴吃饭，我必须多开些地、多种些粮食。于是，我又划了一块较大的地，像以前一样把地圈起来。星期五对这工作不仅心甘情愿、非常卖力，而且干得非常开心。

这是我在这个地方度过的最开心的一年。星期五差不多开始会说话了，也差不多明白我要他拿的每件东西的名称和我派他去的每个地方的名字，而且总是对我侃大山。因此，我真的开始喜欢上了这个人。同时，我相信，他本人爱我可能胜过爱以前所有的一切。

有一次，我一心想试试看他是不是有回家的愿望。这时，我认识到他的英语说得很好，几乎能回答我的任何问题。我问他，他的部族是不是在战争中从未战胜过。听了这个问题，他微微一笑，说："不，不，我们总是打得比较好。"于是，我们就开始了下面的对话：

"你们总是打得比较好，"我说，"那你怎么会被俘虏了呢，星期五？"

星期五：尽管我被抓了，但我的部族打赢的多。

主人：怎么打赢？如果你的部族打赢了，你怎么会被抓住呢？

星期五：在我参战的那个地方，他们比我们人多。他们抓住了一个、两个、三个，还有我。在我没有参战的另一个地方，我的部族打败了他们。我的部族在那里抓了一两千人。

主人：可你们的人为什么不把你们从敌人的手里救回去呢？

Friday: They run one, two, three, and me, and make go in the canoe; my nation have no canoe that time.

Master: Well, Friday, and what does your nation do with the men they take? Do they carry them away, and eat them, as these did?

Friday: Yes, my nation eats men too, eats all up.

Master: Where do they carry them?

Friday: Go to other place where they think.

Master: Do they come hither?

Friday: Yes, yes, they come hither; come other else place.

Master: Have you been here with them?

Friday: Yes, I been here; (points to the northwest side of the island, which it seems was their side.)

By this I understood that my man Friday had formerly been among the savages who used to come on shore on the farther part of the island, on the same man-eating occasions that he was now brought for; and some time after, when I took the courage to carry him to that side, he presently knew the place and told me he was there once when they eat up twenty men, two women, and one child; he could not tell twenty in English; but he numbered them by laying so many stones on a row and pointing to me to tell them over.

After I had had this discourse with him, I asked him how far it was from our island to the shore, and whether the canoes were not often lost; he told me there was no danger, no canoes ever lost; but that after a little way out to the sea, there was a current and wind, always one way in the morning, the other in the afternoon.

This I understood to be no more than the sets of the tide, as going out or coming in; but I afterwards understood it was occasioned by the great draft and reflux of the mighty river Oroonooko; in the mouth of which river, as I found afterwards, our island lay; and this land which I perceived to the west and northwest was the great island Trinidad, on the north point of the mouth of the river. I asked Friday a thousand questions about the country, the inhabitants, the sea, the coast, and what nation were near; he told me all he knew with the greatest openness imaginable; I asked him the names of the several nations of his sort of people; but could get no other name than Caribs; from whence I easily understood that these were the Caribbees, which our maps place on the part of America which reaches from the mouth of the river Oroonooko to Guiana, and onwards to St. Martha.

星期五：他们把一个、两个、三个，还有我，放到了独木舟里跑了。我们的部族当时没有独木舟。

主人：那么，星期五，你们的部族怎么处理抓到的人？他们是把俘虏带走，像这些敌人那样把他们吃掉吗？

星期五：是的，我们的部族也吃人，吃得精光。

主人：他们把人带到什么地方？

星期五：带到他们想去的别的地方。

主人：他们到这里来吗？

星期五：来，来，他们来这里，也去别的地方。

主人：你跟他们来过这里吗？

星期五：是的，我来过这里。（用手指了指岛的西北边。好像那是他们的地方。）

由此，我明白我的仆人星期五以前也常和那些野人在岛上的远处那边上岸吃人，就像他这次被带到这里来一样。过了一段时间，我鼓起勇气，把他带到岛上那边。他马上就认出了那个地方，并对我说，他到过这里一次，吃了 20 个男人、两个女人和一个孩子。他还不会用英语说20，就把许多石块摆成一行，用手指给我看。

我和他谈过这次话后，问他我们的小岛离大陆海岸有多远，独木舟是不是经常沉没。他告诉我说没有任何危险，独木舟从来没有沉没过。不过，在出海口不远处有一股急流和风，总是上午一个方向，下午又换一个方向。

我理解这不过是潮水的流向而已，有时向外流，有时向里流。可是，后来我才明白，那是由奥罗诺诺科大河浩浩荡荡流进流出引起的。后来我发现我们的岛处在这条河的河口。我在西面和西北面发现的这块陆地是特立尼达大岛，处在河口北端。我向星期五问了无数问题，都是有关地形、居民、海洋、海岸和附近是什么国家这些问题。他以最坦率的态度尽其所能一一告诉了我。我问他，他这个民族分成几个部落，这几个部落叫什么名字，但只能问出"加勒比人"一个名字。由此，我立刻明白，这是加勒比群岛，我们的地图上是处在美洲地区，从奥罗诺科河河口延伸到圭亚那，然后又延伸到圣马大。

He told me that up a great way beyond the moon, that was, beyond the setting of the moon, which must be west from their country, there dwelt white bearded men, like me, and pointed to my great whiskers; and that they had killed much mans, that was his word; by all which I understood he meant the Spaniards, whose cruelties in America had been spread over the whole countries and was remembered by all the nations from father to son.

I enquired if he could tell me how I might come from this island and get among those white men; he told me, "Yes, yes, I might go in two canoe"; I could not understand what he meant, or make him describe to me what he meant by "two canoe" till at last with great difficulty, I found he meant it must be in a large great boat, as big as two canoes.

This part of Friday's discourse began to relish with me very well and from this time I entertained some hopes that one time or other, I might find an opportunity to make my escape from this place and that this poor savage might be a means to help me to do it.

他告诉我说，月亮那边很远的地方就是月亮落下的地方，那一定是他们国家的西边，那里住着像我这样有络腮胡的白人，他说着指了指我的大络腮胡，他们在那边杀了好多人。从他的话里，我明白他指的是西班牙人。他们在美洲的暴行传遍了所有国家，并被所有部族世代铭记。

　　我问他能不能告诉我怎样才能从这个岛走到那些白人中间去，他告诉我说："能，能，我可以坐两只独木舟去。"我不明白坐两只独木舟去是什么意思，也无法使他说明两只独木舟是什么意思。最后，费了很大劲儿，我才明白他指的是必须要坐一只大船，像两只独木舟那样大。

　　星期五的这部分谈话开始使我很感兴趣。从这时起，我就抱着一些希望，但愿有一天我能有机会从这个地方逃出去，这个可怜的野人可能会助我一臂之力。

XXIII

The conversation which employed the hours between Friday and I was such as made the three years which we lived there together perfectly and completely happy. We had here the Word of God to read, and no farther off from His Spirit to instruct than if we had been in England.

I always applied myself in reading the Scripture to let him know, as well as I could, the meaning of what I read; and he again, by his serious enquiries and questionings, made me a much better scholar in the Scripture knowledge than I should ever have been by my own private mere reading.

After Friday and I became more intimately acquainted, and that he could understand almost all I said to him, and speak fluently, though in broken English, to me; I acquainted him with my own story. I let him into the mystery, for such it was to him, of gunpowder and bullet, and taught him how to shoot. I gave him a knife, which he was wonderfully delighted with, and I made him a belt, with a frog hanging to it; and in the frog, instead of a hanger, I gave him a hatchet.

I described to him the country of Europe, and particularly England, which I came from; how we lived, how we worshipped God, how we behaved to one another; and how we traded in ships to all parts of the world. I gave him an account of the wreck which I had been on board of, and showed him as near as I could, the place where she lay; but she was all beaten in pieces before, and gone.

I showed him the ruins of our boat, which we lost when we escaped, and which I could not stir with my whole strength then; but was now fallen almost all to pieces. Upon seeing this boat, Friday stood musing a great while, and said nothing; I asked him what it was he studied upon, at last said he, "Me see such boat like come to place at my nation."

23

在我和星期五相处的三年中，因为有许多时间跟他谈话，所以日子过得幸福美满。我们在这里有《圣经》可读，离圣灵不远，可以得到他的教导，就像在英国一样。

我总是诵读《圣经》，尽可能把我所读的话的意思告诉他。由于星期五认真提问，因此我对《圣经》的认识比一个人阅读时要好得多。

我和星期五成了莫逆之交，我对他说的话，他几乎都能听懂；尽管他说的英语非常蹩脚，但对我说起来非常流利。这时，我就把自己的身世告诉了他。我又把火药和子弹的秘密告诉他，因为在他看来这确实是一个秘密，我还教会了他开枪，送给了他一把刀。他对此高兴得不得了。我给他做了一条皮带，皮带上挂了一个佩刀的扣环。我没有让他挂腰刀，而是给了他一把短柄斧。

我把欧洲的情况——尤其是我的故乡英国的情况——说给他听，告诉他我们怎样生活、怎样崇拜上帝、人与人之间怎样相处，以及怎样乘船到世界各地做买卖。我把我乘的那条船出事的经过告诉他，并尽可能指给他看沉船的大致地方。然而，那条船早已被风浪打得粉碎，不见了踪影。

我又把那只小船的残骸指给他看，也就是我们逃命时丢掉的那只救生艇。我曾竭尽全力也无法移动小艇，而现在它差不多烂成了碎片。星期五看到这只小艇，站在那里想了好一阵子，没说一句话。我问他在想什么。最后，他说，我看到过这样的小船到过我们的地方。

I did not understand him a good while; but at last, when I had examined farther into it, I understood by him that a boat such as that had been came on shore upon the country where he lived; that is, as he explained it, was driven thither by stress of weather. I presently imagined that some European ship must have been cast away upon their coast, and the boat might get loose and drive a shore; but was so dull that I never once thought of men making escape from a wreck thither.

Friday said, "We save the white men from drown." Then I presently asked him if there was any white man in the boat. "Yes," he said, "the boat full of white men." I asked him how many; he told upon his fingers seventeen. I asked him then what become of them; he told me, "They live, they dwell at my nation."

This put new thoughts into my head; for I presently imagined that these might be the men belonging to the ship that was cast away in sight of my island; and who after the ship was struck on the rock, and they saw her inevitably lost, had saved themselves in their boat, and were landed upon that wild shore among the savages.

Upon this I enquired of him more critically what was become of them? He assured me they lived still there; that they had been there about four years; that the savages let them alone, and gave them victuals to live. I asked him how it came to pass they did not kill them and eat them. He said, "No, they make brother with them." And then he added, "They no eat men but when make the war fight."

It was after this some considerable time, that being upon the top of the hill, at the east side of the island, from whence as have said, I had in a clear day discovered the main, continent of America; Friday, the weather being very serene, looks very earnestly towards the mainland, and in a kind of surprise, falls a jumping and dancing, and calls out to me, for I was at some distance from him. I asked him what was the matter. "O joy!" said he, "O glad! There see my country! There see my nation!"

This observation of mine put a great many thoughts into me. If Friday could get back to his own nation again, he would not only forget all his religion, but all his obligation to me; and would be forward enough to give his countrymen an account of me, and come back perhaps with a hundred or two of them, and make a feast upon me, at which he might be as merry as he used to be with those of his enemies, when they were taken in war.

我好一阵子都不明白他的意思。最后，我进一步询问，才明白他的意思：曾有一只同这只一模一样的小艇在他们住的地方靠岸。据他解释，小艇是被风浪冲到那里的。我马上想到，这一定是某艘欧洲的商船在他们海岸附近的海面上失事，那只小艇可能脱离了大船，漂到了海岸上。当时，我头脑迟钝，怎么也没想到有人也许从失事船上乘小艇逃生，到了他们那边。

星期五说：我们救出了那些快要淹死的白人。随后，我马上问他，小艇上有没有白人。他说：有，满满一船白人。我问他有多少。他扳着手指告诉我，17个。我又问他们现在的下落。他告诉我说：他们都活着，他们就住在我的部落里。

这使我产生了新的联想，因为我马上想到，这些白人一定是我上次在岛上看到出事的那条大船上的船员。大船触礁后，他们知道船肯定会沉没，就爬上小艇逃命去了。他们在野人聚居的蛮荒海岸上上了岸。

因此，我更仔细地打听了那些白人的下落。星期五向我保证，他们还住在那里，已经住大约四年了。野人们不去打扰他们，还送给他们粮食吃。我问他，他们为什么不把那些白人杀吃了呢？他说："不，他们成了兄弟。"接着，他又补充说："除了打仗，他们平时不吃人。"

此后，过了相当长一段时间。有一天，天气晴朗，我和星期五登上岛东边的那座小山顶。在那里，也是在一个晴天，我曾看到了美洲大陆。当时，星期五聚精会神地眺望着大陆，然后出乎意外地手舞足蹈起来，并朝我大声叫喊，因为我离他有一段距离。我问他怎么了。他说："噢，真高兴！噢，真开心！我看到了我的国家！我看到了我的部族！"

看到他这样，我浮想联翩。如果星期五能重新回到自己的部族，他不但会忘掉他所有的宗教，而且会忘掉他对我的全部义务。他一定会马上把我的情况告诉他部族里的人，也许还会把一两百同胞带到岛上，并拿我来开一次人肉宴。那时，他一定会像吃战争中抓获的那些俘虏那样欢天喜地。

But I wronged the poor honest creature very much, for which I was very sorry afterwards. However, as my jealousy increased, and held me some weeks, I was a little more circumspect[1], and not so familiar and kind to him as before; in which I was certainly in the wrong too, the honest grateful creature having no thought about it.

While my jealousy of him lasted, I was every day pumping him to see if he would discover any of the new thoughts which I suspected were in him; but I found everything he said was so honest and so innocent that I could find nothing to nourish[2] my suspicion.

One day walking up the same hill, but the weather being hazy at sea so that we could not see the continent, I called to him, and said, "Friday, do not you wish yourself in your own country, your own nation?" "Yes," he said, he be much O glad to be at his own nation. "What would you do there?" said I. "Would you turn wild again, eat men's flesh again, and be a savage as you were before?" He looked full of concern, and shaking his head said, "No, no, Friday tell them to live good, tell them to pray God, tell them to eat corn-bread, cattle-flesh, milk, no eat man again." "Why then," said I to him, "they will kill you." He looked grave at that, and then said, "No, they no kill me, they willing love learn." He meant by this, they would be willing to learn. He added, they learned much of the bearded-men that come in the boat. Then I asked him if he would go back to them. He smiled at that, and told me he could not swim so far. I told him I would make a canoe for him. He told me, he would go, if I would go with him. "I go!" said I, "why, they will eat me if I come there!" "No, no," said he, "me make they no eat you; me make they much love you." He meant he would tell them how I had killed his enemies and saved his life, and so he would make them love me; then he told me as well as he could, how kind they were to seventeen white-men, who came on shore there in distress.

---

[1] circumspect   *adj.* 慎重的，周到的
[2] nourish   *vt.* 滋养，怀有（希望、仇恨等）

可是，我大大冤枉了这个可怜的老实人。为此，我后来感到非常抱歉。然而，当时我的猜忌与日俱增，持续了好几周，更加小心翼翼，对待他也没有像以前那样和蔼亲热了。这样做，我也大大错了。这个忠实感恩的人根本就没想到这一点。

我对他的猜忌消除之前，每天都在盘问他，看他是不是会把我怀疑他的新想法露出来。但我发现他说的每一句话都那么诚实、那么单纯，实在无法找出任何让我怀疑的东西。

有一天，我们又走上了那座小山，但这次海上烟雾弥漫，无法看见大陆。我对星期五喊道："星期五，你不想回到自己的国家，回到自己的部落去吗？""不，"他说，他非常高兴回到自己的部族去。我说："你想回去做什么？你要重过野蛮生活，再吃人肉，像从前那样做个野人吗？"他看上去忧心忡忡，摇着头说："不，不，星期五要告诉他们做好人，告诉他们要向上帝祈祷，告诉他们要吃谷物面包，吃牛羊肉，喝奶，不再吃人。"我说："那他们就会杀你。"一听这话，他神情严肃，然后说道："不，他们不会杀我。他们爱学习。"他是说，他们一定会愿意学习。他又补充说，他们从小艇上来的那些有胡子的人那里学了很多东西。接着，我又问他是不是愿意回到他们身边。他微微一笑，告诉我说，他游不了那么远。我告诉他，我会给他做一条独木舟。他说，如果我愿意跟他去，他就去。"我去！"我说，"哎呀，我去了他们会吃掉我的！""不会，不会，"他说，"我叫他们不吃你，我叫他们非常爱你。"他是说，他会告诉他们我怎样杀死了他的敌人，救了他的命，所以他会让他们爱我。接着，他又尽可能告诉我他们对那 17 个白人多么好。那些白人是在船只遇难后上岸到那里的。

From this time I confess I had a mind to venture over, and see if I could possibly join with these bearded-men, who I made no doubt were Spaniards or Portuguese; not doubting but if I could we might find some method to escape from thence, being upon the continent, and a good company together, better than I could from an island 40 miles off the shore, and alone without help. So after some days I took Friday to work again, and told him I would give him a boat to go back to his own nation; and accordingly I carried him to my frigate[1] which lay on the other side of the island, and having cleared it of water, for I always kept it sunk in the water, I brought it out, showed it him, and we both went into it.

I found he was a most dextrous fellow at managing it, would make it go almost as swift and fast again as I could; so when he was in, I said to him, "Well now, Friday, shall we go to your nation?" He looked very dull at my saying so, which it seems was because he thought the boat too small to go so far. I told him then I had a bigger; so the next day I went to the place where the first boat lay which I had made, but which I could not get into water. He said that was big enough; but then as I had taken no care of it, and it had lain two or three and twenty years there, the sun had split and dried it, that it was in a manner rotten. Friday told me such a boat would do very well and would carry "much enough victual, drink, bread."

Upon the whole, I was by this time so fixed upon my design of going over with him to the continent, that I told him we would go and make one as big as that, and he should go home in it. He answered not one word, but looked very grave and sad. I asked him what was the matter with him. He asked me again thus, "Why you angry mad with Friday? What me done?" I asked him what he meant; I told him I was not angry with him at all. "No angry! No angry!" said he, repeating the words several times, "Why send Friday home away to my nation?" "Why," said I. "Friday, did you not say you wished you were there?" "Yes, yes," said he, "wish be both there, no wish Friday there, no master there." In a word, he would not think of going there without me.

---

[1] frigate   *n.* 三帆快速战舰，护卫舰

从这段时间，我承认，我很想冒险渡过海去，看是不是能和那些有胡子的人会合。我毫不怀疑，那些人不是西班牙人，就是葡萄牙人；我也毫不怀疑，一旦我能与他们会合，就能设法从那里逃走，因为到了大陆上我们会相伴而行，这要比我一个人孤立无援，从离大陆 40 海里的小岛上逃出去强。所以，过了几天后，我又带星期五外出干活，告诉他说，我将送给他一条船，让他回到自己的部族去。于是，我把他带到小岛另一边存放小船的地方。因为我总是把船沉到水底，所以到了那里，我先把船里的水排干，再让船从水里浮上来，给他看。随后，我们就坐了进去。

　　我发现他是一个划船能手，划得和我差不多一样快。所以，他一上船，我就对他说："好了，星期五，我们到你的部族去好吗？"听我这么说，他神情呆滞，好像是因为他认为这船太小，走不了那么远。随后，我告诉他说，我还有一只较大的船。于是，第二天，我就去了我存放我造的第一只船的地方，但我当时无法让那条船下水。他说，那船够大的。不过，由于我根本没有保护它，而且在那里躺了二十二三年，因此太阳将它晒得干裂，有些地方已经朽烂了。星期五告诉我说，这样的船很好，可以载"足够的食物、饮水和面包"。

　　总之，我这时一门心思打算和他一起到大陆上去了。我对他说，我们要去造一条跟这一样大的船，这样他就可以坐上去回家。他一句话也没说，但神情非常严肃，一副非常难过的样子。我问他怎么了。他这样反问我："你为什么生星期五的气？我做了什么？"我问他是什么意思，并告诉他，我根本没有生他的气。"没有生气！没有生气！"他把这句话重复了好几遍。"为什么要把星期五打发到我的部族？"我说："哎呀，星期五，你不是说你想去那里吗？""是的，是的，"他说，"我想我们俩都去，不是星期五去，主人不去。"总之，没有我，他不想去那里。

"I go there! Friday," said I. "what shall I do there?" He turned very quick upon me at this: "You do great deal much good," said he, "you teach wild men be good sober tame men; you tell them know God, pray God, and live new life." "Alas! Friday," said I. "thou knowest not what thou sayest; I am but an ignorant man myself." "Yes, yes," said he, "you teachee me good, you teachee them good." "No, no, Friday," said I. "you shall go without me, leave me here to live by myself as I did before." He looked confused again at that word, and running to one of the hatchets which he used to wear, he took it up hastily, came and gave it me. "What must I do with this?" said I to him. "You take, kill Friday." said he. "What must I kill you for?" said I again. He returned very quick, "What you send Friday away for? Take, kill Friday, no send Friday away." This he spoke so earnestly that I saw tears stand in his eyes.

Upon the whole, as I found by all his discourse a settled affection to me, and that nothing should part him from me, so I found all the foundation of his desire to go to his own country was laid in his ardent affection to the people and his hopes of my doing them good; a thing which, as I had no notion of myself, so I had not the least thought of undertaking it. But still I found a strong inclination to my attempting an escape as above, founded on the supposition[1] gathered from the discourse, viz., that there were seventeen bearded men there; and therefore, without any more delay, I went to work with Friday to find out a great tree proper to fell, and make a large canoe to undertake the voyage. There were trees enough in the island to have built a fleet. But the main thing I looked at was to get one so near the water that we might launch it when it was made, to avoid the mistake I committed at first.

At last, Friday pitched upon a tree, for I found he knew much better than I what kind of wood was fittest for it. Friday was for burning the hollow of this tree out to make it for a boat. But I showed him how rather to cut it out with tools; and in about a month's hard labour, we finished it; after this, however, it cost us near a fortnight's time to get her along as it were inch by inch upon great rollers into the water.

---

[1] supposition   *n.* 假定，推测

我说:"我去!星期五,我去那里会做什么呢?"他马上回答说:"你可以做很多很多的好事。你教野人们成为节制、听话的好人。你教他们知道上帝,祈祷上帝,过新生活。""唉!星期五,"我说,"你不知道你说什么。我自己也不过是一个无知的人。""行,行,"他说,"你教我好,你教他们好。""不,不,星期五,"我说,"你一个人去吧,让我独自留在这里,仍像以前一样生活。"听了我的话,他又糊涂了。他马上跑去拿来了他平常佩带的其中一把短柄斧,递给我。"我用这斧干什么?"我对他说。"你拿着,杀了星期五。"他说。"我为什么要杀你?"我又说。他马上回答说:"你为什么要赶走星期五?拿住。杀了星期五,也不要赶星期五走。"他说这话时,非常认真,眼里噙着泪。

总之,从他全部的谈话看来,他对我是忠心耿耿,任何东西也无法让他与我分开,我发现他想回到自己的家乡,完全是出于他对族人的热爱,并希望我对他们有好处。因为我对此一无所知,所以我根本不想去对面的大陆,但我仍有一种想设法从这里逃走的强烈愿望,根据就是从他的谈话里得知,那里有 17 个有胡子的人。于是,我马上就跟星期五一起去找一棵适合砍伐的大树,造一只大独木舟,进行航行。岛上的树木足以造一支船队,但我主要是要找一棵靠近水边的树,这样造好船后就可以下水,避免我起先犯的错误。

最后,星期五选中了一棵树,因为用哪种木料造船,他比我内行得多。星期五要用火把这棵树烧成中空,做成一只船,但我教他用工具凿空更合适。经过大约一个月的辛劳,我们造好了小船。然而,这以后,我们用大转木一寸一寸地将它推到水里,花了将近两星期时间。

When she was in the water, and though she was so big it amazed me to see with what dexterity and how swift Friday would manage her, turn her and paddle her along; so I asked him if we might venture over in her; Yes, he said, he venture over in her very well, though great blow wind. However, I had a farther design that he knew nothing of, and that was to make a mast and sail and to fit her with an anchor and cable.

I was near two months performing this last work. After all this was done too, I had Friday to teach as to what belonged to the navigation of my boat; for though he knew very well how to paddle a canoe, he knew nothing what belonged to a sail and a rudder. As to the compass, I could make him understand very little of that. On the other hand, as there was very little cloudy weather, and seldom or never any fogs in those parts, there was the less occasion for a compass, seeing the stars were always to be seen by night, and the shore by day, except in the rainy seasons, and then nobody cared to stir abroad.

I was now entered on the seven and twentieth year of my captivity[1] in this place; though the three last years that I had this creature with me, ought rather to be left out of the account, my habitation being quite of another kind than in all the rest of the time. I kept the anniversary of my landing here with the same thankfulness to God for his mercies as at first. I had an invincible impression upon my thoughts that my deliverance was at hand, and that I should not be another year in this place. However, I went on with my husbandry, digging, planting, fencing, as usual; I gathered and cured my grapes.

The rainy season was in the meantime upon us, when I kept more within doors than at other times; so I had stowed our new vessel as secure as we could, bringing her up into the creek, where, as I said in the beginning, I landed my rafts from the ship and, hauling her up to the shore, at high water mark, I made Friday dig a little dock, just big enough to hold her, and just deep enough to give her water enough to fleet in; and then when the tide was out, we made a strong dam cross the end of it, to keep the water out; and so she lay dry, as to the tide from the sea; and to keep the rain off, we laid a great many boughs of trees so thick that she was as well thatched as a house; and thus we waited for the months of November and December, in which I designed to make my adventure.

---

[1] captivity   *n.* 囚禁，被关

船下水后，尽管很大，但星期五驾着它灵巧敏捷回转自如，使我大吃一惊。于是，我就问他，我们敢不敢坐这只船过海。他说，敢，我们敢坐它过海，就是刮大风也不要紧。不过，我对船有进一步的设计，他对此一无所知，那就是给船做桅杆和船帆，并配上锚和锚索。

这最后一项工作花了我将近两个月时间。小船也装备完毕后，我就把小船航行的方法教给星期五，因为尽管他船划得不错，但对船帆和船舵一窍不通。至于罗盘，我却无法让他明白它是怎么回事，好在这一带几乎没有多云天气，很少或从来没有见过雾，白天总能看到海岸，晚上总能看到星星，所以很少用罗盘。除了雨季，因为雨季没有人喜欢外出。

我流落到这个地方现在已是第 27 个年头了，尽管最后三年可以不算在内，因为我有了星期五作伴后，生活和以往所有的时间大不一样了。我像起先一样怀着感激天恩的心情度过了我到这里的纪念日。我明显感到，我获救的日子近在咫尺，知道自己不会在这里再呆一年了。然而，我仍像往常一样继续耕作、挖土、种植、筑围墙、采集和晒制葡萄。

同时，雨季快要到了，那时我大部分时间都呆在家里。所以，我尽可能把我们的新船放置妥当。我把船移到从前从大船上卸木排的那条小河里，并在涨潮时把它拖到岸边。我让星期五挖了个小船坞，大得足以容下小船，深得足以划进小船。然后，在退潮时，我们在船坞口筑了一道坚固的水坝挡住海水。这样，就是海水涨潮，船也不会浸湿。为了遮住雨水，我们又搭了好多好多大树枝，密密麻麻，看上去就像个茅草屋顶。就这样，我们等候着 11 月和 12 月的到来，我计划到那个时候冒险。

XXIV

When the settled season began to come in, as the thought of my design returned with the fair weather, I was preparing daily for the voyage; and the first thing I did was to lay by a certain quantity of provisions, being the stores for our voyage; and intended, in a week or a fortnight's time, to open the dock, and launch out our boat. I was busy one morning upon something of this kind, when I called to Friday, and bid him go to the seashore, and see if he could find a turtle, a thing which we generally got once a week, for the sake of the eggs as well as the flesh. Friday had not been long gone when he came running back and flew over my outer wall; and before I had time to speak to him, he cries out to me, "O Master! O Master! O sorrow! O bad!" "What's the matter, Friday?" said I; "O yonder, there," said he, "one, two, three canoe! One, two, three!" By his way of speaking, I concluded there were six; but on enquiry, I found it was but three. "Well, Friday," said I, "do not be frightened"; so I heartened him up as well as I could. However, I saw the poor fellow was most terribly scared; for nothing ran in his head but that they were come to look for him, and would cut him in pieces and eat him; and the poor fellow trembled, so that I scarce knew what to do with him. I comforted him as well as I could, and told him I was in as much danger as he, and that they would eat me as well as him. "But," said I, "Friday, we must resolve to fight them; can you fight, Friday?" "Me shoot," said he, "but there come many great number." "No matter for that," said I again, "our guns will fright them that we do not kill"; so I asked him whether if I resolved to defend him, he would defend me and stand by me and do just as I bid him. He said, "Me die, when you bid die, master"; so I went and fetched a good dram of rum, and gave him; for I had been so good a husband of my rum that had a great deal left. When he had drank it, I made him take the two fowling-pieces, which we always carried, and load them with large swan-shot, as big as small pistol bullets; then I took four muskets, and loaded them with two slugs and five small bullets each; and my two pistols I loaded with a brace of bullets each; I hung my great sword as usual, naked by my side, and gave Friday his hatchet.

24

　　旱季开始来临，随着天气晴好，我又想起了冒险的计划，每天都在为航行做准备。我做的第一件事就是储备一定量的粮食供航行用，并打算用一两周时间打开船坞，让船出海。一天早上，我正在忙着这种事儿时，冲星期五喊叫，让他去海边，看能不能抓到海龟。我们一般每周抓一次，一是为了吃龟肉，二是为了吃龟蛋。星期五去了没多久，就跑了回来，飞身跳进了外墙。还没等我对他说话，他就对我大声叫道："噢，主人！噢，主人！噢，不好了！噢，坏事了！"我说："怎么了，星期五？"他说："噢，那边，那里有一只，两只，三只独木舟！一只，两只，三只！"听了他这种说法，我还以为有六只独木舟；但又问了问，我才发现只有三只。我说："噢，星期五，不要害怕。"于是，我尽量给他壮胆。然而，我看到这可怜的家伙吓得魂飞魄散，因为他只想到他们是来找他的，而且一定会把他切成一块块吃掉。可怜的家伙浑身发抖，我简直不知道拿他怎么办。我尽可能安慰他，并告诉他，我也和他一样处在危险中，他们也会吃掉我。"不过，"我说，"星期五，我们必须下定决心和他们决战。你能打仗吗，星期五？"他说："我会打枪，可来了好多好多人。"我说："不要紧，我们的枪就是打不死他们，也会把他们吓住。"于是，我又问他，如果我决心保卫他，他会不会保卫我，支持我，听我吩咐。他说："主人，你叫我死我就死。"于是，我去拿了一大杯朗姆酒，送给他，因为朗姆酒我一向喝得很省，所以还剩有很多。他把酒喝下去后，我让他去把我们平常总是携带的那两支鸟枪拿来，并装上大子弹，那些大子弹像手枪子弹一样大。随后，我也取了四支，每支枪里都装上两颗弹丸和五颗小子弹，两支手枪各装了一对子弹。我像往常一样在腰间挎着那把无鞘长剑，将那把斧头给了星期五。

When I had thus prepared myself, I took my perspective glass and went up to the side of the hill, to see what I could discover; and I found quickly, by my glass, that there were one and twenty savages, three prisoners, and three canoes; and that their whole business seemed to be the triumphant banquet upon these three human bodies.

I observed also that they were landed not where they had done when Friday made his escape; but nearer to my creek, where the shore was low and where a thick wood came close almost down to the sea. This, with the abhorrence of the inhuman errand these wretches came about, filled me with such indignation that I came down again to Friday, and told him I was resolved to go down to them, and kill them all; and asked him if he would stand by me. He was now gotten over his fright, and his spirits being a little raised with the dram[1] I had given him, he was very cheerful and told me, as before, he would die when I bid die.

In this fit of fury, I took first and divided the arms which I had charged, as before, between us; I gave Friday one pistol to stick in his girdle[2], and three guns upon his shoulder; and I took one pistol, and the other three myself; and in this posture we marched out. I took a small bottle of rum in my pocket and gave Friday a large bag with more powder and bullets; and as to orders, I charged him to keep close behind me, and not to stir or shoot or do anything till I bid him; and in the meantime, not to speak a word. In this posture I fetched a compass to my right hand of near a mile, as well to get over the creek, as to get into the wood; so that I might come within shoot of them before I should be discovered, which I had seen by my glass, it was easy to do.

While I was making this march, my former thoughts returning, I began to abate my resolution; I do not mean that I entertained any fear of their number; for as they were naked, unarmed wretches, 'tis certain I was superior to them; but it occurred to my thoughts what call, what occasion, much less what necessity, I was in to go and dip my hands in blood, to attack people who had neither done or intended me any wrong; who, as to me, were innocent, and whose barbarous customs were their own disaster.

---

[1] dram *n.* 打兰，微量
[2] girdle *n.* 带，腰带，带状物

这样作好准备后，我拿着望远镜跑上山坡去看动静。我从望远镜里很快发现有 21 个野人、3 个俘虏，还有 3 只独木舟。他们来这里好像是要拿这三个活人开一次得胜宴。

我还注意到，他们这次登陆的地点不是上次星期五逃走的那个地方，而是更靠近我那条小河。那一带海岸低，并有一片密林几乎延伸到海边。看到他们登岸，想到这些坏蛋要干的野蛮勾当，真让人痛恨。我义愤填膺，跑下山告诉星期五，我决心下去把他们统统杀掉，然后问他愿不愿意支持我。他现在已经战胜了恐惧，我给他喝的那点朗姆酒也为他提了点儿精神。他兴高采烈，像先前那样告诉我，我叫他死他就死。

我就这样义愤填膺，先把已经装好弹药的武器分作两份，交给星期五一支手枪，叫他插在腰带上，三支长枪让他背在肩上。我自己也拿了一支手枪和三支长枪。我们就这样出发了。我口袋里带了一小瓶朗姆酒，将一大袋火药和子弹交给星期五，吩咐他紧跟在我身后，没有我的命令，不许乱动，不许开枪，不许行动，也不许说话。我按这种姿势向右走了差不多有一英里，以便越过小河，钻进树林。我要在他们发现我之前，进入射程内，根据我用望远镜观察，这很容易做到。

在这次前进过程中，我从前的一些想法又回到了心头，决心开始减弱。我不是说怕他们人多，因为他们都是赤身露体、没有武器的坏蛋，这我肯定比他们占优势。但我想到的是，我有什么命令、什么理由、更没有什么必要去杀人流血，去袭击这些人，他们既没有伤害过我，也无意要伤害我。对我来说，他们是无辜的。他们那种野蛮的风俗是他们自己的不幸。

But God did not call me to take upon me to be a judge of their actions, much less an executioner of his justice; that it was true, Friday might justify it, because he was a declared enemy and in a state of war with those people; and it was lawful for him to attack them. At last I resolved I would only go and place myself near them, that I might observe their barbarous feast, and that I would act then as God should direct.

With this resolution I entered the wood, and with all possible wariness[1] and silence, Friday following close at my heels, I marched till I came to the skirt of the wood, on the side which was next to them; only that one corner of the wood lay between me and them; here I called softly to Friday, and showing him a great tree, which was just at the corner of the wood, I bade him go to the tree, and bring me word if he could see there plainly what they were doing; he did so and came immediately back to me, and told me they might be plainly viewed there; that they were all about their fire, eating the flesh of one of their prisoners; and that another lay bound upon the sand, a little from them, which he said they would kill next; and which fired all the very soul within me; he told me it was not one of their nation; but one of the bearded men, who he had told me of that came to their country in the boat. I was filled with horror at the very naming the white-bearded man, and going to the tree, I saw plainly by my glass a white man who lay upon the beach of the sea, with his hands and his feet tied with flags, or things like rushes; and that he was an European, and had clothes on.

There was another tree, and a little thicket beyond it, about fifty yards nearer to them than the place where I was, which by going a little way about, I saw I might come at undiscovered, and that then I should be within half shot of them; so I withheld my passion, and going back about twenty paces, I got behind some bushes, which held all the way, till I came to the other tree; and then I came to a little rising ground, which gave me a full view of them, at the distance of about eighty yards.

I had now not a moment to lose; for nineteen of the dreadful wretches sat upon the ground, all close huddled together, and had just sent the other two to butcher the poor Christian, and bring him perhaps limb by limb to their fire, and they were stooped down to untie the bands at his feet.

---

[1] wariness *n.* 谨慎，注意，小心

不过，上帝并没有召唤我去做他们行动的审判者，更没有要我去做审判的执行者。诚然，星期五有充分理由那样做，因为他是他们公开的敌人，和他们处于交战状态。他要攻击他们是合法的。最后，我决定只去站在他们附近，观察一下他们的野蛮宴会，然后根据上帝的指示见机行事。

这样决定后，我就进入了树林。星期五紧随我后，小心翼翼、悄无声息，直至我走到树林边缘，那里离他们最近，我和他们中间只隔着一角树木。到了这里，我悄声招呼星期五，指着林角上的一棵大树，吩咐他走到那棵树边，如果他能看清他们的行动，就告诉我。他就这样去了，然后马上回来告诉我说，他从那里看得一清二楚，他们正围着火堆吃一个俘虏的肉；另一个俘虏被捆绑着，躺在离他们不远的沙地上。他说他们接着就要杀他。听了他的话，我怒火中烧。他又告诉我说，那不是他们的族人，而是他曾对我说过的坐小船到他们部落里去的一个有胡子的人。我一听说是有胡子的白人，就吓得发抖。我走到那棵大树边，通过望远镜清晰地看到一个白人躺在海滩上，手脚被菖蒲或灯心草类的东西捆绑着，他是个欧洲人，身上穿着衣服。

那里还有一棵树，树那边有一小丛灌木，比我所在的地方离他们要近大约 50 码。我看到我绕一点路，就可以神不知鬼不觉走到那边。那样，我和他们的距离就不到一半射程了。于是，我强压怒火，往回走了大约 20 步，来到一片矮树丛后面。我借着这片矮树丛的掩护，一直走到另一棵树边，然后来到一个小高地，那里一览无余，离那些野人大约有 80 码远。

我现在一刻也不能浪费了，因为 19 个可怕的坏蛋挤在一起坐在地上，并派出另两个坏蛋去屠杀那可怜的基督徒，可能是要肢解他，拿到火上去烤。我看到那两个野人弯下腰，解他脚边的那些带子。

I turned to Friday. "Now, Friday," said I, "do as I bid thee"; Friday said he would; "Then, Friday," said I, "do exactly as you see me do; fail in nothing." So I set down one of the muskets and the fowling piece upon the ground, and Friday did the like by his; and with the other musket I took my aim at the savages, bidding him do the like; then asking him if he was ready. He said, "Yes." "Then fire at them," said I; and the same moment I fired also.

Friday took his aim so much better than I that on the side that he shot he killed two of them and wounded three more; and on my side, I killed one and wounded two. They were in a dreadful consternation; and all of them, who were not hurt, jumped up upon their feet, but did not immediately know which way to run, or which way to look; for they knew not from whence their destruction came. Friday kept his eyes close upon me, that, as I had bid him, he might observe what I did; so as soon as the first shot was made, I threw down the piece and took up the fowling piece, and Friday did the like; he saw me cock and present, he did the same again. "Are you ready, Friday?" said I. "Yes," said he. "Let fly then," said I, "in the name of God," and with that I fired again among the amazed wretches, and so did Friday; and as our pieces were now loaden with what I called swanshot, or small pistol bullets, we found only two drop; but so many were wounded that they run about yelling and screaming like mad creatures, all bloody, and miserably wounded most of them; whereof three more fell quickly after, though not quite dead.

"Now, Friday," said I, laying down the discharged pieces, and taking up the musket, which was yet loaden. "follow me," said I, which he did, with a great deal of courage; upon which I rushed out of the wood and showed myself, and Friday close at my foot; as soon as I perceived they saw me, I shouted as loud as I could, and bade Friday do so too; and running as fast as I could, which, by the way, was not very fast, being loaden with arms as I was, I made directly towards the poor victim, who was lying upon the beach between the place where they sat and the sea; the two butchers who were just going to work with him had left him at the surprise of our first fire and fled in a terrible fright to the seaside and had jumped into a canoe, and three more of the rest made the same way.

我转身对星期五说:"好,星期五,听我的命令行动。"星期五说他一定。我说:"那好,星期五,看我怎么做你就怎么做,不许失手。"于是,我把一支火铳和那支鸟枪放在地下,星期五也把他的一支火铳和一支鸟枪放在地下。我用剩下的一支瞄准那些野人,同时吩咐星期五也用枪瞄准他们,然后问他是不是准备好。他说:"好了。""那就向他们开火,"我说着,也开了火。

星期五的枪法比我好多了。他那边打死了两个,还打伤了三个。我这边打死了一个,打伤了两个。他们吓得惊慌失措,所有没有受伤的从地上跳了起来,但一时间不知道朝哪个方向跑,也不知道朝哪个方向看,因为他们不知道这场灾祸来自哪里。星期五两眼紧盯着我,因为我吩咐过他要观察我的动作。于是,我放完第一枪,就马上放下那支枪,拿起那支鸟枪;星期五也照着做了。他看见我歪头举枪瞄准,他又如此这般照做。我说:"星期五,你准备好了吗?"他说:"好了。"我说:"那就以上帝的名义开火吧!"说着,我就向那群大惊失色的坏蛋又开了一枪,星期五也开了一枪。因为这次我们枪里装的都是大子弹或小手枪子弹,所以我们发现只打倒了两个,但受伤的很多。他们像疯子似的乱跑乱叫,浑身是血,大多数受了重伤;很快又倒下了三个,尽管还没有完全死去。

"好了,星期五,"我放下开过火的鸟枪,拿起那支装好弹药的火铳说:"跟我来。"他勇气十足地跟着我。于是,我冲出树林,出现在那些野人眼前,星期五紧随我后。我一察觉到他们看见我,就尽可能大声呐喊,然后吩咐星期五也跟着我大声呐喊。我一边呐喊,一边向前飞跑。我跑得不是很快,因为我身上背满了武器。我径直向那可怜的俘虏跑去。他正躺在他们坐的地方和大海之间的海滩上。那两个正要动手杀他的坏蛋在我们放第一枪时,早已吓得魂不附体,丢下俘虏,向海边跑去,跳进了一只独木舟。还有三个也朝同一方向逃跑。

I turned to Friday, and bid him step forwards and fire at them; he understood me immediately, and running about forty yards, to be near them, he shot at them, and I thought he had killed them all; for I saw them all fall of a heap into the boat; though I saw two of them up again quickly. However, he killed two of them and wounded the third; so that he lay down in the bottom of the boat, as if he had been dead.

While Friday fired at them, I pulled out my knife and cut the flags that bound the poor victim, and, loosing his hands and feet, I lifted him up, and asked him in the Portuguese tongue what he was. He answered in Latin, "Christianus"; but was so weak and faint that he could scarce stand or speak; I took my bottle out of my pocket and gave it him, making signs that he should drink, which he did; and I gave him a piece of bread, which he ate; then I asked him what countryman he was. And he said, "Espagniole"; and being a little recovered, let me know by all the signs he could possibly make how much he was in my debt for his deliverance; "Seignior," said I, with as much Spanish as I could make up, "we will talk afterwards; but we must fight now; if you have any strength left, take this pistol and sword and lay about you." He took them very thankfully, and no sooner had he the arms in his hands, but as if they had put new vigour into him, he flew upon his murderers like fury and had cut two of them in pieces in an instant; for the truth is, as the whole was a surprise to them, so the poor creatures were so much frightened with the noise of our pieces that they fell down and had no more power to attempt their own escape than their flesh had to resist our shot; and that was the case of those five that Friday shot at in the boat; for as three of them fell with the hurt they received, so the other two fell with the fright.

I kept my piece in my hand still, without firing, being willing to keep my charge ready, because I had given the Spaniard my pistol and sword; so I called to Friday and bade him run up to the tree from whence we first fired and fetch the arms which lay there that had been discharged, which he did with great swiftness; and then giving him my musket, I sat down myself to load all the rest again, and bade them come to me when they wanted.

我转向星期五，吩咐他追上去向他们开火。他马上明白了我的意思，向前跑了大约 40 码，靠近他们，向他们开枪。我以为他把他们都打死了，因为我看到他们扎成一堆都倒进了船里。我看到其中两个人很快又坐了起来。不过，他打死了两个，打伤了一个，所以那个受伤的倒在船底，像死了一般。

星期五向他们开火时，我拔出刀子，割断那可怜的受害者身上捆着的菖蒲草，然后解开他的手脚，扶他起来。我用葡萄牙话问他是什么人。他用拉丁话回答说："基督徒。"他浑身无力，无精打采，几乎站不起来，也说不出话来。我从口袋里拿出那瓶酒，递给他，同时打手势让他喝。他喝了几口。我又给了他一块面包，他也吃了下去。随后，我又问他是哪个国家的人。他说："西班牙人。"这时，他稍微恢复了精神，做出各种手势告诉我说他多么感激我对他的救命之恩。"先生，"我尽可能用西班牙语凑合着说，"我们以后再说。我们现在必须打仗。你要是还有力气，就拿上这支手枪和这把刀杀过去。"他非常感激地接过它们。他手里一拿到武器，好像注入了新的活力，飞身扑向要杀他的那些凶手，立马就砍倒了两个，把他们剁成了肉酱。因为，事实上，这完全出乎他们的意料，这帮可怜的家伙被我们的枪声吓得心惊胆战，倒在地上，无力逃跑，只好拿他们的肉体来抵挡我们的枪弹。星期五打死打伤在小船上的那五个也一样，因为其中三个就是受伤倒下的，另两个则是吓昏倒下的。

这时，我手里仍拿着一支装好弹药的枪，但我没有开枪，因为我已经把手枪和刀给了那个西班牙人。于是，我把星期五叫过来，吩咐他赶快跑到我们第一次开火的那棵大树边，把那几支空枪拿过来。他飞快地取了回来。随后，我把自己的火铳交给他，坐下来给所有的枪又装上弹药，并吩咐他想用枪时随时可以来我这里拿。

While I was loading these pieces, there happened a fierce engagement between the Spaniard and one of the savages, who made at him with one of their great wooden swords, the same weapon that was to have killed him before, if I had not prevented it. The Spaniard, who was as bold and as brave as could be imagined, though weak, had fought this Indian a good while and had cut him two great wounds on his head; but the savage being a stout lusty fellow, closing in with him, had thrown him down and was wringing my sword out of his hand, when the Spaniard, though undermost[1] wisely quitting the sword, drew the pistol from his girdle, shot the savage through the body and killed him upon the spot, before I, who was running to help him, could come near him.

Friday being now left to his liberty, pursued the flying wretches with no weapon in his hand, but his hatchet; and with that he dispatched those three, who were wounded at first and fallen, and all the rest he could come up with, and the Spaniard coming to me for a gun, I gave him one of the fowling pieces, with which he pursued two of the savages, and wounded them both; but as he was not able to run, they both got from him into the wood, where Friday pursued them and killed one of them; but the other was too nimble for him, and though he was wounded, yet had plunged himself into the sea and swam with all his might off to those two who were left in the canoe, which three in the canoe, with one wounded, who we know not whether he died or no, were all that escaped our hands of one and twenty.

Those that were in the canoe worked hard to get out of gunshot; and though Friday made two or three shot at them, I did not find that he hit any of them. Friday would fain have had me took one of their canoes and pursued them; and indeed I was very anxious about their escape, least carrying the news home to their people, they should come back perhaps with two or three hundred of their canoes and devour us by mere multitude; so I consented to pursue them by sea, and running to one of their canoes, I jumped in and bade Friday follow me; but when I was in the canoe, I was surprised to find another poor creature lie there alive, bound hand and foot, as the Spaniard was, for the slaughter, and almost dead with fear, not knowing what the matter was; for he had not been able to look up over the side of the boat.

---

[1] undermost   *adj.* 最下的，最低的

我正在给这些枪装弹药时，那个西班牙人和一个野人勇猛地打了起来。那个野人手里拿着一把大木刀跟西班牙人拼杀。这正是他们先前用来杀他的那种武器，要不是我阻止，早就把他杀了。那个西班牙人虽然身体虚弱，却非常大胆勇敢，已经和那野人打了好一阵子，在那野人头上砍了两个大口子。可是，那野人结实健壮，抱住西班牙人，把他撂倒在地，伸手去夺西班牙人手里的刀。这时，那个西班牙人急中生智，松开手里的刀，从腰间拔出手枪，没等我来得及跑过去帮忙，他早已射穿那野人的身体，当场结果了那野人的性命。

此时，星期五信马由缰，手里没带武器，只拿着一把斧头，向那些溃逃的坏蛋追去。他先用斧头结果了先前受伤倒下的三个野人的性命，然后把他能追上的野人杀了个精光。这时，那个西班牙人过来向我要枪，我给了他一支鸟枪。他拿住鸟枪，追上了两个野人，把他们都打伤了，但因为他无力再跑，所以那两个受伤的野人钻进了树林里。星期五又追上他们，砍死了一个；但另一个行动敏捷，尽管受了伤，却还是跳到了海里，拼命朝留在独木舟上的那两个野人游去。21个野人中，这三个人连同一个受了伤、生死不明的野人，从我们手里逃走了。

那些逃上独木舟的野人拼命划船，想逃出我们的射程。尽管星期五向他们开了两三枪，但我没有看到他打中任何人。星期五渴望我把其中一只独木舟弄过来去追他们。确实，我非常担心他们逃走，万一他们把消息带回家，也许会有两三百只独木舟卷土重来，仅凭他们人多势众，就会把我们吃光。所以，我同意星期五到海上去追他们。我跑向一只独木舟，跳了上去，并吩咐星期五跟着我。但我一跳上独木舟，就吃惊地发现船上还一个可怜的家伙活着躺在那里，也像那个西班牙人一样，手脚捆绑，等着屠杀。他不知道是怎么回事，吓得半死，因为他无法从船边抬起头。

I immediately cut the twisted flags, which they had bound him with, and would have helped him up; but he could not stand or speak, but groaned most piteously, believing it seems still that he was only unbound in order to be killed.

When Friday came to him, I bade him speak to him, and tell him of his deliverance, and pulling out my bottle, made him give the poor wretch a dram, which, with the news of his being delivered, revived him, and he sat up in the boat; but when Friday came to hear him speak, and look in his face, it would have moved any one to tears, to have seen how Friday kissed him, embraced him, hugged him, cried, laughed, hallooed, jumped about, danced, sung, then cried again, wrung his hands, beat his own face and head, and then sung, and jumped about again, like a distracted creature. It was a good while before I could make him speak to me, or tell me what was the matter; but when he came a little to himself, he told me that it was his father.

It is not easy for me to express how it moved me to see what ecstasy[1] and filial[2] affection had worked in this poor savage, at the sight of his father, and of his being delivered from death. He went into the boat and out of the boat a great many times. When he went in to him, he would sit down by him, open his breast, and hold his father's head close to his bosom[3], half an hour together, to nourish it; then he took his arms and ankles, which were numbed and stiff with the binding, and chafed[4] and rubbed them with his hands; and I, perceiving what the case was, gave him some rum out of my bottle to rub them with, which did them a great deal of good.

This action put an end to our pursuit of the canoe with the other savages, who were now gotten almost out of sight; and it was happy for us that we did not; for it blew so hard within two hours after, and before they could be gotten a quarter of their way, and continued blowing so hard all night, and that from the northwest, which was against them, that I could not suppose their boat could live, or that they ever reached to their own coast.

---

[1] ecstasy　*n.*　入迷；狂喜
[2] filial　*adj.*　子女的，孝顺的
[3] bosom　*n.*　胸部，胸
[4] chafe　*v.*　（将皮肤等）擦热，擦破

我马上割断捆在他身上的菖蒲草，想扶他起来，但他站不起来，也说不出话来，只是可怜巴巴地呻吟着，他以为松绑只是为了杀他。

　　星期五来到他身边时，我让他跟那人说话，告诉他已经得救了。同时，我又拿出酒瓶，叫星期五给这个可怜的人喝一口。那人听到自己获救的消息，精神为之一振，在船里坐了起来。星期五一听到他说话，又看了看他的脸，又亲又抱，又哭又笑，又喊又跳，载歌载舞，然后又是哭嚎，又是绞手，又是打自己的脸和头，随后又唱又跳，就像个疯子似的。任何人看了都会感动得流泪。过了好一阵子，我才让他开口说话，让他告诉我是怎么回事。他稍微恢复了意识，才告诉我说，这是他的父亲。

　　这可怜的野人见到父亲，见到父亲绝处逢生，居然流露出这样的孝心和狂喜，我深受感动，难以言表。只见他时而跳上小船，时而又跳下小船，来来回回反复了好多次。每次上船，他总会坐到父亲身边，敞开胸膛，将父亲的头紧贴在胸口，一坐就是半小时，让父亲的头得以恢复。之后，他又双手捧住父亲被绑得麻木和僵硬的手臂和脚踝来回搓揉。见此情景，我就给他倒了一些朗姆酒搓揉，这样效果好多了。

　　这一举动终止了我们去追那条独木舟上的其他野人。他们现在差不多连影子都看不见了。我们没有去追正好，因为之后不到两小时，他们还没能走四分之一路程，海上就刮起了大风，而且狂刮了整整一夜。风是从西北方刮来的，对他们来说正好是逆风，我想他们的船闯不过去，也到不了自己的海岸。

But to return to Friday; he was so busy about his father that I could not find in my heart to take him off. But after I thought he could leave him a little, I called him to me, and he came jumping and laughing, and pleased to the highest extreme; then I asked him if he had given his father any bread. He shook his head and said, "None; Ugly dog eat all up self." So I gave him a cake of bread out of a little pouch[1] I carried on purpose; I also gave him a dram for himself, but he would not taste it, but carried it to his father. I had in my pocket also two or three bunches of my raisins, so I gave him a handful of them for his father. He had no sooner given his father these raisins but I saw him come out of the boat and run away, as if he had been bewitched[2]; and though I called, and hallooed, too, after him, it was all one, away he went, and in a quarter of an hour, I saw him come back again; and as he came nearer, I found his pace was slacker, because he had something in his hand.

When he came up to me, I found he had been quite home for an earthen jug to bring his father some fresh water, and that he had got two more cakes, or loaves of bread. The bread he gave me, but the water he carried to his father. However, as I was very thirsty too, I took a little sup of it. This water revived his father more than all the rum I had given him; for he was just fainting with thirst.

When his father had drank, I called to him to know if there was any water left; he said, "Yes"; and I bade him give it to the poor Spaniard, who was in as much want of it as his father; and I sent one of the cakes that Friday brought to the Spaniard too, who was indeed very weak, and was reposing himself upon a green place under the shade of a tree; and whose limbs were also very stiff, and very much swelled with the rude bandage he had been tied with. When I saw that upon Friday's coming to him with the water, he sat up and drank, and took the bread and began to eat, I went to him, and gave him a handful of raisins; he looked up in my face with all the tokens of gratitude and thankfulness that could appear in any countenance; but was so weak, notwithstanding he had so exerted himself in the fight that he could not stand up upon his feet; he tried to do it two or three times, but was really not able, his ankles were so swelled and so painful to him; so I bade him sit still, and caused Friday to rub his ankles and bathe them with rum, as he had done his father's.

---

[1] pouch *n.* 小袋，烟草袋
[2] bewitched *adj.* 中魔法的

现在再回头说星期五。他正在父亲身边忙活，所以我不忍心让他离开。等我认为他可以离开一会儿时，才把他叫到我身边。他走过来时，又跳又笑，兴高采烈。随后，我问他是不是给他父亲吃了面包。他摇摇头说："没有，我这丑狗把面包吃光了。"于是，我从自己特意带的一只小袋里给他掏出一块面包，又给了他一点儿酒，让他自己喝。可是，他连尝都没尝一下，就送给了他父亲。我口袋里还有两三串葡萄干，就给了他一把，让他也送给父亲。他把这把葡萄干一送给父亲，我就看到他又跳出小船，像着了魔似的跑走了。尽管我对他大声叫喊，但他还是一个劲儿地跑走了。不到一刻时间，我看到他又跑了回来。他走近时，我发现他的步子跑得比较缓慢，因为他手里拿着一些东西。

他来到我面前时，我才明白他是跑回家去拿一只泥罐，为他父亲弄了一些淡水，还带来了两块面包。他把面包交给我，却把水送给了父亲。不过，我也很渴，就喝了一小口。这水让他父亲恢复了精神，比我给他的朗姆酒还有效，因为他确实快要渴昏了。

他父亲喝完水后，我将星期五叫过来，想知道罐子里还有没有水。他说："有。"我就吩咐他把水送给那个西班牙人，他和星期五的父亲一样缺水。我又让星期五把他带来的面包也给那个西班牙人送一块。那个西班牙人确实非常虚弱，正躺在一棵树下的绿地上休息，四肢因被捆得太狠，现在又硬又肿。我看到星期五一把水给他送过去，他就坐起来喝，然后又接过面包，开始吃了起来。我走到他面前，又给了他一把葡萄干。他抬起头，带着无限感激之情望着我的脸。可是，他的身体非常虚弱，尽管他在和野人战斗时奋力拼搏，现在却连站都站不起来了。他试了两三次，但确实无法站起来，脚踝肿得非常厉害，疼痛难忍。于是，我让他坐下别动，要星期五像他替父亲搓揉手脚那样给那人揉脚踝，并用朗姆酒搓洗。

I observed Friday, every two minutes, all the while he was here, turned his head about to see if his father was in the same place and posture as he left him sitting; and at last he found he was not to be seen; at which he started up, and without speaking a word, flew with that swiftness to him. But when he came, he only found he had laid himself down to ease his limbs; so Friday came back to me presently, and I then spoke to the Spaniard to let Friday help him up and lead him to the boat, and then he should carry him to our dwelling, where I would take care of him. But Friday took the Spaniard quite up upon his back and carried him away to the boat and set him down softly upon the side of the canoe, with his feet in the inside of it, and then lifted him quite in and set him close to his father, and presently stepping out again, launched the boat off, and paddled it along the shore faster than I could walk, though the wind blew pretty hard too; so he brought them both safe into our creek; and leaving them in the boat, runs away to fetch the other canoe. As he passed me, I asked him whither he went; he told me, "Go fetch more boat"; so away he went like the wind; and he had the other canoe in the creek almost as soon as I got to it by land; so he wafted me over, and then went to help our new guests out of the boat; but they were neither of them able to walk; so that poor Friday knew not what to do.

To remedy this, I went to work in my thought, and calling to Friday to bid them sit down on the bank, I soon made a kind of hand-barrow to lay them on, and Friday and I carried them up both together upon it between us. But when we got them to the outside of our wall, we were at a worse loss than before; for it was impossible to get them over; and I was resolved not to break it down. So I set to work again; and Friday and I, in about two hours' time, made a very handsome tent, covered with old sails, and above that with boughs[1] of trees, being in the space without our outward fence, and between that and the grove of young wood which I had planted. And here we made them two beds of good rice-straw, with blankets laid upon it to lie on, and another to cover them on each bed.

---

[1] bough   *n.* 大树枝，主枝

我观察到，在此期间，星期五每隔两分钟就回头看他父亲是不是还坐在原地，是不是还是他离开时让父亲坐的那个坐姿。最后，他发觉父亲不见了，就惊跳起来，一句话也不说，飞快地跑到父亲那里。但他过去时，只见父亲为了放松四肢，躺了下去。于是，星期五又马上回到了我身边。这时，我对西班牙人说，让星期五扶他走到小船上去，然后坐船到我们的住处，这样我就能照顾他。然而，星期五一下子背起那个西班牙人，走到了小船边，脚朝里轻轻地把他放到船沿上，然后又完全把他提起来放在他父亲身边。星期五马上又跳出小船，把船推到水里，沿岸划了起来。尽管风相当大，但他划得比我走得还快。于是，他就把他俩安全地送到了那条小河，让他们留在船里，又跑去弄另一只独木舟。他经过我身边时，我问他去哪里，他告诉我说："再去弄一只小船。"说完，他一阵风似的跑走了。我从陆路刚走到小河边，他就已经把另一只独木舟划进了河里。于是，他先把我渡过小河，又去帮我们的两位新客人下了船。可是，他俩都无法走动，所以可怜的星期五不知道该怎么办。

　　为了解决这个问题，我想了又想，然后叫星期五吩咐他俩在河岸上坐下。不久，我就做了一个手推车一样的东西，让他俩坐上去，我和星期五一前一后抬着他们往前走。然而，我们抬到住处墙外时，却比先前更不知所措了，因为不可能把他俩背过墙去，但我又绝不愿推倒围墙。于是，我又开始忙活起来，我和星期五用了大约不到两小时搭了一个非常漂亮的帐篷，篷顶上盖着旧帆布，帆布上又压了一些大树枝。帐篷就搭在我们外墙外面的那块空地上，处在外墙和我种植的那片幼林之间。我们在帐篷里搭了两张干爽的稻草床，上面铺上毯子，又给每张床上加了一条盖的毯子。

XXV

As soon as I had secured my two weak rescued prisoners and given them shelter and a place to rest them upon, I began to think of making some provision for them. And the first thing I did, I ordered Friday to take a yearling goat, betwixt[1] a kid and a goat, out of my particular flock, to be killed; when I cut off the hinder quarter, and chopping it into small pieces, I set Friday to work to boiling and stewing, and made them a very good dish of flesh and broth, having put some barley and rice also into the broth; and as I cooked it without doors, for I made no fire within my inner wall, so I carried it all into the new tent; and having set a table there for them, I sat down and ate my own dinner also with them, and, as well as I could, cheered them and encouraged them; Friday being my interpreter, especially to his father, and indeed to the Spaniard too; for the Spaniard spoke the language of the savages pretty well.

After we had dined, I ordered Friday to take one of the canoes, and go and fetch our muskets and other fire-arms, which for want of time we had left upon the place of battle, and the next day I ordered him to go and bury the dead bodies of the savages, which lay open to the sun, and would presently be offensive; and I also ordered him to bury the horrid remains of their barbarous feast. When I went again, I could scarce know where it was, otherwise than by the corner of the wood pointing to the place.

I then began to enter into a little conversation with my two new subjects; and first I set Friday to enquire of his father what he thought of the escape of the savages in that canoe, and whether we might expect a return of them with a power too great for us to resist.

---

[1] betwixt *prep.* 在···之间，在···中间

25

　　我一安顿好解救出来的身体虚弱的两个俘虏，使他们有遮风避雨和休息的地方，就开始想到给他们弄一些吃的东西。我先吩咐星期五从我特殊的羊圈里挑了一只不大不小的山羊宰掉。我把山羊的后半截砍下来，切成小块，让星期五着手去炖煮，然后又在汤里加了一些大麦和大米，做成了味道鲜美的羊肉粥。这顿饭我是在门外做的，因为我从不在内墙生火，所以就把羊肉粥端进了新帐篷，又在那里为他们摆上一张桌子，坐下来和他们一块吃，而且尽可能谈笑风生，鼓励他们。星期五给我当翻译，尤其是把我的话译给他父亲听，当然也译给那个西班牙人，因为那个西班牙人说他们野人的话相当不错。

　　饭后，我命令星期五划独木舟去把我们的火铳和其他武器运回来，因为时间仓促，这些武器留在了战场上。第二天，我又命令他去埋掉那几个野人的尸体，因为尸体晾在太阳下，很快就会发臭。我还吩咐他埋掉野蛮人肉宴留下的可怕的残骨剩肉。我再到那边去时，要不是靠那片树林的一角辨别方向，简直认不出那是什么地方。

　　随后，我开始和那两个新臣民进行了一次短暂交谈。首先，我让星期五问他父亲，他认为那几个逃跑的野人会怎么样，他们是不是会带大批野人卷土重来，人数会不会多得我们难以抵抗。

His first opinion was that the savages in the boat never could live out the storm which blew that night they went off but must of necessity be drowned or driven south to those other shores where they were as sure to be devoured; but as to what they would do if they came safe on shore, he said he knew not; but it was his opinion that they were so dreadfully frightened with the manner of their being attacked, the noise and the fire, that he believed they would tell their people, they were all killed by thunder and lightning, not by the hand of man, and that the two which appeared, viz., Friday and me, were two heavenly spirits or furies, come down to destroy them, and not men with weapons. This he said he knew, because he heard them all cry out so in their language to one another, for it was impossible to them to conceive that a man could dart fire and speak thunder and kill at a distance without lifting up the hand, as was done now. And this old savage was in the right; for the savages never attempted to go over to the island afterwards.

This, however, I knew not, and therefore was under continual apprehensions for a good while, and kept always upon my guard, me and all my army; for as we were now four of us, I would have ventured upon a hundred of them fairly in the open field at any time.

In a little time, however, no more canoes appearing, the fear of their coming wore off, and I began to take my former thoughts of a voyage to the main into consideration; being likewise assured by Friday's father that I might depend upon good usage from their nation on his account, if I would go.

But my thoughts were a little suspended when I had a serious discourse with the Spaniard and when I understood that there were sixteen more of his countrymen and Portuguese, who, having been cast away, and made their escape to that side, lived there at peace indeed with the savages, but were very sore put to it for necessaries, and indeed for life. I asked him all the particulars of their voyage and found they were a Spanish ship bound from the Rio de la Plata to the Havana, being directed to leave their loading there, which was chiefly hides and silver, and to bring back what European goods they could meet with there; that they had five Portuguese seamen on board, who they took out of another wreck; that five of their own men were drowned when the first ship was lost, and that these escaped through infinite dangers and hazards, and arrived almost starved on the cannibal coast, where they expected to have been devoured every moment.

他的第一个意见就是，那条小船绝逃不过那天夜里的风暴，那些野人不是被淹死，就是被刮到了南方其他海岸，他们肯定会被当地的野人吃掉。至于安全靠岸，他们会采取什么行动，星期五的父亲说他不得而知，但他认为，他们受到我们那种袭击，被枪声和火光吓得半死，所以他相信，他们一定会告诉自己的族人，说那些没有逃出来的人是被霹雳和闪电击死的，而不是被人用手打死的；那两个露面的人，也就是我和星期五，是天兵神将从天上下来消灭他们，而不是手持武器的凡人。他说，这他知道，因为他听到他们都用土话这样传来传去，因为他们无法想像，一个人居然既能喷火又能响雷，而且连手都不抬，就能从远处把人打死。这个老野人说的不错，因为后来那些野人再也没有企图到岛上来。

然而，我开始并不知道，所以提心吊胆了好一阵子，总是带着我的全部军队严加防守。我们现在已有 4 个人了，所以哪怕他们来上 100 人，只要他们在开阔地，我就敢跟他们决战。

然而，过了一小段时间，并没有见独木舟出现，我害怕他们来的担心渐渐消失了，又开始考虑坐船到大陆上去的老问题，因为星期五的父亲向我保证，如果我愿意去，他们的族人会看在他的面上优待我。

不过，我和那个西班牙人认真交谈后，又把那些念头暂时收了起来。我明白他们那边还有 16 个西班牙人和葡萄牙人。自从船只遇难，他们逃到那边后，确实和那些野人相安无事，但生活必需品非常匮乏，实在难以活命。我询问了他们航行的所有细节，发现他们乘的是一条西班牙船，从拉普拉塔河出发，前往哈瓦那，准备在哈瓦那卸货（船上装的主要是皮革和银子），然后再看看能在那里碰上什么欧洲货带回去。他们船上有 5 个葡萄牙船员，是从另一条遇难船上救下来的。后来，他们自己的船也出事了，淹死了 5 个西班牙船员，其余人历尽艰难险阻，逃到吃人族海岸时，差不多都快饿死了；上岸后，他们时刻担心被那些野人吃掉。

He told me they had some arms with them, but they were perfectly useless, for that they had neither powder or ball, the washing of the sea having spoiled all their powder but a little, which they used at their first landing to provide themselves some food.

I asked him what he thought would become of them there, and if they had formed no design of making any escape. He said they had many consultations about it, but that having neither vessel, or tools to build one, or provisions of any kind, their councils always ended in tears and despair.

I asked him how he thought they would receive a proposal from me, which might tend towards an escape; and whether, if they were all here, it might not be done. I told him with freedom, I feared mostly their treachery[1] and ill usage of me, if I put my life in their hands; for that gratitude was no inherent virtue in the nature of man; nor did men always square their dealings by the obligations they had received so much as they did by the advantages they expected. I told him it would be very hard that I should be the instrument of their deliverance and that they should afterwards make me their prisoner in New Spain, where an Englishman was certain to be made a sacrifice, what necessity or what accident soever[2] brought him thither. And that I had rather be delivered up to the savages and be devoured alive than fall into the merciless claws of the priests and be carried into the Inquisition[3]. I added that otherwise I was persuaded, if they were all here, we might, with so many hands, build a bark large enough to carry us all away, either to the Brazils southward, or to the islands or Spanish coast northward. But that if in requital[4] they should, when I had put weapons into their hands, carry me by force among their own people, I might be ill used for my kindness to them and make my case worse than it was before.

---

[1] treachery   *n.* 背叛，背信弃义
[2] soever   *adv.* 无论，不论何种
[3] Inquisition   *n.* （中世纪天主教审判异教徒）宗教裁判所
[4] in requital   为酬谢…，为报答…

他告诉我说，他们本来随身带了一些武器，但因为既无火药又无子弹，所以毫无用处。他们所有的火药，除了一丁点儿之外，都被海水浸湿了，这一丁点儿也在他们初次上岸打猎充饥时用光了。

我问他，他认为，那些人在那里会怎样，有没有逃跑的打算。他说，他们对这件事商量过许多次，但一没有船，二没有造船工具，三没有任何粮食，所以他们商量的结果总是以眼泪和失望而结束。

我问他，如果我提出一个逃生的建议，他认为他们是不是会接受，如果让他们都到这里来，这是不是能做到。我坦率地告诉他，我最怕的是，一旦我把自己的生命交到他们手里，他们说不定会背信弃义、恩将仇报，因为感恩戴德并不是人性中与生俱来的美德，人们也往往不是以其所受的恩泽来规范自己的行为，而常常是见利忘义。我又告诉他说，如果我帮助他们逃生，他们随后把我当成俘虏押往新西班牙，那将会非常艰难，因为英国人在那里肯定会成为牺牲品，无论是迫不得已还是他偶然到那里。我说，我宁愿把自己交给那些野人，让他们活活吞吃，也不愿落入那些残忍的僧侣的魔掌，受到宗教法庭的审判。我又补充说，如果不是这样，我相信，只要他们都到这里来，我们有这么多人手，就可以造一条大船，把我们都载走，要么向南开往巴西，要么向北开往西印度群岛或西班牙海岸。然而，如果我把武器交到他们手里，他们恩将仇报用武力把我劫持到他们自己人那里去，我就可能好心不得好报，处境比以前更糟。

He answered that their condition was so miserable and they were so sensible of it that he believed they would abhor the thought of using any man unkindly that should contribute to their deliverance; and that, if I pleased, he would go to them with the old man and discourse with them about it, and return again and bring me their answer. That he would make conditions with them upon their solemn oath, that they should be absolutely under my leading, as their commander and captain; and that they should swear upon the Holy Sacraments[1] and the Gospel[2] to be true to me and to go to such Christian country as that I should agree to, and no other; and to be directed wholly and absolutely by my orders, till they were landed safely in such country as I intended; and that he would bring a contract from them, under their hands, for that purpose.

Then he told me, he would first swear to me himself that he would never stir from me as long as he lived, till I gave him orders; and that he would take my side to the last drop of his blood, if there should happen the least breach of faith among his countrymen.

He told me they were all of them very civil honest men, and they were under the greatest distress imaginable, having neither weapons or clothes, nor any food, but at the mercy and discretion of the savages; out of all hopes of ever returning to their own country; and that he was sure, if I would undertake their relief, they would live and die by me.

Upon these assurances, I resolved to venture to relieve them, if possible, and to send the old savage and this Spaniard over to them to treat. But when we had gotten all things in a readiness to go, the Spaniard himself started an objection, which had so much prudence in it on one hand and so much sincerity on the other hand that I could not but be very well satisfied in it; and, by his advice, put off the deliverance of his comrades for at least half a year. The case was thus:

---

[1] Holy Sacraments （基督教）《圣经》
[2] Gospel *n.* 福音；《福音书》

他回答说，他们处境非常悲惨，而且都通情达理，所以他相信，他们痛恨对任何能帮助他们脱险的人有恩将仇报的念头。同时，他又说，如果我愿意的话，他将和那个老人一起去见他们，同他们谈谈这件事，然后再把他们的答复给我带回来。他说他一定会跟他们订好条件，让他们郑重宣誓，绝对服从我的领导，把我当成他们的司令和船长，同时还要让他们向《圣经》和《福音书》发誓，对我忠心耿耿，我同意去哪个基督教国家就去哪个国家，他们完全彻底服从我的命令，直到他们平安把我送到我想去的那个国家，而且他一定要让他们专门亲手签约。

接着，他又告诉我说，他本人愿意首先向我宣誓，没有我的命令，他一辈子绝不离开我；万一他的同胞背信弃义，他将站在我这边，直到流尽最后一滴血。

他还告诉我说，他们都是非常礼貌诚实的人，正处在极端的危难之中。他们既没有武器，也没有衣服，更没有食物，任凭那些野人摆布处置，没有重返故乡的一切希望。他敢保证，只要我救他们脱险，他们一定会跟我出生入死。

听了他这些保证，我决定尽可能冒险解救他们，并想派那个老野人和这个西班牙人渡海过去同他们交涉。可是，当我们一切准备就绪要出发时，那个西班牙人自己提出了反对意见。他的意见不仅非常慎重，而且非常真挚，这使我非常高兴。因此，我听从了他的劝告，把解救他同伴的计划推迟了至少半年。情况是这样的：

He had been with us now about a month; during which time, I had let him see in what manner I had provided, with the assistance of Providence, for my support; and he saw evidently what stock of corn and rice I had laid up; which as it was more than sufficient for myself, so it was not sufficient, at least without good husbandry, for my family; now it was increased to number four. But much less would it be sufficient, if his countrymen, who were, as he said, fourteen still alive, should come over. And least of all should it be sufficient to victual our vessel, if we should build one, for a voyage to any of the Christian colonies of America. So he told me he thought it would be more advisable to let him and the two other dig and cultivate some more land, as much as I could spare seed to sow; and that we should wait another harvest, that we might have a supply of corn for his countrymen when they should come.

His caution was so seasonable and his advice so good that I could not but be very well pleased with his proposal as well as I was satisfied with his fidelity. So we fell to digging, all four of us, as well as the wooden tools we were furnished with permitted; and in about a month's time, by the end of which it was seed time, we had gotten as much land cured and trimmed up, as we sowed 22 bushels of barley on and 16 jars of rice, which was, in short, all the seed we had to spare; nor indeed did we leave ourselves barley sufficient for our own food for the six months that we had to expect our crop, that is to say, reckoning from the time we set our seed aside for sowing; for it is not to be supposed it is six months in the ground in the country.

Having now society enough, and our number being sufficient to put us out of fear of the savages, if they had come, unless their number had been very great, we went freely all over the island, wherever we found occasion; and as here we had our escape or deliverance upon our thoughts, it was impossible, at least for me, to have the means of it out of mine; to this purpose, I marked out several trees which I thought fit for our work, and I set Friday and his father to cutting them down; and then I caused the Spaniard, to whom I imparted my thought on that affair, to oversee and direct their work. I showed them with what indefatigable pains I had hewed a large tree into single planks, and I caused them to do the like, till they had made about a dozen large planks of good oak, near two feet broad, thirty-five feet long, and from two inches to four inches thick.

他现在已经和我们相处了大约一个月。在此期间，我让他看到，在上帝的帮助下，我是用什么方法来维持自己的生活。他也明显看到我的谷物大米储备有多少。这粮食我自己吃绰绰有余，但如果不厉行节约，就不够现在一家人吃了，现在增加到了四口人。如果他那几个同胞从对岸过来，那肯定不够吃。他说，他们那边还有 14 个人活着。尤其是我们还要造一条船，航行到美洲的一个基督教国家的殖民地去，这粮食肯定不够全船人吃。因此，他对我说，他认为，让他和星期五父子再开垦一些土地，把我尽可能省下来的粮食全部做种子种下去，更明智。这样，等到再收获一季庄稼，他的同胞过来时，就有粮食吃了。

他的警告非常及时，建议也非常好，所以我不仅对他的建议非常高兴，而且对他的忠诚也很满意。于是，我们四人就一起动手用现有的那些木头工具掘地。大约不到一个月，就开垦好一大片土地，赶在播种季节之前正好整好。我们种下了 22 蒲式耳大麦和 16 罐大米。总之，我们把能省下来的全部粮食都当作了种子。其实，在收获前的六个月中间，我们保留下来的大麦甚至还不够我们吃。这六个月是指从我们节省种子准备播种算起，因为这个地区从播种到收获不需要六个月。

现在我们有了足够的居民，即使那些野人再来，我们也不用害怕了，除非他们来的人数非常多。于是，我们一发现有机会，就在全岛自由走动。因为我们的脑海里都想着逃走或脱险的事儿，所以不想办法是不可能的，至少对我来说是这样。为了这个目的，我把几棵适合造船的树做了记号，让星期五父子把它们砍倒，然后又把自己的想法告诉了那个西班牙人，叫他监督和指挥星期五父子干活。我把自己以前砍好的一些厚木板给他们看，告诉他们我是怎样不辞辛劳把一棵大树削成木板的，并让他们照着去做。最后，他们用上好的橡树做成了大约 12 块大木板，每块将近两英尺宽，35 英尺长，两到四英寸厚。

At the same time I contrived to increase my little flock of tame goats as much as I could; and to this purpose, I made Friday and the Spaniard go out one day, and myself with Friday the next day; for we took our turns. And by is means we got above twenty young kids to breed up with the rest; for whenever we shot the dam, we saved the kids, and added them to our flock. But above all, the season for curing the grapes coming on, I caused such a prodigious quantity to be hung up in the sun, that I believe, had we been at Alicante, where the raisins of the sun are cured, we could have filled sixty or eighty barrels; and these with our bread was a great part of our food.

It was now harvest, and our crop in good order; it was not the most plentiful increase I had seen in the island, but it was enough to answer our end; for from our 22 bushels of barley, we brought in and thrashed out above 220 bushels; and the like in proportion of the rice, which was store enough for our food to the next harvest, though all the 16 Spaniards had been on shore with me; or if we had been ready for a voyage, it would very plentifully have victualed our ship, to have carried us to any part of the world, that is to say, of America.

When we had thus housed and secured our magazine of corn, we fell to work to make more great baskets in which we kept it; and the Spaniard was very handy and dexterous at this part.

And now having a full supply of food for all the guests I expected, I gave the Spaniard leave to go over to the main, to see what he could do with those he had left behind him there. I gave him a strict charge in writing not to bring any man with him who would not first swear in the presence of himself and of the old savage that he would no way injure, fight with, or attack the person he should find in the island, who was so kind to send for them in order to their deliverance; but that they would stand by and defend him against all such attempts, and wherever they went, would be entirely under and subjected to his commands; and that this should be put in writing and signed with their hands. How we were to have this done, when I knew they had neither pen or ink; that indeed was a question which we never asked.

Under these instructions, the Spaniard, and the old savage the father of Friday, went away in one of the canoes.

同时，我又设法尽可能把我的小羊群繁殖起来。为此，我让星期五和那个西班牙人第一天出去，我和星期五的父亲第二天出去，采用这种轮流出动的办法，捉了20多只小山羊，把它们和原有的羊圈养在一起。我们每打到母羊，就把小羊留下来送到羊群中去饲养。而最重要的是，当晒制葡萄的季节到来时，我叫大家采集大量葡萄，把它们挂在太阳下晒干。我相信，如果我们是在阿利坎特，这次制成的葡萄干能装满60至80桶。这些葡萄干和面包是我们的主要食品。

　　现在到了收获的季节，我们的收成不错，尽管这不能说是我在岛上见到的大丰收年，但足够满足我们的需要了，因为我们从种下去的20蒲式耳大麦中收进并打出了220多蒲式耳，稻米收成同样是这个比例。这些存粮，就是那边16个西班牙人都到我这边来，也足够我们吃到下一个收获季节；要么，我们准备航海的话，也可以在船上装上大量粮食，开到世界上任何地方，也就是说，美洲的任何地方。

　　于是，我们把这些存粮搬进屋里藏好后，又着手编制更多的大筐用来保管存粮。那个西班牙人是这方面的行家里手，编得既快又巧。

　　现在，我们的粮食足够供应我盼望的所有客人了。于是，我就决定让那个西班牙人到大陆上去，看看他能帮那些滞留在那里的人做些什么。我向他下了一道严格的书面指示：如果不先在他本人和那个老野人面前发誓，上岛后绝不对我进行任何伤害、攻击或与我作战，就不得带任何人到岛上来，因为我是好心派他们去营救，遇到有人哗变时，他们一定要和我站在一起，保卫我，而且无论到什么地方，都要完全服从命令。我要求他们把这都写下来，并亲笔签名。我知道他们既没有笔也没有纸，他们怎么能做到呢，这个问题我们居然都没有问过。

　　那个西班牙人和那个老野人——星期五的父亲——在接受了我的这些指示后，就坐着一只独木舟出发了。

I gave each of them a musket with a firelock[1] on it and about eight charges of powder and ball, charging them to be very good husbands of both and not to use either of them but upon urgent occasion.

This was a cheerful work, being the first measures used by me in view of my deliverance for now 27 years and some days. I gave them provisions of bread and of dried grapes sufficient for themselves for many days, and sufficient for all their countrymen for about eight days' time; and wishing them a good voyage, I see them go, agreeing with them about a signal they should hang out at their return, by which I should know them again, when they came back, at a distance, before they came on shore.

They went away with a fair gale on the day that the moon was at full by my account, in the month of October. But as for an exact reckoning of days, after I had once lost it I could never recover it again; nor had I kept even the number of years so punctually as to be sure that I was right, though as it proved, when I afterwards examined my account, I found I had kept a true reckoning of years.

It was no less than eight days I had waited for them, when a strange and unforeseen accident intervened. I was fast asleep in my hutch[2] one morning, when Friday came running in to me and called aloud, "Master, master, they are come, they are come!"

I jumped up, and regardless of danger I went out, as soon as I could get my clothes on, through my little grove, which, by the way, was by this time grown to be a very thick wood; I say, regardless of danger, I went without my arms, which was not my custom to do. But I was surprised, when turning my eyes to the sea, I presently saw a boat at about a league and half's distance, standing in for the shore, with a shoulder-of-mutton sail, and the wind blowing pretty fair to bring them in; also I observed presently that they did not come from that side which the shore lay on, but from the southernmost end of the island. Upon this I called Friday in, and bid him lie close, for these were not the people we looked for, and that we might not know yet whether they were friends or enemies.

---

[1] firelock　*n.* 以燧石发火的旧式枪；明火枪
[2] hutch　*n.*　笼；茅屋，小舍

我送给了他们每人一支带火绳的火铳和八份弹药，命令他们好好节约使用，不到紧急时刻不要用。

　　这是一件令人愉快的工作，因为 27 年来这是第一次我为解救自己采取的实际步骤。我给了他们许多面包和葡萄干，足够他们吃好几天了，也足够那些西班牙人吃 8 天左右。于是，我祝他们一路顺风，为他们送行，同时和他们约定他们回来时船上应挂出的信号。这样，他们回来时，还没等他们靠岸，我就会在远处认出他们。

　　他们出发时，正好是顺风，据我估计，那是 10 月当中月圆之日。但至于准确日期的计算，在我把日历记错后，就再也无法改过来了；我甚至连年份有没有记准也拿不准了。后来我检查记录时，发现年份记的没错。

　　我刚等了他们 8 天，这时发生了一件出人意料的怪事。那天早晨，我在自己的茅屋里酣睡，星期五跑进来，冲我大声喊道："主人，主人，他们来了，他们来了!"

　　我一跃而起，不顾危险，一穿上衣服，就穿过小树林（此时已长成了一片密林），跑了出去。我说不顾危险，是说我没带武器就跑出来了。这不是我平时的习惯。我转眼向海上望去时，吃了一惊，很快就看到大约一里格半外有一只小船，上面正挂着一面羊肩帆向岸边驶来。当时正好顺风，将船送了过来。同时，我马上注意到，他们不是来自大陆方向，而是来自岛的最南端。于是，我把星期五叫过来，吩咐他不要远离，因为这些人不是我们要找的人，我们还不知道他们是敌人还是朋友。

In the next place, I went in to fetch my perspective glass, to see what I could make of them; and having taken the ladder out, I climbed up to the top of the hill.

I had scarce set my foot on the hill, when my eye plainly discovered a ship lying at an anchor, at about two leagues and an half's distance from me, south-southeast, but not above a league and an half from the shore. By my observation it appeared plainly to be an English ship, and the boat appeared to be an English longboat.

I cannot express the confusion I was in, though the joy of seeing a ship, and one who I had reason to believe was manned by my own countrymen, and consequently friends, was such as I cannot describe; but yet I had some secret doubts hung about me, I cannot tell from whence they came, bidding me keep upon my guard. In the first place, it occurred to me to consider what business an English ship could have in that part of the world, since it was not the way to or from any part of the world, where the English had any traffic; and I knew there had been no storms to drive them in there, as in distress; and that if they were English really, it was most probable that they were here upon no good design; and that I had better continue as I was than fall into the hands of thieves and murderers.

其次，我跑回家去取望远镜，想看看他们是什么人。我搬出梯子，爬上山顶。

我一上小山，就发现一条大船在我东南偏南的地方停泊着，距离我大约有两里格半，离岸边不超过一里格半。我一看就知道，那显然是一艘英国船，那只小船似乎是一条英国大艇。

我无法描述自己当时的茫然状态。尽管看到一艘大船，而且有理由相信是由自己的同胞和朋友们驾驶，心里有说不出的高兴，但又有一些疑惑不定。我不知道这些疑惑从何而来，却使我警惕起来。首先，我想到，一条英国船开到这一带来干什么，因为这里不是英国人在世界上进行贸易往来的要道。而且，我知道，近来并没有发生过什么暴风雨，把他们的船刮到那里。如果真是英国人，他们到这一带来，十有八九居心不良。我与其落到盗贼和凶犯手里，还不如像以前那样继续活下去。

XXVI

I had not kept myself long in this posture, but I saw the boat draw near the shore, as if they looked for a creek to thrust in at for the convenience of landing; however, as they did not come quite far enough, they did not see the little inlet where I formerly landed my rafts; but run their boat on shore upon the beach, at about half a mile from me, which was very happy for me; for otherwise they would have landed just as I may say at my door, and would soon have beaten me out of my castle and perhaps have plundered me of all I had.

When they were on shore, I was fully satisfied that they were English men, at least most of them; one or two I thought were Dutch; but it did not prove so. There were in all eleven men, whereof three of them I found were unarmed, and, as I thought, bound; and when the first four or five of them were jumped on shore, they took those three out of the boat as prisoners. One of the three I could perceive using the most passionate gestures of entreaty[1], affliction and despair, even to a kind of extravagance; the other two lifted up their hands sometimes, and appeared concerned indeed, but not to such a degree as the first.

I was perfectly confounded[2] at the sight, and knew not what the meaning of it should be. Friday called out to me in English as well as he could, "O Master! You see Englishmen eat prisoner as well as savage men." "Why," said I, "Friday, do you think they are a-going to eat them then?" "Yes," said Friday, "They will eat them." "No, no, said I, "Friday, I am afraid they will murder them indeed, but you may be sure they will not eat them."

---

[1] entreaty *n.* 恳求，乞求
[2] confounded *adj.* 糊涂的，困惑的

26

　　我在小山上这样望了没多久，就看见那只小船靠近了岸边。他们好像在寻找河湾，以便把船开进来上岸。不过，他们沿着海岸走得不够远，所以没看到我从前卸木排的那个小河湾，只好把小船停在离我大约半英里远的沙滩上靠岸。这让我非常高兴，因为如果他们进入河湾，就会在我的家门口上岸，那样他们一定会马上把我赶出城堡，也许还会把我洗劫一空。

　　他们上岸后，我完全确信他们都是英国人，至少大部分是。其中有一两个我想是荷兰人，但后来证明并不是这样。他们共有 11 个人，其中三个我发现没带武器，而且我想是被绑起来的。船一靠岸，就有四、五个人首先跳上了岸，然后把三个人押下船来。我可以看到三个人其中有一个正作出最强烈的恳求、痛苦和失望的手势，甚至有点儿过火。另外两个人有时也举起双手，显得忧心忡忡，但程度没有第一个人那样激烈。

　　看到这情景，我感到莫名其妙，不知道是什么意思。星期五在旁边一直用英语对我喊道："噢，主人！你看英国人也和野人一样吃俘虏。""怎么，"我说，"星期五，你以为他们会吃那几个人吗？""是的，"星期五说，"他们一定会吃的。""不，不，"我说，"星期五，我怕他们会杀死他们，但我敢担保他们不会吃这些人。"

All this while I had no thought of what the matter really was; but stood trembling with the horror of the sight, expecting every moment when the three prisoners should be killed; nay[1], once I saw one of the villains lift up his arm with a great cutlass[2] to spike one of the poor men; and I expected to see him fall every moment, at which all the blood in my body seemed to run chill in my veins.

I wished heartily now that I had any way to have come undiscovered within shot of them, that I might have rescued the three men; for I saw no firearms they had among them; but it fell out to my mind another way.

After I had observed the outrageous usage of the three men by the insolent seamen, I observed the fellows run scattering about the land, as if they wanted to see the country. I observed that the three other men had liberty to go also where they pleased; but they sat down all three upon the ground, very pensive, and looked like men in despair. This put me in mind of the first time when I came on shore.

It was just at the top of high water when these people came on shore, and while partly they stood parleying[3] with the prisoners they brought, and partly while they rambled about to see what kind of a place they were in; they had carelessly stayed till the tide was spent, and the water was ebbed considerably away, leaving their boat aground.

They had left two men in the boat, who as I found afterwards, having drank a little too much brandy, fell asleep; however, one of them waking sooner than the other, and finding the boat too fast aground for him to stir it, hallooed for the rest who were straggling about, upon which they all soon came to the boat; but it was past all their strength to launch her, the boat being very heavy, and the shore on that side being a soft oozy[4] sand, almost like a quicksand.

In this condition, they gave it over, and away they strolled about the country again; and I heard one of them say aloud to another, calling them off from the boat, "Why, let her alone, Jack, she will float next tide"; by which I was fully confirmed in the main enquiry, of what countrymen they were.

---

[1] nay *adv.* <书>不仅如此，而且.

[2] cutlass *n.* 短剑，弯刀

[3] parley *n.* 会谈

[4] oozy *adj.* 软泥的

304

此时，我不知道到底是怎么回事，只是站在那里，看着这可怕的情景发抖，料想着那三个俘虏随时会被杀掉。而且，有一次，我看到一个坏蛋举起一把腰刀向其中一个可怜的人砍去，而且料想着会看到他随时都会倒下来，这使我不寒而栗。

这时，我真希望能有什么办法神不知鬼不觉地走到对他们的射程内，把那三个人救出来，因为我看到他们这伙人都没有带火铳。不过，我又想了一个办法。

我看到那伙粗野无礼的水手残暴虐待了那三个人后，都在岛上四散开来，好像他们想看看这里的地形。我观察到，另外那三个人行动自由，想去哪里就去哪里，但他们三个都在地上坐下来，心事重重，一副绝望的神情。这使我想起了自己第一次上岸的情景。

这些人上岸时，正是潮水涨得最高的时候。他们中的一部分人站在那里同带来的俘虏谈判，另一部分人在四周游逛，看看他们到了什么地方，由于一时大意，他们呆到了潮水退去，而且潮水退得相当远，把他们的小船搁浅在了沙滩上。

他们本来在小船上留有两个人，但我后来发现，他俩喝多了点儿白兰地就倒头睡着了。不过，其中一个先醒来，发现小船搁浅，怎么也推不动，就向四散在各处的其他人高声喊叫。他们都马上跑到小船边。可是，因为小船很重，那边的海岸又是松软的沙土，差不多像流沙一样，所以他们用尽了全力也无法把船推向海里。

在这种情况下，他们不再推船，又到四处遛达去了。我听见一个水手向另一个水手大声说话，叫他离开小船："嗨，杰克，别管它了。潮水上来，船就会浮起来。"我一听这话，就完全证实他们是哪国人了。

All this while I kept myself very close, not once daring to stir out of my castle, any farther than to my place of observation near the top of the hill; and very glad I was to think how well it was fortified. I knew it was no less than ten hours before the boat could be on float again, and by that time it would be dark, and I might be at more liberty to see their motions, and to hear their discourse, if they had any.

In the meantime, I fitted myself up for a battle, as before; though with more caution, knowing I had to do with another kind of enemy than I had at first. I ordered Friday also, who I had made an excellent marksman with his gun, to load himself with arms. I took myself two fowling-pieces, and I gave him three muskets; my figure, indeed, was very fierce; I had my formidable goat-skin coat on, with the great cap, a naked sword by my side, two pistols in my belt, and a gun upon each shoulder.

It was my design not to have made any attempt till it was dark. But about two o'clock being the heat of the day, I found that they were all gone straggling into the woods, and as I thought were laid down to sleep. The three poor distressed men, too anxious for their condition to get any sleep, were, however, set down under the shelter of a great tree, at about a quarter of a mile from me, and as I thought out of sight of any of the rest.

Upon this I resolved to discover myself to them and learn something of their condition. Immediately I marched, Friday at a good distance behind me, as formidable for his arms as I.

I came as near them undiscovered as I could, and then before any of them saw me, I called aloud to them in Spanish, "What are ye, gentlemen?"

They started up at the noise, but were ten times more confounded when they saw me. They made no answer at all, but I thought I perceived them just going to fly from me, when I spoke to them in English. "Gentlemen," said I, "do not be surprised at me; perhaps you may have a friend near you when you did not expect it." "He must be sent directly from Heaven then," said one of them very gravely to me, and pulling off his hat at the same time to me, "for our condition is past the help of man." "All help is from Heaven, sir," said I. "But can you put a stranger in the way how to help you, for you seem to me to be in some great distress? I saw you when you landed, and when you seemed to make applications to the brutes that came with you, I saw one of them lift up his sword to kill you."

在此期间，我总是严密隐蔽，除了到附近的小山顶上观察，不敢离开自己的城堡一步。想到自己城堡是那样坚固，我心里非常高兴。我知道那小船至少要过 10 小时才能再次浮起来。到那时，天就要黑了，我就可以更自由地留意他们的行动、听到他们任何的谈话。

与此同时，我像以前那样作好战斗准备。这次我比过去更加谨慎，因为我知道我要对付的敌人和从前不一样。我把星期五训练成了一名神枪手。我命令他也把自己武装起来。我自己拿了两支鸟枪，给了他三支火铳。我现在的样子确实非常凶猛，身上穿可怕的羊皮外套，头上戴大帽子，腰间挎着一把无鞘剑，皮带上插着两把手枪，肩上各背了一支枪。

我计划到天黑采取任何行动。可是，两点左右天气正热时，我发现他们都纷纷跑进了树林里，我想是躺下睡觉去了。那三个可怜的不幸人为自己的处境忧心忡忡，怎么也睡不着，只好在一棵大树的凉阴下坐下来，离我大约有四分之一英里。我想其他任何人看不见他们坐的地方。

于是，我决定亲自去看一下他们，了解一下他们的情况，便马上出发了，星期五远远地跟在我后面，像我一样全副武装，样子非常可怕。

我尽可能神不知鬼不觉地走近他们，然后还没等到他们任何人看见我，就用西班牙语向他们大声喊道："先生们，你们是什么人？"

他们听到我的喊声，惊跳起来，但他们看到我，更加惊慌失措，连话都说不出来了。我察觉到他们准备逃跑，就用英语对他们说："先生们，不要对我吃惊。也许你们想不到，你们眼前的人是你们的朋友。""那他一定是天上直接派来的，"其中一个一本正经地对我说，同时脱帽向我致礼。"因为我们的处境，人是救不了的。""一切拯救都来自天堂，先生，"我说，"你们能让一个陌生人来帮助你们吗？因为在我看来你们似乎正在危难之中。你们上岸时，我就看见你们了。你们向跟你们一块来的那帮畜生哀求时，我看到其中有一个人举起刀要杀你们。"

The poor man with tears running down his face, and trembling, looking like one astonished, returned, "Am I talking to God, or man? Is it a real man, or an angel?" "Be in no fear about that, sir," said I, "if God had sent an angel to relieve you, he would have come better clothed, and armed after another manner than you see me in; pray lay aside your fears, I am a man, an Englishman, and disposed to assist you, you see; I have one servant only; we have arms and ammunition; tell us freely, can we serve you? What is your case?"

"Our case," said he, "sir, is too long to tell you, while our murderers are so near; but in short, sir, I was commander of that ship, my men have mutinied[1] against me; they have been hardly prevailed on not to murder me, and at last have set me on shore in this desolate place, with these two men with me; one my mate, the other a passenger, where we expected to perish, believing the place to be uninhabited, and know not yet what to think of it."

"Where are those brutes, your enemies," said I, "do you know where they are gone?" "There they lie, sir," said he, pointing to a thicket of trees; "my heart trembles for fear they have seen us and heard you speak; if they have, they will certainly murder us all."

"Have they any firearms?" said I. He answered they had only two pieces, and one which they left in the boat. "Well then," said I, "leave the rest to me; I see they are all asleep, it is an easy thing to kill them all; but shall we rather take them prisoners?" He told me there were two desperate villains among them that it was scarce safe to show any mercy to; but if they were secured, he believed all the rest would return to their duty. I asked him which they were. He told me he could not at that distance describe them; but he would obey my orders. "Well," said I, "let us retreat out of their view or hearing, least they awake"; so they willingly went back with me, till the woods covered us from them.

"Look you, sir," said I, "if I venture upon your deliverance, are you willing to make two conditions with me?" He anticipated my proposals, by telling me, that both he and the ship, if recovered, should be wholly directed and commanded by me in everything; and if the ship was not recovered, he would live and die with me in what part of the world soever I would send him; and the two other men said the same.

---

[1] mutiny *v.* 叛变，造反，兵变

那个可怜人泪流满面，浑身发抖，样子非常吃惊。他回答说："我是在对上帝还是在对人说话？你是真人还是天使？""绝不要害怕，先生，"我说，"如果上帝派一位天使来拯救你们，他一定会比我穿得好，你们看到的武器也会是另一种样子。请你们放心。我是一个人，是一个英国人，是受命来救你们的，你们明白。我只有一个仆人。我们都有武器和弹药。直接告诉我们，我们能为你们效劳吗？你们发生了什么事儿？"

"先生，"他说，"我们的事儿说来话长，那些凶手又近在咫尺。先生，长话短说吧，我是那条船的船长，我手下的人已经叛变了我。我好不容易才说服他们不杀我，最后他们把我和这两个人一起押送到了这个荒岛上。一个是我的大副，另一个是旅客。我们相信这是一个没有人烟的荒岛，我们一定会饿死，不知道该怎么办。"

"你们的敌人，那些畜生在哪里？"我说，"你们知道他们到哪里去了吗？""他们在那边躺着，先生。"他指着一个灌木林说。"我心里发抖，怕他们看到我们，听到你说话。如果那样的话，他们肯定把我们统统杀掉。"

"他们有火铳吗？"我问。他回答说，他们只有两支枪，其中一支留在船上。"那就好了，"我说，"其他的一切交给我处理。我看到他们都睡着了，把他们统统杀掉是一件轻而易举的事儿。不过，是不是活捉更好？"他告诉我说，他们中有两个是亡命徒，要对他们仁慈就不会有安全。只要把他们搞定，他相信其他所有人就会回到工作岗位。我问他是哪两个人。他告诉我说距离太远，他无法描述清楚他们，但他一定服从我的命令。"那好吧，"我说，"让我们退远点儿，以免他们醒来时看到或听到。"于是，他们欣然跟着我往回走，直到树林遮住我们。

"注意，先生，"我说，"如果我冒险救你们，我有两个条件，你们愿意答应吗？"没等我把条件说出来，他就抢先说道，只要收回大船，他和他的船就完全听从我的指挥和命令。如果收不回船，他也愿和我同生死，不管我派他去世界上哪个地方都行。另两个人也都这样说。

309

"Well," said I, "my conditions are but two. 1. That while you stay on this island with me, you will not pretend to any authority here; and if I put arms into your hands, you will upon all occasions give them up to me and do no prejudice to me or mine upon this island, and in the meantime be governed by my orders. 2. That if the ship is or may be recovered, you will carry me and my man to England passage free.

He gave me all the assurances.

"Well then," said I, "here are three muskets for you, with powder and ball; tell me next what you think is proper to be done." He showed all the testimony of his gratitude that he was able; but offered to be wholly guided by me. I told him I thought it was hard venturing anything; but the best method I could think of was to fire upon them at once, as they lay; and if any was not killed at the first volley[1], and offered to submit, we might save them.

He said very modestly that he was loath to kill them, but that those two were incorrigible[2] villains and had been the authors of all the mutiny in the ship, and if they escaped, we should be undone still; for they would go on board and bring the whole ship's company, and destroy us all. "Well then," said I, "necessity legitimates my advice; for it is the only way to save our lives."

In the middle of this discourse, we heard some of them awake, and soon after, we saw two of them on their feet. I asked him if either of them were of the men who he had said were the heads of the mutiny. He said, "No." "Well then," said I. "you may let them escape, and Providence seems to have wakened them on purpose to save themselves. Now, if the rest escape you, it is your fault."

Animated[3] with this, he took the musket I had given him in his hand, and a pistol in his belt, and his two comrades with him, with each man a piece in his hand. The two men who were with him, going first, made some noise, at which one of the seamen who was awake, turned about, and seeing them coming, cried out to the rest; but it was too late then.

---

[1] volley   *n.* （箭、子弹、枪、炮等）群射，齐发
[2] incorrigible   *adj.* 无药可救的，不能被纠正的
[3] animate   *v.* 鼓舞

"好吧，"我说，"我的条件只有两个。一、你们和我呆在这个岛上时，绝不要对这里的权威阳奉阴违；如果我发给你们武器，你们要随时交还给我。在这岛上，不要对我或我的人抱有成见，同时要服从我的统治。二、如果收回那只大船，你们要把我和我的人免费送到英国。"

他向我做了种种保证。

"那好，"我说，"给你们三支火铳，还有火药和子弹。告诉我你们想下一步怎么办合适。"他竭尽感谢之能事，愿意完全听从我的指挥。我告诉他说，我认为很难冒任何险。不过，我能想起的最好办法就是趁他们在睡觉时，马上向他们开火。如果放过第一排枪后还有没打死的，并愿意投降，我们可以饶他们一命。

他说话非常谨慎，不情愿杀死他们，但那两个人是不可救药的坏蛋，是船上所有哗变的罪魁祸首。如果他们逃脱，我们肯定会完蛋，因为他们回到船上，就会发动全体船员，把我们统统杀掉。"那好吧，"我说，"我的建议也是迫不得已，因为这是救我们自己性命的唯一办法。"

正在谈话时，我们听到他们中间有几个人醒来了。稍后，我们看到有两个人站了起来。我问他这两个人中有没有哗变的头头。他说："没有。""那好，"我说，"你可以让他们逃命。上天好像有意叫醒他们，让他们自救。听着，如果你让其他人逃跑，那就是你的过错。"

听了我的话，他受到了鼓舞，把我给他的火铳拿在手里，然后把一支手枪插进皮带，他的两个手下跟着他，每人手里各拿着一支枪，走在前面，弄出了一些声响，那两个醒来的水手中有一人听到了响动，转过身，看到他们过来，就向其他人大声叫喊，但为时已晚。

For the moment he cried out, they fired; I mean the two men, the captain wisely reserving his own piece. They had so well aimed their shot at the men they knew, that one of them was killed on the spot, and the other very much wounded; but not being dead, he started up upon his feet, and called eagerly for help to the other; but the captain stepping to him, told him, it was too late to cry for help, he should call upon God to forgive his villainy[1], and with that word knocked him down with the stock of his musket, so that he never spoke more. There were three more in the company, and one of them was also slightly wounded. By this time I was come, and when they saw their danger, and that it was in vain to resist, they begged for mercy. The captain told them he would spare their lives, if they would give him any assurance of their abhorrence of the treachery they had been guilty of and would swear to be faithful to him in recovering the ship and afterwards in carrying her back to Jamaica, from whence they came. They gave him all the protestations of their sincerity that could be desired, and he was willing to believe them, and spare their lives, which I was not against, only that I obliged him to keep them bound hand and foot while they were upon the island.

While this was doing, I sent Friday with the captain's mate to the boat, with orders to secure her and bring away the oars and sail, which they did; and by and by, three straggling men that were (happily for them) parted from the rest, came back upon hearing the guns fired, and seeing their captain, who before was their prisoner, now their conqueror, they submitted to be bound also; and so our victory was complete.

It now remained that the captain and I should enquire into one another's circumstances. I began first, and told him my whole history, which he heard with an attention even to amazement; and particularly at the wonderful manner of my being furnished with provisions and ammunition; and, indeed, as my story is a whole collection of wonders, it affected him deeply; but when he reflected from thence upon himself, and how I seemed to have been preserved there on purpose to save his life, the tears ran down his face, and he could not speak a word more.

---

[1] villainy *n.* 邪恶，坏事，恶行

他刚一叫出声，他们就开了火。我是说那两个手下。船长很精明，没有开枪。他们都瞄得很准，当场打死了一个，另一个受了重伤，但没有死。他惊跳起来，向另一个人急切呼救。这时，船长一步跨到他面前，对他说，现在呼救太晚了，他应该请求上帝宽恕他的罪恶。说着，船长一枪把他打倒在地，所以他再也开不了口了。这伙人中还有三个人，其中有一个也受了轻伤。此时，我也已经赶到。他们看到了危险，知道抵抗也是徒然，就哀求饶命。船长告诉他们说，如果他们向他保证痛恨自己所犯的反叛罪行，并发誓效忠于他，夺回大船，然后再把船开回他们来的地方牙买加，他可以饶他们不死。他们纷纷竭力向船长表示自己的诚意。他表示愿意相信他们，并饶他们不死。我对此没有反对，只是责成他在他们留在岛上时捆住他们的手脚。

与此同时，我派星期五和船长手下的大副到那小船上去，命令他们扣留小船，拿下上面的几只桨和帆。他们都言听计从。过了一会儿，有三个到别处遛达的人因听到枪声，也赶了回来。幸亏，他们没有跟其他人在一起。他们看到他们的船长（先前是他们的俘虏，现在成了他们的征服者），也就俯首就擒。这样，我们就大获全胜。

现在剩下的就是船长和我相互打听彼此的情况。我先开口，把自己的全部经历告诉了他。他全神贯注，甚至惊奇地听着我讲，尤其是对我弄到粮食和弹药的奇妙方式。他听了我的故事，深受感动，因为我的经历确实让人叹为观止。可是，当他从我的故事想到自己，想到上帝好像有意让我活下来救他的命时，他泪流满面，连一句话都说不出来了。

After this communication was at an end, I carried him and his two men into my apartment, leading them in, just where I came out, viz., at the top of the house, where I refreshed them with such provisions as I had, and showed them all the contrivances[1] I had made during my long, long inhabiting that place.

All I showed them, all I said to them, was perfectly amazing; but above all, the captain admired my fortification, and how perfectly I had concealed my retreat with a grove of trees, which having been now planted near twenty years, and the trees growing much faster than in England, was become a little wood, and so thick that it was unpassable in any part of it, but at that one side, where I had reserved my little winding passage into it. I told him, this was my castle and my residence; but that I had a seat in the country, as most princes have, whither I could retreat upon occasion, and I would show him that too another time; but at present our business was to consider how to recover the ship. He agreed with me as to that; but told me, he was perfectly at a loss what measures to take; for that there were still six and twenty hands on board, who having entered into a cursed conspiracy, by which they had all forfeited their lives to the law, would be hardened in it now by desperation; and would carry it on, knowing that if they were reduced, they should be brought to the gallows[2] as soon as they came to England or to any of the English colonies; and that therefore there would be no attacking them, with so small a number as we were.

I mused[3] for some time upon what he had said; and found it was a very rational conclusion; and that therefore something was to be resolved on very speedily, as well to draw the men on board into some snare for their surprise, as to prevent their landing upon us, and destroying us; upon this it presently occurred to me that in a little while the ship's crew wondering what was become of their comrades and of the boat, would certainly come on shore in their other boat to see for them, and that then perhaps they might come armed and be too strong for us; this he allowed was rational.

---

[1] contrivance   *n.* 发明，想出的办法
[2] gallows   *n.* 绞架，绞刑
[3] muse   *v.* 沉思

谈话结束后，我把他和他的两个手下带到我的住处。我是从哪里出来的，也从哪里领他们进去，也就是爬过屋顶进去。我拿出所有食品招待他们，还把我长期以来住在此地制造的所有装置指给他们看。

我给他们看的一切，我对他们说的话，都让他们感到非常惊奇。但船长最欣赏的是我的防御工事，欣赏我用一片小树林把隐身处隐蔽起来是多么完美。这片小树林现在已经栽了将近 20 年了，因为这里的树木比英国的长得快得多，所以现在已经成了一片小森林，而且非常茂密。我在树林的其中一边留了一条弯弯曲曲的通道，其他任何地方都无法通过。我告诉他说，这是我的城堡，也是我的住处，但像大多数皇宫贵族一样，我在乡间还有一所别墅，我有时会去那里休养。我说，改日我也会带他到那里去看看，而现在我们的任务是要考虑如何收回那条大船。他同意我的意见，但他告诉说，他完全想不起来采取什么措施，因为大船上还有 26 个人，他们已经参加了该死的叛乱，在法律上都犯了死罪，所以他们都会铤而走险破釜沉舟干下去，他们知道，如果被打败，他们一回英国或任何英国殖民地，就会被送上绞架。因此，靠我们这区区几个人，肯定无法向他们进攻。

我对他的话沉思了一段时间，发现他的结论非常合理，因此我们必须当机立断，既要出其不意让船上那些人落入某种圈套，又要阻止他们上岸攻打我们、消灭我们。于是，我马上想到，再过一会儿，大船上的船员不知道他们的同伙和小船发生了什么事儿；那时，他们就会坐上另一只小船上岸来找他们。他们到时候说不定会带武器来，那对我们来说太强大了。他认为我说的有道理。

Upon this, I told him the first thing we had to do was to stave[1] the boat, which lay upon the beach, so that they might not carry her off; and taking everything out of her, leave her so far useless as not to be fit to swim; accordingly we went on board, took the arms which were left on board, out of her, and whatever else we found there, which was a bottle of brandy, and another of rum, a few biscuit cakes, a horn of powder, and a great lump of sugar in a piece of canvas; the sugar was five or six pounds; all which was very welcome to me, especially the brandy and sugar, of which I had had none left for many years.

When we had carried all these things on shore (the oars, mast, sail, and rudder of the boat were carried away before, as above) we knocked a great hole in her bottom, that if they had come strong enough to master us, yet they could not carry off the boat.

Indeed, it was not much in my thoughts that we could be able to recover the ship; but my view was that if they went away without the boat, I did not much question to make her fit again to carry us away to the Leeward Islands and call upon our friends, the Spaniards, in my way, for I had them still in my thoughts.

While we were thus preparing our designs and had first by main strength heaved the boat up upon the beach so high that the tide would not fleet her off at high-water-mark; and besides, had broken a hole in her bottom, too big to be quickly stopped and were sat down musing what we should do; we heard the ship fire a gun, and saw her make a waft[2] with her ancient as a signal for the boat to come on board; but no boat stirred; and they fired several times, making other signals for the boat.

At last, when all their signals and firings proved fruitless, and they found the boat did not stir, we saw them, by the help of my glasses, hoist another boat out and row towards the shore; and we found, as they approached, that there was no less than ten men in her, and that they had firearms with them.

---

[1] stave   *vt.* 击穿，弄破
[2] waft   *n.* 飘荡；信号，遇难信号

于是，我告诉他，我们首先必须做的是击穿搁浅在沙滩上的那只小船，这样他们就不可能划走小船了，然后我们把船上所有的东西都拿下来，使它失去航行能力，无法下水。于是，我们上了小船，把留在船上的那支枪拿了下来，又把上面所能找到的东西统统拿了下来。其中有一瓶白兰地，还有一瓶朗姆酒、几块饼干、一角筒火药，以及用一块帆布包着的一大块糖，糖有五、六磅重。这些东西对我非常管用，尤其是白兰地和糖，我已经吃完好多年了。

船上的桨、桅杆、帆和舵早已拿走了，所以我们把所有这些东西搬上岸后，又在船底凿了个大洞。这样，即使他们有足够实力战胜我们，也没法划走小船。

确实，我认为收回大船的把握不大。我的意见是，只要他们不把那只小船弄走，我把它重新修好没多大问题，然后让它把我们送到背风群岛去，顺路还有去拜访那些西班牙朋友，因为我心里还时刻记着他们。

于是，我们按计划准备起来，首先我们竭尽全力把小船推到沙滩的高地；这样，即使潮水上涨，也不会把船浮起来；再说，我们已在船底凿了个洞，洞子太大不会马上堵住。我们坐在地上正寻思着该怎么办时，听到大船上放了一枪，然后看到上面摇动旗帜发出了信号，让小船到大船上去，但小船毫无动静。于是，他们又放了几枪，同时向小船又发出了其他一些信号。

最后，所有的信号和放枪都没有效果，小船还是没有动静，我们在望远镜里看到他们把另一只小船放下来，向岸边划来。当他们靠近时，我们发现小船上多达 10 个人，而且他们都带着武器。

As the ship lay almost two leagues from the shore, we had a full view of them as they came, and a plain sight of the men even of their faces, because the tide having set them a little to the east of the other boat, they rowed up under shore, to come to the same place, where the other had landed and where the boat lay.

By this means, I say, we had a full view of them, and the captain knew the persons and characters of all the men in the boat, of whom he said, that there were three very honest fellows, who he was sure were led into this conspiracy by the rest, being overpowered and frightened. But that as for the boatswain[1], who, it seems, was the chief officer among them, and all the rest, they were as outrageous as any of the ship's crew, and were no doubt made desperate in their new enterprise; and terribly apprehensive he was that they would be too powerful for us.

I smiled at him and told him that men in our circumstances were past the operation of fear. That seeing almost every condition that could be was better than that which we were supposed to be in, we ought to expect that the consequence, whether death or life, would be sure to be a deliverance. I asked him what he thought of the circumstances of my life and whether a deliverance were not worth venturing for. "And where, sir," said I, "is your belief of my being preserved here on purpose to save your life, which elevated you a little while ago? For my part, there seems to be but one thing amiss[2] in all the prospect of it." "What's that?" said he. "Why," said I, " 'tis that, as you say, there are three or four honest fellows among them, which should be spared; had they been all of the wicked part of the crew, I should have thought God's Providence had singled them out to deliver them into your hands; for depend upon it, every man of them that comes a-shore are our own and shall die or live as they behave to us."

As I spoke this with a raised voice and cheerful countenance, I found it greatly encouraged him; so we set vigorously to our business. We had, upon the first appearance of the boat's coming from the ship, considered of separating our prisoners, and had indeed secured them effectually.

---

[1] boatswain *n.* 水手长
[2] amiss *adj.* 有毛病的，出差错的

318

那条大船停泊在离岸将近两里格的地方。他们坐小船划过来时，我们一览无余，甚至连他们的脸都看得一清二楚。因为潮水把他们冲到了另一只小船偏东一点儿，所以他们又沿着海岸往西划，划向第一只小船靠岸和停泊的那个地方。

　　我是说，我们对他们一览无余，船长认识小船上那些人，也知道他们所有人的性格。他说，其中有三个非常老实的人，他相信他们参与谋反，是因为势单力孤，受到了其他人的威吓。那个水手长好像是其中的主谋。他和其他所有船员一样蛮横无礼。因为他们既然发动了这次叛乱，毫无疑问会铤而走险，所以船长非常担心他们人多势众，我们不是对手。

　　我向他微微一笑，对他说，处在我们这种境地的人早已无所畏惧了。你明白几乎每一种情况都比我们现在所处的境地强，所以我们应该预料到，不管结果是死是活，都肯定会是一种解脱。我问他对我生活的处境有什么看法，为了解脱，是不是值得去冒险。"先生，"我说，"你刚才还认为上帝让我活在这里是为了特意救你的命，并使你振奋精神，你这种信心到哪里去了？在我看来，在这件事的整个前景中，好像只有一件事儿不合适。""什么事儿？"他问。"那就是你说的，他们当中有三、四个老实人，我们应该饶他们一命。如果他们也是船员中的坏分子，我会认为是上帝把他们挑出来送到了你手里，因为他们每个上岸的人都是我们的俘虏，他们是死是活，要看他们对我们的表现。"

　　我说话时，提高嗓门，面带笑容，发现这大大鼓起了船长的勇气。于是，我们精神抖擞地行动起来。他们一从大船上放下小船，我们就考虑到要疏散俘虏，而且这件事我们确实已经作了有力安排。

Two of them, of whom the captain was less assured than ordinary, I sent with Friday and one of the three (delivered men) to my cave, where they were remote enough and out of danger of being heard or discovered, or of finding their way out of the woods, if they could have delivered themselves. Here they left them bound, but gave them provisions, and promised them, if they continued there quietly, to give them their liberty in a day or two; but that if they attempted their escape, they should be put to death without mercy. They promised faithfully to bear their confinement[1] with patience and were very thankful that they had such good usage as to have provisions and a light left them; for Friday gave them candles (such as we made ourselves) for their comfort; and they did not know but that he stood sentinel[2] over them at the entrance.

The other prisoners had better usage; two of them were kept pinioned[3] indeed, because the captain was not free to trust them; but the other two were taken into my service upon their captain's recommendation and upon their solemnly engaging to live and die with us; so with them and the three honest men, we were seven men, well armed; and I made no doubt we should be able to deal well enough with the ten that were a coming, considering that the captain had said there were three or four honest men among them also.

As soon as they got to the place where their other boat lay, they run their boat in to the beach, and came all on shore, hauling the boat up after them, which I was glad to see; for I was afraid they would rather have left the boat at an anchor, some distance from the shore, with some hands in her, to guard her; and so we should not be able to seize the boat.

Being on shore, the first thing they did, they ran all to their other boat, and it was easy to see that they were under a great surprise to find her stripped of all that was in her, and a great hole in her bottom.

---

[1] confinement　*n.*　（被）限制，（被）禁闭
[2] sentinel　*n.*　哨兵
[3] pinion　*vt.*　（常与 to 连用）绑住；束缚

其中有两个人，船长非常不放心。我派星期五和船长手下的一个人把这两个人送到我的洞室里去。那地方很远，不会有被人听到或发现的危险，即使他们自己能逃出洞外，在树林里也找不到出路。他们把这两个人都在这里绑了起来，但供给他们吃喝，并答应他们，如果他们继续安静地呆在洞里，一两天后就给他们自由；但如果他们企图逃跑，就会被毫不留情地处死。他们都诚心诚意地保证，愿意耐心地被关起来，并非常感谢我们对他们的优待，给他们吃喝，还给他们点灯，因为星期五给了他们几支蜡烛（都是我们自己做的），以示安慰。他们不知道星期五就站在洞口看守着他们。

其他俘虏受到的待遇要好些。其中有两个一直没有松绑，因为船长对他们仍不放心，但另外两个因船长推荐而被我聘用，同时他们本人也郑重允诺要和我们同生死。因此，他们和三个老实人，我们一共是 7 个人，全副武装。我毫不怀疑，我们完全能对付即将上岛的那 10 个人，船长说过，其中还有三、四个老实人。

他们一来到另一只小船停泊的地方，便马上把他们的小船推到沙滩上，随后船上的人都下了船，同时把小船拖到岸上。看到这一情景，我非常高兴，因为我就怕他们把小船在离岸有一段距离的地方下锚，并留几个人在船上看守。那样的话，我们就无法夺取小船了。

一上岸，他们做的第一件事就是一起跑去看另一只小船。他们一目了然，发现船上拆卸一空，船底还有一个大洞，都大吃了一惊。

After they had mused a while upon this, they set up two or three great shouts, hallooing with all their might, to try if they could make their companions hear; but all was to no purpose. Then they came all close in a ring, and fired a volley of their small arms, which indeed we heard, and the echoes made the woods ring; but it was all one, those in the cave we were sure could not hear, and those in our keeping, though they heard it well enough, yet durst give no answer to them.

They were so astonished at the surprise of this, that as they told us afterwards, they resolved to go all on board again to their ship, and let them know that the men were all murdered and the longboat staved; accordingly they immediately launched their boat again, and got all of them on board.

The captain was terribly amazed and even confounded at this, believing they would go on board the ship again and set sail, giving their comrades for lost, and so he should still lose the ship, which he was in hopes we should have recovered; but he was quickly as much frightened the other way.

They had not been long put off with the boat, but we perceived them all coming on shore again; but with this new measure in their conduct, which it seems they consulted together upon, viz., to leave three men in the boat, and the rest to go on shore, and go up into the country to look for their fellows.

This was a great disappointment to us; for now we were at a loss what to do; for our seizing those seven men on shore would be no advantage to us, if we let the boat escape; because they would then row away to the ship, and then the rest of them would be sure to weigh and set sail, and so our recovering the ship would be lost.

However, we had no remedy but to wait and see what the issue of things might present; the seven men came on shore, and the three who remained in the boat put her off to a good distance from the shore, and came to an anchor to wait for them; so that it was impossible for us to come at them in the boat.

Those that came on shore kept close together, marching towards the top of the little hill under which my habitation lay; and we could see them plainly, though they could not perceive us. We could have been very glad they would have come nearer to us, so that we might have fired at them, or that they would have gone farther off, that we might have come abroad.

他们对看到的情况沉思了一会儿，就尽力大喊了两三次，想叫他们的同伴们听见，却没有任何结果。接着，他们又围成一圈，用小武器放了一排枪，这枪声我们确实听见了，而且枪声的回声使树林都回响起来，但结果还是一样。我们确信那些关在洞里的人无法听见；我们看守的那些人，尽管听得一清二楚，却不敢对他们有任何回应。

这出乎他们的意料，使他们非常惊讶。事后，他们告诉我们说，他们决定都回到大船上去，告诉船上的人，那些人都被杀光，大艇也被击穿沉没了。于是，他们马上把小船又推到水里，都纷纷上了船。

船长对此非常吃惊，甚至不知所措。他相信，他们一定会回到大船上去，扬帆起航，让同伴们没有生还的希望。那样的话，他原来想收回大船的希望就会落空，但他很快又惊慌失措起来。

他们把小船划出没多久，我们就看到他们又都回到了岸上。这次行动他们采取了新的措施。看来，他们刚才已经商量好了，也就是把3个人留在小船上，其他人一齐上岸，然后深入小岛，去寻找他们的同伴。

这使我们大失所望，因为我们现在不知道怎么办，因为如果我们让小船开跑，即使我们把岸上的7个人都抓住，那也没有任何好处，因为那3个人会把小船划回大船，大船上的人肯定会起锚扬帆，那我们收回大船的希望也会落空。

然而，我们除了等待观望事情的发展，没有什么补救措施。那7个人上了岸，3个留在船上的人把船划得离岸很远，然后抛锚等待岸上的人，因为我们不可能向小船的人发动攻击。

那些上岸的人紧走在一起，向那个小山顶前进。我的住处就在小山下。我们可以把他们看得一清二楚，尽管他们无法看到我们。我们很高兴他们走近我们。这样，我们就可以向他们开枪。要么他们走远点，这样我们可以到外面去。

But when they were come to the brow of the hill, where they could see a great way into the valleys and woods, which lay towards the northeast part, and where the island lay lowest, they shouted and hallooed till they were weary; and not caring, it seems, to venture far from the shore, nor far from one another, they sat down together under a tree, to consider of it. Had they thought fit to have gone to sleep there, as the other party of them had done, they had done the job for us; but they were too full of apprehensions of danger to venture to go to sleep, though they could not tell what the danger was they had to fear neither.

The captain made a very just proposal to me, upon this consultation of theirs, viz., that perhaps they would all fire a volley again, to endeavour to make their fellows hear, and that we should all sally[1] upon them, just at the juncture when their pieces were all discharged, and they would certainly yield, and we should have them without bloodshed. I liked the proposal, provided it was done while we were near enough to come up to them before they could load their pieces again.

But this event did not happen, and we lay still a long time, very irresolute[2] what course to take; at length I told them there would be nothing to be done in my opinion till night, and then, if they did not return to the boat, perhaps we might find a way to get between them and the shore, and so might use some stratagem[3] with them in the boat, to get them on shore.

We waited a great while, though very impatient for their removing; and were very uneasy, when, after long consultations, we saw them start all up and march down towards the sea. It seems they had such dreadful apprehensions upon them of the danger of the place that they resolved to go on board the ship again, give their companions over for lost, and so go on with their intended voyage with the ship.

As soon as I perceived them go towards the shore, I imagined it to be as it really was, that they had given over their search, and were for going back again; and the captain, as soon as I told him my thoughts, was ready to sink at the apprehensions of it; but I presently thought of a stratagem to fetch them back again, and which answered my end to a tittle.

---

[1] sally   *vt.* 突围，出击
[2] irresolute   *adj.* 犹豫不决的
[3] stratagem   *n.* 战略，计谋

到达小山顶时，可以看到那些山谷和森林远远地向东北延伸，那是岛上地势最低的地方。他们一上去就大喊大叫，直到筋疲力尽。看来他们不想冒险远离海岸，也不想彼此离得很远。他们一块坐在一棵树下想办法。如果他们也像另一些人那样想先睡一觉，那正中我们的下怀，但他们却非常担心有危险，不敢睡觉，尽管他们说不清楚自己害怕的是什么危险。

他们正在那里商量时，船长向我提出了一个合情合理的建议，那就是他们也许还会打一排枪，是想尽力让他们的同伴们听见。我们应该趁他们全打完枪的关头，就向他们出击。那时他们肯定会束手就擒，我们就可以不流一滴血制服他们。我喜欢这个建议。要做到这一点，我们要在他们重新装弹药前足够靠近他们。

然而，他们并没有开枪。我们一动不动在那里趴了很长时间，举棋不定，不知道该怎么办。最后，我告诉他们说，我认为，我们到天黑再采取行动。到那时，如果他们不回到小船上去，我们说不定可以想出一个办法包抄到他们和海岸中间，这样就可以用策略对付小船上的那几个人，使他们上岸。

我们又等了好一阵子，尽管忐忑不安，盼他们离开。我们看到他们商议了好长时间后，突然一起跳起来，向海边走去。我们感到心神不安。看来，他们非常害怕这里真有什么危险，认为他们那些同伴已经完蛋，所以要回大船上去继续他们原定的航行计划。

我一见他们向海边走去，就想到他们已经放弃搜寻，准备回去。事实也确实如此。我把自己的想法一告诉船长，他就因担忧而沮丧起来。不过，我马上想出了一个把他们再引回来的办法，而且这完全达到了我的目的。

I ordered Friday and the captain's mate to go over the little creek westward, towards the place where the savages came on shore when Friday was rescued; and as soon as they came to a little rising ground, at about half a mile distance, I bade them halloo as loud as they could and wait till they found the seamen heard them; that as soon as over they heard the seamen answer them, they should return it again, and then keeping out of sigh, take a round, always answering when the other hallooed, to draw them as far into the island and among the woods as possible and then wheel about again to me, by such ways as I directed them.

They were just going into the boat, when Friday and the mate hallooed; and they presently heard them, and answering, run along the shore westward towards the voices they heard, when they were presently stopped by the creek, where, the water being up, they could not get over, and called for the boat to come up and set them over, as indeed I expected.

When they had set themselves over, I observed that the boat being gone up a good way into the creek, and, as it were, in a harbour within the land, they took one of the three men out of her to go along with them, and left only two in the boat, having fastened her to the stump of a little tree on the shore.

This was what I wished for, and immediately leaving Friday and the captain's mate to their business, I took the rest with me, and crossing the creek out of their sight, we surprised the two men before they were aware; one of them lying on shore, and the other being in the boat; the fellow on shore was between sleeping and waking and going to start up, the captain who was foremost, ran in upon him, and knocked him down, and then called out to him in the boat to yield, or he was a dead man.

There needed very few arguments to persuade a single man to yield[1], when he saw five men upon him and his comrade knocked down; besides, this was, it seems, one of the three who were not so hearty in the mutiny as the rest of the crew, and therefore was easily persuaded, not only to yield, but afterwards to join very sincere with us.

---

[1] yield *v.* 屈服，投降

我命令星期五和那位大副越过小河往西走，一直走到星期五得救、那些野人登陆的那个地方；我吩咐他们一来到大约半英里外的那片小高地，就尽可能大声叫喊，一直喊到让那些水手听见为止。我还吩咐他们一听到那些水手回答，就再回叫几声，然后不要让他们看见，兜上一个圈子，一边叫一边应，尽可能把他们引向小岛深处，然后再按我指定的路线绕到我这里来。

　　那些人刚要上小船，星期五和大副就大声喊叫起来。他们马上听到了，就一边回答，一边沿海岸往西朝喊话的方向跑去。他们跑了一会儿，就被那条小河挡住了去路。河水正在上涨，他们没法过河，便把那只小船叫过来，渡他们过去。确实像我预料的那样。

　　他们渡过河后，我观察到小船已向上游走了很长一段路程，进入了一个好像内陆港口的地方。他们把三个人中的其中一个从船上叫下来跟他们一块走，船上只剩下了两个人，小船拴在岸边的一棵小树桩上。

　　这正合我意。我让星期五和大副继续干他们的事儿，自己马上带其他人避开他们的视线渡过小河，出其不意地向那两个人扑去。其中一个人正躺在岸上，另一个人还在船里。岸上那个人半睡半醒，正要跳起来，走在最前面的船长一下跑到他面前，将他打倒在地，然后向船上那个人大声喊叫，让他投降，否则他就死定了。

　　当一个人看到有 5 个人向他扑来，同伴被打倒在地时，劝他投降用不着多费口舌。何况，在叛乱中，他们三个不像其他人那样热心，所以他毫不费力就被我们说服，不但举手投降，而且后来还真心实意地参加了我们的队伍。

In the meantime, Friday and the captain's mate so well managed their business with the rest, that they drew them by hallooing and answering, from one hill to another, and from one wood to another, till they not only heartily tired them but left them, where they were very sure they could not reach back to the boat before it was dark; and indeed they were heartily tired themselves also by the time they came back to us.

We had nothing now to do but to watch for them in the dark and to fall upon them, so as to make sure work with them.

It was several hours after Friday came back to me, before they came back to their boat; and we could hear the foremost of them long before they came quite up, calling to those behind to come along, and could also hear them answer and complain how lame and tired they were and not able to come any faster, which was very welcome news to us.

At length they came up to the boat; but 'tis impossible to express their confusion, when they found the boat fast aground in the creek, the tide ebbed out, and their two men gone we could hear them call to one another in a most lamentable manner, telling one another, they were gotten into an enchanted island.

They hallooed again, and called their two comrades by their names, a great many times, but no answer. After some time, we could see them, by the little light there was, run about wringing their hands like men in despair; and that sometimes they would go and sit down in the boat to rest themselves, then come ashore again, and walk about again, and so over the same thing again.

My men would fain have me given them leave to fall upon them at once in the dark; but I was willing to take them at some advantage, so to spare them, and kill as few of them as I could; and especially I was unwilling to hazard the killing any of our own men, knowing the other were very well armed. I resolved to wait to see if they did not separate; and therefore to make sure of them, I drew my ambuscade[1] nearer and ordered Friday and the captain to creep upon their hands and feet as close to the ground as they could that they might not be discovered and get as near them as they could possibly before they offered to fire.

---

[1] ambuscade   *n.* 埋伏，埋伏处

与此同时，星期五和大副也出色地控制了其他几个人。他们一边喊一边应，把他们从一座小山引向另一座小山，从一片树林引向另一片树林，直到那些人疲惫不堪，而且他们确信那些人不到天黑不可能返回小船。其实，星期五他们自己回来时也是疲惫不堪。

我们现在无事可做，只有在黑暗中监视他们，向他们突然进攻，以确保打败他们。

星期五回来好几小时后，他们才回到了小船。我们很远就能听到走在最前面的几个向跟在后面的几个叫喊，让他们跟上。我们还能听到那后面的几个人一边答应一边抱怨说他们又瘸又累，不能走再快了。这对我们是一个大好消息。

最后，他们走到了小船边，发现潮水已退，小船搁浅在小河里。那两个人又离去，他们慌乱的样子，真是难以描述。我们听见他们彼此呼喊相告，样子非常可悲。他们都说是上了一座魔岛。

他们又大声叫喊起来，无数次地喊着他们那两个同伴的名字，但没有任何回音。过了一会儿，我们借着微光看见他们紧握着双手绝望地跑来跑去，时而跑去小船上坐下来休息，时而又跑到岸上走来走去，反复了好多次。

我手下的人要我下令让他们趁着夜色马上发动进攻，但我想利用某种有利时机抓住他们，饶他们一命，尽可能少杀几个。我尤其不愿让我们自己人冒被杀的危险，因为我知道对方全副武装。我决定等等看他们是不是会散开。因此，为了有把握，我把埋伏点向前靠近了些，吩咐星期五和船长尽可能贴着地面匍匐前进，这样他们就不会被发现，并在他们动手开火之前，尽可能爬得离他们近些。

They had not been long in that posture, but that the boatswain, who was the principal ringleader[1] of the mutiny and had now shown himself the most dejected and dispirited[2] of all the rest, came walking towards them with two more of their crew; the captain was so eager that he could hardly have patience to let him come so near as to be sure of him; for they only heard his tongue before. But when they came nearer, the captain and Friday starting up on their feet, let fly at them.

The boatswain was killed upon the spot, the next man was shot into the body, and fell just by him, though he did not die till an hour or two after; and the third run for it.

At the noise of the fire, I immediately advanced with my whole army, which was now eight men, viz., myself generalissimo[3], Friday my lieutenant-general, the captain and his two men, and the three prisoners of war, who we had trusted with arms.

We came upon them indeed in the dark, so that they could not see our number; and I made the man they had left in the boat, who was now one of us, call to them by name, to try if I could bring them to a parley, and so might perhaps reduce them to terms, which fell out just as we desired. For indeed it was easy to think, as their condition then was, they would be very willing to capitulate[4]; so he calls out as loud as he could to one of them, "Tom Smith! Tom Smith!" Tom Smith answered immediately, "Who's that, Robinson?" For it seems he knew his voice. The other answered, "Ay, ay; for God's sake, Tom Smith, throw down your arms and yield, or you are all dead men this moment."

"Who must we yield to? Where are they?" said Smith again. "Here they are," said he, "here's our captain, and fifty men with him, have been hunting you this two hours; the boatswain is killed, Will Frye is wounded, and I am a prisoner; and if you do not yield, you are all lost."

---

[1] ringleader   n. 魁首，头目
[2] dispirited   adj. 沮丧的
[3] generalissimo   n. 大元帅，总司令
[4] capitulate   vi. 有条件投降，认输，屈服

他们向前爬了没多久，那个水手长就带着另外两个水手朝他们走来。那个水手长是这次哗变的主要头目，在所有其他人中最垂头丧气。船长迫不及待，因为他们以前只听到过他的声音，不等他走近看清楚，就和星期五一起跳起来向他们开了枪。

那个水手长当场被打死，另一个身上中弹，倒在了水手长身边，一两小时后才死去。第三个人拔腿就跑。

一听见枪响，我就马上带领全军前进。我这支军队现在一共有 8 个人，也就是：我自己是总司令，星期五是我的副总司令，船长和他的两个手下，还有 3 个我们信得过、发有武器的战俘。

我们确实是趁着夜色向他们进攻，所以他们无法看清我们有多少人。他们留在小船上的那个人，现在成了我们的人。我命令他喊那些水手的名字，看能否让他们谈判，这样也许迫使他们屈服。结果我们如愿以偿，因为确实不难想像，他们处在当时那种情况下甘愿屈服。于是，他尽可能提高嗓门喊着其中一个人的名字："汤姆·史密斯！汤姆·史密斯！"汤姆·史密斯马上回答说："是谁，是鲁滨逊吗？"因为好像他知道那人的声音。另一个回答说："唉，唉；看在上帝的份上，汤姆·史密斯，放下武器投降吧，否则你们此刻都死定了。"

"我们必须向谁投降？他们在哪里？"史密斯又说道。"他们在这里，"他说。"我们船长就在这里，他带了 50 个人，一直搜寻你们两个小时了。水手长已被打死，威尔·弗赖伊受了伤，我也被俘虏了。你们要不投降，都会没命的。"

"Will they give us quarter[1] then," said Tom Smith. "and we will yield?" "I'll go and ask, if you promise to yield," said Robinson; so he asked the captain, and the captain then calls himself out, "You Smith, you know my voice. If you lay down your arms immediately and submit, you shall have your lives all but Will Atkins."

Upon this, Will Atkins cried out, "For God's sake, captain, give me quarter; what have I done? They have been all as bad as I"; which, by the way, was not true neither; for it seems this Will Atkins was the first man that laid hold of the captain, when they first mutinied, and used him barbarously, in tying his hands, and giving him injurious[2] language.

However, the captain told him he must lay down his arms at discretion and trust to the governor's mercy, by which he meant me; for they all called me governor.

In a word, they all laid down their arms and begged their lives; and I sent the man that had parleyed with them and two more, who bound them all; and then my great army of 50 men, which, particularly with those three, were all but eight, came up and seized upon them all and upon their boat, only that I kept myself and one more out of sight, for reasons of state.

---

[1] quarter   *n.* 慈悲；饶恕
[2] injurious   *adj.* 有害的

"我们投降，"汤姆·史密斯说，"他们会饶我们一命吗？""你们要答应投降，我就去问一下，"鲁滨逊说。于是，他就问船长。这时，船长亲自喊道："你，史密斯，你熟悉我的声音。只要你们马上放下武器投降，我就饶你们一命，只有威尔·阿特金斯除外。"

听到这话，威尔·阿特金斯大声喊道："船长，看在上帝的份上，饶了我吧。我做了什么？他们都和我一样坏。"看样子，他说的并不是实话，因为好像他们最初哗变时，正是这个威尔·阿特金斯首先把船长抓起来，野蛮地对待他，绑住他的两只手，并对他恶语相加。

不管怎样，船长还是告诉他说，他必须自行放下武器，听候总督处理。所谓总督指的就是我，因为他们都叫我总督。

总之，他们都放下了武器，请求饶命。于是，我派那个和他们谈判的人以及另两个水手把他们都绑起来。随后，我那 50 人大军（就是加上他们 3 人，我们才 8 个人）走上前，抓住他们，并扣留了他们的小船。只有我和另一个人因身份缘故，没有露面。

XXVII

Our next work was to repair the boat and think of seizing the ship; and as for the captain, now he had leisure to parley with them. He expostulated[1] with them upon the villainy of their practices with him, and at length upon the farther wickedness of their design, and how certainly it must bring them to misery and distress in the end, and perhaps to the gallows.

They all appeared very penitent and begged hard for their lives; as for that, he told them they were none of his prisoners, but the commander of the island; that they thought they had set him on shore in a barren uninhabited island, but it had pleased God so to direct them that the island was inhabited, and that the governor was an Englishman; that he might hang them all there, if he pleased; but as he had given them all quarter, he supposed he would send them to England to be dealt with there as justice required, except Atkins, who he was commanded by the governor to advise to prepare for death; for that he would be hanged in the morning.

Though this was all a fiction of his own, yet it had its desired effect; Atkins fell upon his knees to beg the captain to intercede[2] with the governor for his life; and all the rest begged of him for God's sake, that they might not be sent to England.

It now occurred to me that the time of our deliverance was come, and that it would be a most easy thing to bring these fellows in to be hearty in getting possession of the ship; so I retired in the dark from them, that they might not see what kind of a governor they had, and called the captain to me; when I called, as at a good distance, one of the men was ordered to speak again and say to the captain, "Captain, the commander calls for you"; and presently the captain replied, "Tell his excellency, I am just a-coming." This more perfectly amused them; and they all believed that the commander was just by with his fifty men.

---

[1] expostulate   *vi.* 劝诫，忠告
[2] intercede   *v.* 调解

27

　　我们的下一步工作就是修好那只小船，并考虑夺回大船。这时，船长也有空闲和他们谈判了。他告诫他们对他犯下的恶行，最后告诫他们这种图谋的进一步恶果，它最后一定会给他们带来痛苦和不幸，说不定还会上绞架。

　　他们都纷纷悔罪，哀求饶命。对此，船长告诉他们说，他们绝不是他的俘虏，而是岛上司令官的俘虏。他说，他们本来以为把他送到了一个荒无人烟的岛上，但上帝却命令他们把他送到有人居住的岛上，而且岛上的总督是一位英国人。他说，如果总督乐意的话，他可能会把他们统统在岛上吊死。不过，他决定全部饶恕他们，他想他要把他们送回英国，秉公审判，除了阿特金斯。总督下令，要阿特金斯准备受死，明天早上就要把他吊死。

　　尽管这都是船长的杜撰，但达到了预期的效果。阿特金斯跪下来哀求船长向总督求情，饶他一命。其他所有人也哀求船长行行好，不要把他们送回英国。

　　这时，我突然想到，我们获救的时刻已经来临。现在把这些人争取过来，让他们卖力去夺取那只大船，将是一件轻而易举的事儿。于是，我趁着夜色离开了他们，以免他们看见我是怎样一个总督。随后，我将船长叫到身边。我叫他时，因为有很长一段距离，就又派一个人去对船长传话说："船长，司令叫你。"船长马上回答说："告诉阁下，我就来。"这使他们越发深信不疑。他们都相信，司令和50名手下就在附近。

Upon the captain's coming to me, I told him my project for seizing the ship, which he liked of wonderfully well, and resolved to put it in execution the next morning.

But in order to execute it with more art, and secure of success, I told him we must divide the prisoners, and that he should go and take Atkins and two more of the worst of them, and send them pinioned to the cave where the others lay. This was committed to Friday and the two men who came on shore with the captain to convey them to the cave.

The other I ordered to my bower; and as it was fenced in, and they pinioned, the place was secure enough.

To these in the morning I sent the captain, who was to enter into a parley with them; in a word, to try them, and tell me, whether he thought they might be trusted or no, to on board and surprise the ship. He talked to them of the injury done him, of the condition they were brought to; and that though the governor had given them quarter for their lives, as to the present action, yet that if they were sent to England, they would all be hanged in chains, to be sure; but that if they would join in so just an attempt, as to recover the ship, he would have the governor's engagement for their pardon.

Anyone may guess how readily such a proposal would be accepted by men in their condition; they fell down on their knees to the captain and promised with the deepest imprecations that they would be faithful to him to the last drop, and that they should owe their lives to him and would go with him all over the world, that they would own him for a father to them as long as they lived.

"Well," said the captain, "I must go and tell the governor what you say, and see what I can do to bring him to consent to it." So he brought me an account of the temper he found them in; and that he verily believed they would be faithful.

However, that we might be very secure, I told him he should go back again and choose out five of them, and tell them they might see that he did not want men, that he would take out those five to be his assistants, and that the governor would keep the other two, and the three that were sent prisoners to the castle (my cave) as hostages, for the fidelity of those five; and that if they proved unfaithful in the execution, the five hostages should be hanged in chains alive upon the shore.

船长一到，我就把夺取大船的计划告诉了他。船长认为计划非常周密，就决定第二天早晨开始行动。

可是，为了将计划进行得更巧妙、更有成功的把握，我告诉船长说，我们必须把那些俘虏分开。他应该去抓住阿特金斯和另两个最坏的家伙，然后将他们送到关押另几个人的那个石洞里去。这件事交给了星期五和那两个跟船长一起上岸的人，把俘虏押送到石洞里。

我又命令把其他俘虏送到我的乡间别墅，因为那里有围墙，他们又被捆绑着，所以万无一失。

到了第二天早晨，我便派船长去同他们谈判，总之是要考验他们，然后告诉我，看看派他们去夺回大船是不是值得信赖。船长跟他们谈到了他们对他的伤害和他们现在的处境。他还告诉他们说，尽管现在总督已经饶了他们的命，但如果把他们送回英国，他们肯定会被统统用铁链吊死。不过，如果他们愿意参加夺回大船的正义行动，他一定请求总督允诺赦免他们。

任何人都可以猜到，他们在那种处境下对这个建议真是求之不得。他们跪在船长面前，苦苦哀求，答应对他誓死效忠，永远感激他的救命之恩，愿意跟他走遍天涯海角，他们还要终生把他当父亲一样看待。

"好吧，"船长说，"我必须回去，将你们的话告诉总督，看我能不能劝他同意。"于是，他回来把他们现在的思想倾向向我作了汇报，说他完全相信他们会效忠。

然而，为了万无一失，我让他再回去一趟，从中挑出5个人，并要他告诉他们，他现在并不缺少人手，现在要挑选5个人做他的助手，总督要把其他2个人和那3个已经押送到城堡里去的俘虏留下来作人质，以保证那5个人的忠诚。如果他们在执行任务时有不忠的表现，那5个人质就要在岸上用铁链吊死。

This looked severe, and convinced them that the governor was in earnest; however, they had no way left them but to accept it; and it was now the business of the prisoners, as much as of the captain, to persuade the other five to do their duty.

Our strength was now thus ordered for the expedition. 1. The captain, his mate, and passenger. 2. Then the two prisoners of the first gang, to whom having their characters from the captain, I had given their liberty, and trusted them with arms. 3. The other two who I had kept till now, in my bower, pinioned; but upon the captain's motion, had now released. 4. These five released at last. So that they were twelve in all, besides five we kept prisoners in the cave, and the two hostages.

I asked the captain if he was willing to venture with these hands on board the ship; for as for me and Friday, I did not think it was proper for us to stir, having seven men left behind; and it was employment enough for us to keep them asunder[1], and supply them with victuals.

As to the five in the cave, I resolved to keep them fast, but Friday went in twice a day to them, to supply them with necessaries; and I made the other two carry provisions to a certain distance, where Friday was to take it.

When I showed myself to the two hostages, it was with the captain, who told them, I was the person the governor had ordered to look after them, and that it was the governor's pleasure they should not stir anywhere but by my direction; that if they did, they should be fetched into the castle, and be laid in irons; so that as we never suffered them to see me as governor, so I now appeared as another person, and spoke of the governor, the garrison, the castle, and the like, upon all occasions.

The captain now had no difficulty before him, but to furnish his two boats, stop the breach of one, and man them. He made his passenger captain of one, with four other men; and himself and his mate and five more went in the other. And they contrived their business very well; for they came up to the ship about midnight. As soon as they came within call of the ship, he made Robinson hail them and tell them they had brought off the men and the boat, but that it was a long time before they had found them, and the like holding them in a chat till they came to the ship's side when the captain and the mate entering first with their arms, immediately knocked down the second mate and carpenter with the butt-end of their muskets.

---

[1] asunder *adv.* 分离；成碎片

这看起来非常严厉，并使他们相信总督做事认真，他们除了接受，别无办法。现在，那几个俘虏和船长一样认真，劝说那五个人尽心尽责。

因此，我们现在对出征的兵力做了这样的安排：一、船长、大副和旅客；二、然后是第一批俘虏中的两个水手，我从船长那里了解了他们的品行，已经给了他们自由，并信任他们发给了武器；三、还有两个水手直到现在还被捆绑着关在我的别墅里，经船长提议，现已释放；四、这五个最后释放的人。因此，他们总共是 12 人。此外，还有 5 个我们关在石洞里，以及两个人质。

我问船长是不是愿意冒险带领这些人去收回大船，因为我认为我和星期五不宜出动，岛上还有 7 个俘虏，他们又都被分散看守，还得供给他们饮食，够我们忙的。

至于关在洞里的那 5 个人，我决定严加看守。我让星期五一天进去两次，给他们送一些必需品。我让其他两个人先把东西送到一个指定地点，然后再由星期五送去。

我在那两个人质面前露面时，是和船长一起去的。船长告诉他们说，我是总督派来监视他们的。总督命令，没有我的指示，他们不得到处乱跑。如果乱跑，就把他们抓起来送进城堡，并用铁链锁住。这样，为了不让他们知道我就是总督，我现在是以另一个人的身份出现，并不失时机地谈到总督、驻军和城堡等诸如此类的问题。

船长现在只要装备好两只小船，补好其中一只小船的洞，再分别派人上去，就没什么困难了。他指定他的旅客当其中一只小船的船长，再带上另外 4 名水手。他自己、大副和另外 5 名水手上了另一只小船。他们的事情进行得非常顺利，因为大约到午夜，他们就来到了大船边。他们一划到能向大船喊话的距离，船长就让那个也叫鲁滨逊的水手同他们喊话，告诉他们说人和船都已经回来了，他们花了很长时间才找到。他们这样闲聊着，直到靠近了大船边。船长和大副首先带枪上了船，用枪托将二副和木匠打倒在地。

Being very faithfully seconded by their men, they secured all the rest that were upon the main and quarter decks, and began to fasten the hatches to keep them down who were below, when the other boat and their men entering at the fore chains, secured the forecastle of the ship and the scuttle which went down into the cook room, making three men they found there prisoners.

When this was done, and all safe upon deck, the captain ordered the mate with three men to break into the roundhouse where the new rebel captain lay, and having taken the alarm, was gotten up, and with two men and a boy had gotten firearms in their hands, and when the mate with a crow split open the door, the new captain and his men fired boldly among them and wounded the mate with a musket ball which broke his arm, and wounded two more of the but killed nobody.

The mate calling for help, rushed however into the roundhouse, wounded as he was, and with his pistol shot the new captain through the head, the bullet entering at his mouth, and came out again behind one of his ears; so that he never spoke a word; upon which the rest yielded, and the ship was taken effectually, without any more lives lost.

As soon as the ship was thus secured, the captain ordered seven guns to be fired, which was the signal agreed upon with me, to give me notice of his success, which I was very glad to hear, having sat watching upon the shore for it till near two of the clock in the morning.

Having thus heard the signal plainly, I laid me down; and it having been a day of great fatigue to me, I slept very sound, till I was something surprised with the noise of a gun; and presently starting up, I heard a man call me by the name of "Governor, Governor," and presently I knew the captain's voice, when climbing up to the top of the hill, there he stood, and pointing to the ship, he embraced me in arms, "My dear friend and deliverer," said he, "there's your ship, for she is all yours, and so are we and all that belong to her." I cast my eyes to the ship, and there she rode within little more than half a mile of the shore; for they had weighed for as soon as they were masters of her; and the weather being fair, had brought her to an anchor just against the mouth of the little creek; and the tide being up, the captain had brought the pinnace in near the place where I at first landed my rafts, and so landed just at my door.

340

手下的人忠心耿耿，船长和大副在他们协助下又全部制服了前后甲板上的所有其他人，然后关好舱口，把舱底下的人关在下面。这时，第二只小船上的人也从船前的铁索上爬上来，占领了前甲板和通向厨房的舷窗，同时俘虏了在厨房里发现的三个人。

待做完这个，甲板平安无事后，船长命令大副带三个人占领后甲板舱室，那个做了新船长的叛徒就睡在那里。新船长已经听到警报，爬了起来，两个船员和一个见习船员手里都有枪。当大副用橇杠把门撬开时，新船长和他的手下人不知死活地向他们开火。一颗火铳子弹打伤了大副，把他的胳膊打断了，还打伤了其他两个人，但没有打死人。

尽管大副受了伤，但还是一边呼救，一边冲进后甲板舱室，用手枪一枪打穿了新船长的脑袋，子弹从他嘴里进去，又从一只耳朵后面出来，所以他再也没说一句话。见此情景，其他人都纷纷投降。大船就这样被有力地夺了过来，没有再死一个人。

于是，一搞定大船，船长就马上下令开了七枪。这是我和他约定的信号，通知我大功告成。听到这个信号，我非常高兴，因为我一直坐在岸边等候这个信号，一直等到了差不多凌晨两点。

因此，我听清了信号后，便躺下睡觉。我整整劳累了一天，所以睡得很香，直到我被一声枪响惊醒。我立刻一跃而起，听到有人喊我："总督！总督！"我马上听出是船长的声音，就爬上小山顶，只见他站在那里，指着大船，一把将我抱在怀里。"我亲爱的朋友、救命恩人，"他说，"这是你的船，因为它都是你的，我们和船上的一切也都是你的。"我放眼望去，只见大船停泊在离岸不到半英里的地方。因为他们一把大船夺到手就起了锚，当时天气晴朗，所以他们就把船一直开到了小河口。而且当时正好涨潮，于是船长就把大艇划到了当初我的木排靠岸的附近地方，正好在我的门口上岸。

XXVIII

I was at first ready to sink down with the surprise. For I saw my deliverance indeed visibly put into my hands, all things easy, and a large ship just ready to carry me away whither I pleased to go. At first, for some time, I was not able to answer him one word; but as he had taken me in his arms, I held fast by him, or I should have fallen to the ground.

He perceived the surprise, and immediately pulls a bottle out of his pocket, and gave me a dram of cordial, which he had brought on purpose for me; after I had drank it, I sat down upon the ground; and though it brought me to myself, yet it was a good while before I could speak a word to him.

All this while the poor man was in as great an ecstasy as I, only not under any surprise, as I was; and he said a thousand kind tender things to me, to compose me and bring me to myself; but such was the flood of joy in my breast that it put all my spirits into confusion, at last it broke out into tears, and in a little while after, I recovered my speech.

Then I took my turn and embraced him as my deliverer; and we rejoiced together. I told him I look upon him as a man sent from Heaven to deliver me, and that the whole transaction seemed to be a chain of wonders. I forgot not to lift up my heart in thankfulness to Heaven.

When we had talked a while, the captain told me he had brought me some little refreshment. Upon this he called aloud to the boat, and bid his men bring the things ashore that were for the governor; and indeed it was a present, as if I had been one not that was to be carried away along with them, but as if I had been to dwell upon the island still and they were to go without me.

First, he had brought me a case of bottles full of excellent cordial waters, six large bottles of Madera wine; the bottles held two quarts a-piece; two pound of excellent good tobacco, twelve good pieces of the ship's beef, and six pieces of pork, with a bag of peas, and about a hundredweight of biscuit.

28

　　起先，这件意外事差点儿让我晕倒，因为我确实看到自己脱险的事儿显然十拿九稳，一切顺利，而且一艘大船随时准备把我送到任何我想去的地方。起先，我好一阵子答不上一句话。要不是他将我抱在怀里，我紧紧靠住他，早已倒在地上了。

　　他察觉到我这样吃惊，就马上从口袋里取出一只瓶子，让我喝了一口他特地为我带来的提神饮料。喝完后，我在地上坐下来。尽管这使我清醒了过来，但又过了好一阵子，我才对他说出话来。

　　此时，船长也和我一样狂喜，只是不像我那样吃惊。于是，他对我说了无数亲切温暖的话语，让我安定清醒。可是，我心里充满了喜悦之情，精神完全陷入了混乱状态。最后，我失声大哭。又过了一会儿，我才恢复了说话能力。

　　这时，我也抱住了船长，把他当成自己的救命恩人。我们都充满了喜悦。我告诉他说，我把他看成是上天派来解救我的人，而且整个事情仿佛都是一连串的奇迹。我也没有忘记对上天表达自己的感激之情。

　　我们谈了一会儿后，船长对我说，他给我带了一点饮料和食物。说着，他冲小船大喊了一声，吩咐手下人把献给总督的东西搬上岸来。其实，这是一份厚礼，好像还要让我在岛上呆下去，不准备把我带走了。

　　首先，他给我送来了一箱上好的提神酒、六大瓶马德罗葡萄酒（每瓶两夸脱）、两磅上等烟叶、十二块上好的牛肉干、六块猪肉、一袋豆子和大约一英担饼干。

He brought me also a box of sugar, a box of flour, a bag full of lemons, and two bottles of lime-juice, and abundance of other things. But besides these, and what was a thousand times more useful to me, he brought me six clean new shirts, six very good neckcloths, two pair of gloves, one pair of shoes, a hat, and one pair of stockings, and a very good suit of clothes of his own, which had been worn but very little. In a word, he clothed me from head to foot.

After these ceremonies past, and after all his good things were brought into my little apartment, we began to consult what was to be done with the prisoners we had; for it was worth considering whether we might venture to take them away with us or no, especially two of them, who we knew to be incorrigible and refractory[1] to the last degree; and the captain said, he knew they were such rogues that there was no obliging them, and if he did carry them away, it must be in irons, as malefactors, to be delivered over to justice at the first English colony he could come at; and I found that the captain himself was very anxious about it.

Upon this, I told him that if he desired it, I durst undertake to bring the two men he spoke of to make it their own request that he should leave them upon the island. "I should be very glad of that," said the captain, "with all my heart."

"Well," said I, "I will send for them up, and talk with them for you"; so I caused Friday and the two hostages, for they were now discharged, their comrades having performed their promise; I say, I caused them to go to the cave and bring up the five men, pinioned as they were, to the bower, and keep them there till I came.

After some time, I came thither dressed in my new habit, and now I was called governor again; being all met, and the captain with me, I caused the men to be brought before me, and I told them, I had had a full account of their villainous behaviour to the captain, and how they had run away with the ship and were preparing to commit farther robberies, but that Providence had ensnared[2] them in their own ways and that they were fallen into the pit which they had dug for others.

---

[1] refractory *adj.* 难控制的；难熔的
[2] ensnare *vt.* 诱捕

他还给我送来了一箱糖、一箱面粉、满满一袋柠檬、两瓶酸橙汁，以及好多其他东西。但此外，对我要有用上千倍的是，他给我送来了六件干净新衬衫、六条上等围巾、两副手套、一双鞋、一顶帽子、一双长袜，还有他自己穿的一套有穿过几次的上好衣服。总之，他从头到脚都给我提供了穿戴。

这些送礼仪式完毕，他所有的好东西也都搬进了我小小的住处后，我们开始商议如何处置我们抓获的那些俘虏，因为是不是冒风险把他们带走值得考虑，尤其是其中的两个人，我们知道他们俩无可救药、最难驾驭。船长说，他知道他俩都是坏蛋，绝不能对他们心慈手软。如果他真把他们带走，必须把他们像犯罪分子一样关起来，一遇到英国殖民地，就把他们送交法办。我发现船长本人对此也非常担心。

于是，我告诉船长说，如果他想的话，我就斗胆说服他所说的那两个人，让他们自己提出请求留在岛上。"我很高兴那样，"船长说，"我完全同意。"

"那好，"我说，"我现在就派人把他们叫来，替你跟他们谈谈。"于是，我吩咐星期五和那两个人质去，因为我们现在已经释放了他们，他们的同伙实践了他们的诺言。我是说，我让他们到洞室里去，把关在那里仍然绑着的五个人带到我的乡间别墅，然后把他们关在那里，等我来。

过了一会儿，我就穿上新衣服去了那里。现在，我又以总督的身份出现了。我和船长到了那边，跟我们的人都见了面，我让人把那五个人带到我面前。我告诉他们说，我已经获得了他们对待船长的恶行的详尽报告，还有他们如何夺走大船逃跑，并准备继续抢劫。但上帝使他们自投罗网，跌进了他们为别人挖的陷阱。

I let them know that by my direction the ship had been seized, that she lay now in the road; and they might see by and by that their new captain had received the reward of his villainy; for that they might see him hanging at the yardarm[1].

That as to them, I wanted to know what they had to say.

One of them answered in the name of the rest that they had nothing to say but this, that when they were taken, the captain promised them their lives, and they humbly implored my mercy; but I told them, I knew not what mercy to show them; for as for myself, I had resolved to quit the island with all my men, and had taken passage with the captain to go for England. And as for the captain, he could not carry them to England other than as prisoners in irons to be tried for mutiny and running away with the ship; the consequence of which, they must needs know, would be the gallows; so that I could not tell which was best for them, unless they had a mind to take their fate in the island; if they desired, that I did not care, as I had liberty to leave it, I had some inclination to give them their lives, if they thought they could shift on shore.

They seemed very thankful for it, said they would much rather venture to stay there than to be carried to England to be hanged; so I left it on that issue.

However, the captain seemed to make some difficulty of it, as if he durst not leave them there. Upon this I seemed a little angry with the captain, and told him, that they were my prisoners, not his; and that seeing I had offered them so much favour, I would be as good as my word; and that if he did not think fit to consent to it, I would set them at liberty; and if he did not like it, he might take them again if he could catch them.

Upon this they appeared very thankful, and I accordingly set them at liberty, and bade them retire into the woods to the place whence they came, and I would leave them some firearms, some ammunition, and some directions how they should live very well, if they thought fit.

---

[1] yardarm　*n.*　（航海）桁端，横杆端

我告诉他们，在我的指挥下，大船已被夺回，现在正停泊在锚地。他们不久就会看到，新船长的罪行已经得到了报应，因为他们会看到他吊在桁端上。

　　至于他们，我想知道他们还有什么话可说。

　　这时，其中有一个人以其他人的名义回答说，他们没有什么话可说，只是他们被俘时，船长曾答应饶他们一命。他们低声下气恳求我宽恕。但我告诉他们说，我不知道怎样宽恕他们，因为我已经决定带着手下人离开这个岛，跟船长一起乘船前往英国。至于船长，他只能把他们当作囚犯关起来带回英国，并让以哗变罪和劫船逃跑罪审判他们，他们应该都知道其中的结果，肯定是上绞架。所以，我无法为他们想出最好的办法，除非他们决定留在岛上，听任命运的安排。如果他们愿意，我不介意，因为我要离开。只要他们愿意留在岛上，我可以放他们一条生路。

　　他们对此好像非常感激，说他们宁愿冒险留在这里，也不愿被带回英国吊死。所以，我就同意了这个看法。

　　然而，船长对此似乎有些反对，好像他不敢把他们留在岛上。于是，我对船长有点儿生气。我告诉他，他们是我的俘虏，而不是他的俘虏。因为我已经给了他们这么多关照，所以就要说话算数。他要不同意，我就放掉他们。他要不喜欢这样做，可以去把他们抓回来，只要他能抓住。

　　他们对此好像非常感激。于是，我就释放了他们，让他们退回树林，回到他们原来的地方去，我会给他们留一些武器弹药，并指导他们如何在这里好好生活，如果他们认为合适的话。

Upon this I prepared to go on board the ship, but told the captain, that I would stay that night to prepare my things and desired him to go on board in the meantime, and keep all right in the ship, and send the boat on shore the next day for me; ordering him in the meantime to cause the new captain who was killed to be hanged at the yardarm, that these men might see him.

When the captain was gone, I sent for the men up to me to my apartment and entered seriously into discourse with them of their circumstances. I told them I thought they had made a right choice; that if the captain carried them away, they would certainly be hanged. I showed them the new captain hanging at the yardarm of the ship, and told them they had nothing less to expect.

When they had all declared their willingness to stay, I then told them I would let them into the story of my living there, and put them into the way of making it easy to them. Accordingly I gave them the whole history of the place and of my coming to it; showed them my fortifications, the way I made my bread, planted my corn, cured my grapes. I told them the story also of the sixteen Spaniards that were to be expected; for whom I left a letter, and made them promise to treat them in common with themselves.

I left them five muskets, three fowling pieces and three swords. I had above a barrel and half of powder left. I gave them a description of the way I managed the goats, and directions to milk and fatten them, and to make both butter and cheese.

In a word, I gave them every part of my own story; and I told them I would prevail with the captain to leave them two barrels of gunpowder more and some garden-seeds, which I would have been very glad of; also I gave them the bag of peas which the captain had brought me to eat, and bade them be sure to sow and increase them.

Having done all this, I left them the next day and went on board the ship. We prepared immediately to sail, but did not weigh that night. The next morning early, two of the five men came swimming to the ship's side, and making a most lamentable[1] complaint of the other three, begged to be taken into the ship, for God's sake, for they should be murdered and begged the captain to take them on board, though he hanged them immediately.

---

[1] lamentable *adj.* 不快的

于是，我准备上船。我对船长说，我要在岛上待一夜，准备自己的东西，希望他此时回到船上，安排好所有的一切，第二天再派小船到岸上来接我，同时命令他在此期间把那打死的新船长吊在桁端上示众。

船长走后，我派人把那几个人带到我的房间，和他们进行了一次严肃谈话，谈了他们的处境。我告诉他们说，我认为他们已经做出了正确的选择。如果船长把他们带走，他们肯定会被吊死。我指着吊在大船桁端上的新船长，告诉他们没有别的什么指望，只有这种下场。

他们都表示愿意留在岛上。随后，我就告诉他们说，我要让他们了解我在这里生活的情况，并教会他们轻松生活的方法。于是，我向他们谈了小岛的全部情况和我来到这里的全部经历，领他们看了我的城堡，以及我做面包、种庄稼、晒制葡萄干的方法。我还把即将到来的 16 位西班牙人的事儿告诉了他们。我给那些西班牙人留了一封信，并要他们答应对他们一视同仁。

我留给了他们五支火铳、三支鸟枪和三把刀，还留下了一桶半多火药。我还向他们说明了管理山羊的方法，告诉他们如何挤羊奶、如何使羊长膘、如何做奶油和奶酪。

总之，我把自己的经历一一告诉了他们，还对他们说，我要劝船长再给他们留下两桶火药和一些菜种，我当时要是有菜种一定会非常高兴。我还把船长送给我吃的一袋豌豆也送给了他们，吩咐他们一定要播种下去，让它们繁殖起来。

这都做完后，第二天我就离开他们，上了大船。我们准备马上开船，但那天夜里却没有起锚。第二天一大早，那五个人中有两个人游到大船边，闷闷不乐地控诉那三个人，恳求我们行行好把他们带上大船，因为他们会被那三个人杀死。他们苦苦哀求船长带他们上船，就是他马上吊死他们也行。

Upon this the captain pretended to have no power without me; but after some difficulty, and after their solemn promises of amendment[1], they were taken on board, and were some time after soundly whipped and pickled[2]; after which, they proved very honest and quiet fellows.

Some time after this, the boat was ordered on shore, the tide being up, with the things promised to the men, to which the captain at my intercession[3] caused their chests and clothes to be added, which they took and were very thankful for; I also encouraged them by telling them that if it lay in my way to send any vessel to take them in, I would not forget them.

When I took leave of this island, I carried on board for relics[4], the great goat's-skin-cap I had made, my umbrella, and my parrot; also I forgot not to take the money I formerly mentioned, which had lain by me so long useless that it was grown rusty, or tarnished[5], and could hardly pass for silver, till it had been a little rubbed and handled; as also the money I found in the wreck of the Spanish ship.

And thus I left the island, the nineteenth of December, as I found by the ship's account, in the year 1686, after I had been upon it eight and twenty years, two months, and 19 days; being delivered from this second captivity the same day of the month that I first made my escape in the barco-longo, from among the Moors of Sallee.

In this vessel, after a long voyage, I arrived in England, the eleventh of June, in the year 1687, having been thirty and five years absent.

---

[1] amendment *n.* 改善，改正
[2] pickle *vt.* 腌，泡
[3] intercession *n.* 代为求情，调解
[4] relic *n.* 遗物，遗迹；纪念物
[5] tarnish *v.* 失去光泽

见此情景，船长假装说，没有我的允许，他无权决定。但经过一些阻挠和他们郑重其事承诺痛改前非之后，才让他们上了大船。上船后过了一阵子，他们狠狠挨了一顿鞭子，还被用盐擦了背。从那以后，他们果然成了安分守己的人。

之后过了一段时间，潮水上涨，我就命令把我答应给那三个人的东西用小船运到岸上去。我又向船长求情，把他们三人的箱子和衣服一起送去。他们收到后都非常感激。我还鼓励他们，告诉他们说，如果将来我有船从这里经过一定收留他们，我不会忘记他们。

离开这个小岛时，我把自己做的那顶大羊皮帽、雨伞和我的鹦鹉都带上船，作为纪念，同时也没有忘记拿走我以前提到过的那笔钱。这些钱因放了好久没有使用，现在已经生锈，失去了光泽，直到磨一磨用一用，才能认出是银币。我在失事的西班牙大船上发现的钱也是这样。

因此，根据船上的日历，1686 年 12 月 19 日，我离开了这个岛，一共在那里住了 28 年两个月 19 天。我第二次囚禁获救这一天正好和我第一次从萨利的摩尔人手里坐大艇里逃出来是同月同日。

我坐上这条船，经过了漫长的航行，1687 年 7 月 11 日到达英国。我离开家已经 35 年了。